THE LANGUAGE OF
MODERN PHYSICS

THE LANGUAGE OF
MODERN PHYSICS

AN INTRODUCTION TO
THE PHILOSOPHY OF SCIENCE

BY

ERNEST H. HUTTEN

LONDON: GEORGE ALLEN & UNWIN LTD
NEW YORK: THE MACMILLAN COMPANY

*Printed in Great Britain
in 11 point Imprint by
The Blackfriars Press Limited
Smith-Dorrien Road, Leicester*

CONTENTS

PREFACE

A preface presents the author with a privileged occasion where he may explain the aim he had in writing the book and apologize for not having attained it.

There exist already many books on the philosophy of science. However, most of them deal with quantum physics only and, moreover, their authors usually neglect to state clearly the philosophical terms of reference they have used.

My intention has been to give a reasonably complete account of the concepts, both of classical and of quantum physics. And I have tried also to make clear the methodology employed for explaining and arguing about these concepts.

The first part of the book therefore treats of modern logic and semantics ; the discussion is based on the semantic conception of truth and leads up to the criterion of *meaning*. Our prime concern is, after all, to establish what our hypotheses, laws, and theories mean. The second, and main, part of the book is about the basic ideas of physics. Here the *model* which underlies a scientific theory is of greatest import ; in most instances the model is tacitly assumed, but we must bring it out into the open if we want to understand the theory. The third, and last, part deals with the method scientists use for confirming their hypotheses. I have followed my own laboratory experience and tried to describe it in a manner which is closer to scientific practice than the usual 'armchair' accounts. The rôle the concept of *probability* plays in judging the result of an experiment is, in my view, quite different from what it is generally supposed to be.

The book is addressed to the layman who realises that science is an inalienable part of our civilisation and who therefore wants to understand it. The philosopher will find here a discussion of the concepts of physics in a language which I have tried to keep as close as possible to his usual way of speaking. But I hope that the physicist as well may find that to philosophize about his science can be of help in understanding it.

The book was written between the years 1947 and 1951 ; there

7

were several revisions, the last one in April, 1955. I am greatly
indebted to Professor A. J. Ayer and to Professor D. J. O'Connor
whose patient and careful criticism has been of invaluable help
to me.

ERNEST H. HUTTEN

Royal Holloway College,
University of London

I

INTRODUCTION

1. *Science and philosophy*

To-day more than ever it has become clear to everyone what an important rôle science plays in the modern world. And of all the sciences it is physics that has shown itself to be most successful. Physics is the most advanced of the natural sciences. The methods and techniques of physics are more accurate and more reliable than those of any other science, and its results have been strongly confirmed by experience. For this reason physics is best fitted to serve as an example of the ideas of modern science.

The material revolution science has brought about is felt everywhere; but the intellectual revolution, the change in ideas and concepts, has not penetrated far into every-day life. The intellectual climate in which we live lags behind the material or technical climate created by the discoveries of science and the inventions of industry. We may have heard the latest facts, but do we understand them? Can we achieve the intellectual integration which an understanding of science requires? Some years ago Einstein complained that ' . . . many scientists were unable to grasp the meaning of the (relativity) theory itself; all they could understand were its consequences within their special field'. If this criticism holds true even for the average scientist, how much more does it apply to the man in the street?

It may be no exaggeration to say that the intellectual methods, the thinking habits which science requires, are largely unknown even to the educated layman. So far as physics is concerned we may doubt whether the average man has caught up with Galileo and Newton; and there are many who have not yet grasped what Aristotle knew two thousand years ago. People learn by rote certain results of science as applied to every-day life; they know how to manipulate gadgets; they acquire skills. It would be wrong to underestimate the value of this practical knowledge; but it is too limited. Isn't it strange that a man should know how to run a machine, and yet not know what 'makes it tick'? We need to make

9

at least a little clearer what the concepts of modern physics are and how they differ from the corresponding ideas we all implicitly use in ordinary life.

And this is a task necessary for the development of physics itself. For it appears that physics has arrived at a temporary impasse. No new theories have been invented for some time—in fact it was in 1927 that the theory of quantum mechanics made its appearance. For a hundred years at least there has been a brilliant succession of theories in physics. But during the last twenty-five years details have been filled in here and there, and minor developments have occurred: no new, and fundamental, theory has been proposed. Even the atomic bomb, as was often pointed out, is merely an application of principles that have been known for many years. New experiments have been made and a wealth of new data has been accumulated; but present theories cannot cope with them since only partial explanations and insufficient computations can be obtained. Thus it seems obvious to suggest that we must investigate the logical structure of our theories, or analyse the language of physics. We require a better understanding of science, for its own sake as well as for the sake of our civilisation of which science is an inalienable part.

At all times there were people who were aware of this need. Scientists and philosophers alike have tried therefore not only to present the results of science but to explain the intellectual methods. The Enlightenment of the eighteenth century, to some extent, was the attempt to explain and to understand Newtonian physics. And the Victorians, spurred on by the discoveries of biology and geology, tried to translate these new ideas into the language of every-day life. Often misunderstandings arose. But, in principle, one cannot fail to agree that a Philosophy of Science is needed to understand the intellectual discoveries of science.

2. *Philosophy and language*

But what is the philosophy of science and what do we mean by the terms 'science' and 'philosophy'? No dogmatic formulation will do, though we must provide some general explanation in order to delimit the field. A preliminary statement is all we can offer here; only after having discussed some examples can we make clearer what we mean by the 'philosophy of science'.

Most people agree that knowledge is the aim of science; that all knowledge starts with experience; and that controlled experience, i.e. observation and experiment, furnishes the basis upon which all science is built. Experimentation is the method of modern science. An experiment is planned according to a hypothesis and carried out under special conditions in the laboratory; it is more restricted than what we ordinarily call experience. (Since this term is open to almost any interpretation, it would be best to drop it. I do not want to be pedantic, however, and so I shall use the term, on occasion, though always in the sense of 'experiment'.)

But the mere collection of facts is not yet science: it is the systematic, ordered, account of our experiments that represents science. We wish to bring into connexion the various facts we have accumulated in a particular field, and so we have to describe our experiments and create theories. A theory is a description of experiments; a linguistic or, rather, a symbolic description since not only words but mathematical and logical symbols are used. A scientific theory, however, is more than mere description, for it must also permit one to predict future experiments, and in this way a test of the theory is made. The customary statement is to say that a scientific theory describes past experiments and predicts future experiments. But such a statement remains a slogan unless we can make clearer what is involved in describing and predicting experiments.

Astrology, I suppose, is equally based on observation, and its adherents claim that they can predict the future. But we would hardly classify it as a science; rather, it is astronomy that everybody accepts as a scientific discipline. Clearly, then, it is not only the subject-matter but the method of dealing with it that is of importance. Science is based on experiment. But its results must also be confirmed by experiment, and so the methods and procedures of science have to be carefully selected. We start with some statements referring to what has been observed; but we wish to relate these statements to one another and to derive other statements from them, and this cannot be done unless we employ appropriate methods, the methods of logic. In actual science this method is mainly given by mathematics and the rules of logic, in the wider sense of this term, are used in the context in which the formulae appear. It is customary to say that the method of deduction allows us to obtain the formal structure of our theories and that the rules of induction are used to confirm our knowledge formulated in the theories. We shall speak later about what 'deduction' and 'induction' may mean; here it will suffice to say this. Although it may be granted that the process of discovery, as observed in the individual scientist, is a complex psychological process, science requires a *formal* representation. For we want to know exactly what our statements assert about the world, and so we have to separate what is the contribution of language and what is due to the experiment. Otherwise we cannot be sure that the success of our theories is genuine. False theories may be quite successful, particularly if they are vague and their meaning cannot be given clearly. Only if we can state precisely the meaning of our sentences can we accept their test by experience as significant.

The description of experience requires the use of language, and we have to escape the 'tyranny of words'. We cannot neglect to analyse our language since it contains 'chance philosophic prejudices imbibed from a nurse or a schoolmaster or current modes of expression'. Science has to develop its own way of speaking, a more precise language: science is in this sense an *artificial* language. We start with colloquial language. But we cannot simply accept it without criticism since it embodies—for historical and psychological reasons—an interpretation that, to-day, is often obsolete. For the common sense underlying ordinary language is a first, crude, approach to knowledge; and it contains the 'faded mythology' that is the first attempt of man to orient himself in the world. The knowledge embedded in our language is derived from the simple experiences of daily life: we cannot expect it to apply to the detailed experience of laboratory and observatory. So we must re-examine the meaning of our words, for we need to know exactly to what, if anything, they refer.

The practice of science shows how to carry out this task: it is mathematical method, and logic, that provide the tools for analysis. The investigations into the foundations of mathematics, from Boole and de Morgan to Bertrand Russell and his successors, have brought about modern mathematical logic and they have created a new understanding of logic and of language. Philosophy, then, is concerned with the logical analysis of language and, in particular, with the analysis of the language of science. At this point philosophy and science come together: for science cannot do without a *critique* of language, while philosophical argument must be based on the knowledge science alone can provide.

Logic is a method invented for a purpose, and the purpose is to analyse our expressions and to make clear the rules according to which they are used. Modern logic is more comprehensive than the traditional discipline: it includes *meaning analysis* as well as what is usually called 'formal logic'. To distinguish the one from the other the term *'semantics'* is often used.

Many scientific theories started by analysing the meaning of previous theories; and Mach's critique of the concepts of Newton's physics which eventually led to relativity theory is an example. The analysis of scientific language, then, must not be underestimated in its value for the actual development of physics. For old theories, and established formulae, sometimes fail; and new theories must be invented. We need more than mere manipulation of formulae: we have to investigate the concepts that underlie both the scientific and our ordinary way of speaking.

The philosophers have not always succeeded in this task, often from their neglect of science. It is easy to show up the errors of philosophers, but scientists also often adopt the wrong attitude. While philosophers are prone to overestimate the power of ideas and to submit to the fascination of words, scientists often underestimate the value of theoretical work and become enamoured of gadgets. While philosophers may, on occasion, indulge in phantasies, scientists sometimes refuse to employ their imagination. Newton's famous dictum 'hypotheses non fingo' is misunderstood. It is all very well to stick to the facts provided one doesn't get stuck in them. This hard-headed attitude was rebuked by Einstein: 'Everything that they learned up to the age of eighteen is believed to be experience. Whatever they hear about later is theory and speculation'.

The growth of science and the need for specialisation which results from it has turned many a scientist into a technician. It has given rise to the belief that the pair of pliers and the soldering iron of the experimentalist, or perhaps the computing machine of the theoretician, are the only tools of physics; that only a grease-stained laboratory coat and dirty hands are the sign of honest work. But progress in science consists not merely in new experiments: it is equally necessary to formulate new theories to describe these experiments, and this requires us to give new meaning to our symbols.

The actual result of such investigations is often not very spectacular and does not lead immediately to new or sensational experiments. In fact, the outcome sometimes appears to be trivial. Logical difficulties are somehow evanescent: it suffices to give a clear formulation, and the problem seems to disappear. But it is wrong to think, if a problem is verbal, that therefore it is not important. If we do not know what our formulae mean we can hardly be expected to know how to apply them correctly.

II
THEORETICAL CONCEPTS

1. *Logical terms*

The knowledge of science is given by its theories and laws, and is therefore expressed in statements. Science is a linguistic, or symbolic, representation of experience. For a scientific theory consists of sentences and equations, and these are, first of all, a series of signs. Signs, that is words as well as the symbols of mathematics, are arranged in a certain order, and we take account of experience by means of signs.

The notion of sign is very general. We say, for instance, that clouds are a sign of rain; or, we have natural signs which indicate a causal correlation between events. Sometimes, the sign is similar to the thing it stands for, in the manner in which a picture represents, and we have iconic signs. Finally, we have conventional signs, or symbols: the flag is the symbol for the country, or the red cross for medicine. The correlation is arbitrary, and it is a matter of convenience and of convention which sign is chosen. This is the case with language: words are conventional signs, or symbols, invented by men for the purpose of communication. They have arisen during the long history of mankind; but for this reason we are not always clear about the use a particular sign may have in a given situation.

The use of symbols not only presupposes a fixed shape of the physical marks by which they are represented. It requires equally that the symbols, or *expressions* (i.e. sequences of symbols), are combined in a definite manner if they are to function according to the intention of the user. The same word, for instance, is used repeatedly, and so we distinguish between the design, or *type*, of a sign and its individual occurrence, or *token*. But the symbols are also used in a certain way, that is, words (and other expressions) must be used according to *rules* if they are to possess meaning. Only then do we have a language.

This approach may appear unduly general. But it helps to remind us that the expressions of our language do not possess an inherent and fixed meaning, but that we give a meaning to them by usage. And this enables us to separate more clearly the two components in the description of nature which we call science: experience and language. For we may use a symbol to refer to some physical thing or event, or we may take it to refer to other symbols. In modern terminology we so distinguish the *semantic* from the *syntactic* use of expressions.

For any *natural*, or historically given, language we must find out by analysis the rules which govern the use of symbols, or the rules of language. Like the symbols, the rules are of course an invention, and they are not always unique. Grammar re-constructs the actual usage of natural language, and so is a first step in formalising language in order to make clearer the meaning of our sentences. But grammar is not a reliable guide on all occasions. Sometimes we change the rules if the historical usage turns out to be inconsistent or incompatible with the need for taking account of new experience. We may even invent new symbols and rules altogether—such as mathematics—or create an *artificial* language and so achieve our aim. Indeed, it has been the invention of mathematics that is mainly responsible for the advance of modern physics.

A linguistic expression usually consists of many symbols, and the sentence is the normal form in which knowledge is expressed. Language of course has many functions; but for science its *informative* use alone is of interest, and the subsequent discussion deals only with *declarative* sentences. The rules of sentence formation are given by grammar. But the rules of grammar are often obscure, and they are variable. Although they work well enough in ordinary life, they do not suffice if we wish to describe experience more accurately.

Aristotelian logic represents another attempt to clarify the formal structure of language and to provide more detailed and restricted rules for the use of language; it is a step towards making language a more reliable instrument for communication. But traditional logic also does not suffice to disentangle the complexities of actual language and to supply the formal framework for the language of science. Misled by every-day language Aristotle made the subject-predicate relation the only form a sentence can possess. Modern logicians have shown that many other, formal, structures are possible, and needed, for a correct analysis of language.

The dead hand of Aristotle—supported by ecclesiastic authority —lay heavy on logic and prevented its development for nearly two thousand years. Logic became barren, and 'logic chopping' the most fruitless of undertakings, a matter for ridicule. And yet it was known that the Aristotelian system is defective since logical paradoxes can be constructed: a pair of sentences can be derived according to the accepted rules which contradict one another.

Such antinomies have been known since antiquity, e.g. created by a vicious circle argument. 'Epimenides the Cretan said that all Cretans are liars' is one instance of a sentence from which a contradiction can obviously be derived. Most people are apt to treat such an antinomy as a joke. Indeed, if we use reasoning of this kind in every-day life, we do not mean to be serious; and so many people laugh this problem out of existence, even to-day. But to find the reasons why the paradoxes occur has turned out to be of great import. It is the work culminating in the *Principia Mathematica* of Russell and Whitehead, and its continuance until to-day, that has made logic fruitful.

The first result of modern logic which is of interest here concerns the character of logic. Logic deals with the purely formal properties of symbols. The symbols are regarded merely as shapes or marks on paper, and the rules according to which they are combined depend only on this formal character. It enables us to derive one sentence from another, a method which is commonly called *deduction*; and one, rather simple, example is the Aristotelian syllogism. 'Socrates is a man' and 'All men are mortal' imply 'Socrates is mortal'. The sentences are related to each other by deductive inference, and in this manner we can transform one sentence into another. The method of derivation is purely formal, and we need not know what the sentences refer to in experience nor whether they are true or false. We must be able to recognise their grammatical structure, that is, we need to know only their formal or logical meaning, or the syntactic rules; but we do not require their empirical or factual meaning, or to use the semantic rules which tell us to what the sentences refer in experience. So, instead of using words we could have used any other symbols, or individual letters to make the deduction, and this is a frequent illustration in the textbooks of logic. Thus, it is true, deduction does not give us new knowledge; but it makes clear what is implicitly contained in the sentences taken as premisses. The syllogism

B

is of course not of very great interest. It shows one possible schema in which deduction can proceed. Modern logic has found many other ways of statement composition and of deductive inference. It was the generalisation of logic, and the power of symbolic method, that made possible the great progress in the analysis of scientific theory as we know it to-day.

The second result of modern logic concerns the nature of mathematics. Mathematics as well is shown to be purely formal in character, and the whole of mathematics can be derived, in principle, from a few simple logical notions by means of deductive inference. This is a most important result, and it represents the great achievement of *Principia Mathematica*.

The recognition of the formal character of pure mathematics explains the success of the mathematical method in science. It is no mystery that mathematics fits the physical world, and there is no need to invoke intuition or to assume a special power of reason. Because it is formal, mathematics fits all and every kind of experience, and is concerned only with the correct operation of symbols regarding quantity and number. The 'abstract' symbolism of mathematics—the employment of symbols specially invented—has a great advantage over ordinary language. We are less tempted to presuppose a special interpretation for them and so better able, psychologically, to use them in the formal manner for which they are intended. This advantage equally applies to logic, and modern logic is mathematical or symbolic logic. The use of technical symbols permits us to avoid the pitfalls that natural language puts in our way, and we can give logical statements the precise formulation of mathematics.

The third result of mathematical logic arises from the more detailed analysis of the concept of number: it is shown that symbols are of different *logical type*. The theory of logical types was first enunciated by Russell when he investigated the foundations of mathematics and is necessary to solve the contradiction of 'the greatest cardinal number'.

We need not go into technical details in order to understand the notion of logical type. For its application, in a limited sense, to every-day discourse may serve as example—a kind of example which, in a vague and obscure manner, has been known ever since philosophy began. Let us look at our room, where we have chairs, tables, and similar things. All these objects are collectively called 'furniture'. The logical rule states that we must not commit the mistake of confusing types. In ordinary language the word 'furniture' is not of the same type as 'chair' or 'table'. We cannot say, for instance, that one chair, a table, and the furniture make, together, three objects; that is, we cannot simply add. Of course, no one would make this mistake in ordinary life. But in more unfamiliar, or technical, discourse it is not easy to see the difference in logical type, and as a result we end up with meaningless sentences.

'Furniture' is the word used to designate the class of physical things that are designated, in turn, by 'chair' and 'table'; and we must distinguish between the class and its members.

This may be illustrated by an example. Following Russell we may form the assemblage of all classes that are not members of themselves. This is again a class; but the (as it turns out illegitimate) question arises whether or not it is a member of itself. If it is, then it is one of those classes that are not members of themselves: thus it is not a member of itself. If it is not, then it is not one of those classes that are not members of themselves: thus it is a member of itself. Each of the two possible assumptions leads to a contradiction. The confusion of logical types of signs creates sentences that are meaningless. It makes no sense to say that a class either is, or is not, a member of itself. Such a sentence is meaningless since it has been put together in violation of a logical rule. It is not a statement which is either true or false. A false statement is quite meaningful since it asserts something to be the case which, in fact, is not the case. But a meaningless sentence states nothing and is a sequence of idle symbols to which the concept of truth does not apply.

It is not a trivial insight to understand that we may, unwittingly, use symbols in such a way that they no longer symbolise anything. To discover that sentences can be formed correctly according to the usual rules of grammar but all the same be meaningless was of first-rate importance.

Signs, or symbols, that is words, are of different logical types. We have signs to designate or name physical things; then there are signs of signs to designate signs; and so on in a hierarchy of logical types. Of course, this does not mean that a given sign, or word, possesses—by its very nature—a certain type, or that there is an intrinsic type. It depends how the word is *used* in a given context. A word has a certain logical type only by virtue of the manner in which we use it; and we normally follow the usage of every-day language.

For instance, we may speak of the negro race, that is, of the class of negroes: 'race' is a word which in this context denotes the totality of negroes. We cannot attribute the same properties to a class which we believe to apply to the individual members. We may say that negroes are coloured, when we wish to refer to the property of skin pigmentation. We do not say that the class of negroes or the word 'race' is coloured. But we often speak, elliptically, of the 'coloured race': we mean that one of the properties by which we intend to characterize all negroes is to possess a certain kind of skin coloration. In this instance, we closely skirt the danger of unwarranted generalisation, for we attempt to define a class by means of a characteristic found in a limited number of its members. It may turn out that, in fact, a property found to belong to some members of a class does not apply to all of them, and then we must not use it in defining the class.

Or, let us consider the United Nations: it is a class of still higher logical type since it denotes a class of classes in ordinary usage. Its members are nations, that is, classes of people, or peoples, and not people. Individuals are members of nations, but not of the United Nations; and the United Nations is not a new nation which may be added to the number of existing nations. 'The United Nations' is a word denoting a class of classes, or a class which has other classes as members; and these classes, that is the nations of the earth, in turn have individuals as their members. In this context 'individual', 'nation', and 'United Nations', are used as signs of successive logical type.

In ordinary usage we consider that only individuals possess physical properties. We say that physical things have weight, size, or shape, and then we cannot say that classes of physical things have the same properties. Some of the traditional problems of philosophy have their origin in this lack of discrimination, in particular, the problems concerning the use of the word 'to exist'. If we decide to ascribe existence to physical things such as chairs and tables, we cannot in the same sense say that the class exists which contains these things as members. If chairs and tables exist in the physical sense (and this is the normal usage), then furniture does not exist: 'furniture' is a word of higher logical type. There is of course no necessity to use the word 'exist' in this way: we are free to apply it to classes. But if we do so, we cannot use it in the same sense when we speak of the members of the class. Certain philosophers have, to some extent, acknowledged this difference by saying that the class *subsists*. We must then realise that 'subsistence' is a term with a meaning completely different from that of 'existence', otherwise this terminology merely increases the confusion. Take as example a modern version of the problem of universals. Every word, except a proper name, is a universal since it may be applied significantly to more than one instance. So the word 'chair' is a universal, for there are many individual chairs that can be so named, and there is an infinity of words, or tokens (i.e. marks on paper) of the universal word. The question is, then, whether or not universals exist. Since the use of the word 'word' in this instance is ambiguous as to logical type, we must make a decision. If we say in accordance with ordinary language that the individual token of a word exists—that is the mark on paper—then we cannot say that the universal exists in the same sense. There is no doubt that the theory of types at least clarifies, if it does not solve, the problem of universals.

The language of every-day life is not strict regarding the logical type; for instance, it does not prescribe precise rules for the use of quotation marks, and words of different type are used side by side. Though in many contexts not much harm comes from this neglect, in science, and sometimes in ordinary discourse as well, serious puzzles are created if no heed is taken. Sentences are produced that are meaningless, but we fail to recognise them as such and try to find out whether they are true or false.

The notion of logical type is applied not only to individual symbols but to sentences as a whole. Here again the theory of *levels* of language has given us a better insight into the working of language. Language consists of signs, and so we must distinguish between languages constituted by signs of different logical type.

One instance is given by the distinction between a physical thing and its name. When we say that 'London' has six letters, everyone knows that we speak about the word 'London' and not about the city so named, even though in speaking we cannot indicate this difference by the quotation marks we use in writing. The familiar context makes clear that we understand this distinction:

'London' has six letters, but London has some six million inhabitants. So when we say 'London is large', the sentence is about
London and contains 'London': we *mention* London by *using*
its name, or speak about the city by naming it. When we say
' "London" has six letters', the sentence is about 'London' and
contains " 'London' ", for " 'London' " designates 'London'
which, in turn, designates London; and so on.

This appears to be a trivial distinction. Why should the correct
use of quotation marks be of such importance to logic? The
reason is that we do not always deal with such simple examples.
When we discuss 'abstract', or technical, subjects the distinction
is by no means clear at first sight; and we may have also to build
up a whole hierarchy of levels since we might want to speak not
only of things and of their names, but of names of names, etc.
Quotation marks are not indispensable but customary and useful
(we may use different symbols and words to distinguish types and
levels). Actually, we often avoid their use by a circumlocution,
and this is an added difficulty.

We say, then, that the language we speak ordinarily, e.g. to
describe something, is the *object-language*, and the language in
which we speak about the first language is the *meta-language*; and
so on in a hierarchy of levels of language. The distinction is of
course relative. We speak in ordinary English about mathematics.
In this instance the symbols of mathematics constitute an object-
language, while we use every-day language as meta-language. In
fact, it is from mathematics that we have learned to make this
distinction. Hilbert first coined the term 'meta-mathematics' to
distinguish the language in which we speak *about* mathematics
from the language *of* mathematics. In this context 'language'—
strictly speaking—means 'language system', that is, we presuppose that we have succeeded in formalising the language in
question and so assume that we know its axioms, definitions, and
rules.

The term 'language' is ambiguous, particularly in English, and
it is so for two reasons. First, the word means what, e.g. in French,
is distinguished from one another by 'langue' and 'langage': that
is, a historically given, or *natural*, language (as in the phrase 'the
French tongue') and a special way of using this language.

It is only in the latter sense that we may contrast natural and
scientific language. To say that the language of science is *artificial*

merely means that its vocabulary is enriched by certain technical terms and that these terms (and any expressions also current in ordinary discourse it may contain) are used in science according to rules which may differ from those of customary grammar. Though the language of physics, for instance, is often as incomprehensible to the layman as if it were Chinese, it is not a *foreign* language; and speaking scientifically is still speaking English. Indeed, the dichotomy between natural and scientific language is false: there is a continuous range of using language, from the most informal use to the most formal and technical manner of speaking.

But a second ambiguity of the term 'language' remains which arises from the present discussion, i.e. from the distinction between object-language and meta-language. For we sometimes take 'language' as implying a reference to the rules of language. We may mean, e.g. by 'ordinary language', that we intend to express ourselves in accordance with the rules of ordinary grammar. Or we speak of the 'thing-language' meaning that, in such a language, all expressions are construed according to a certain scheme taken from every-day discourse; we speak there about simple things like chairs and tables and this usage is taken as a paradigm, for example, when we are told the rule that nouns are thing-words.

The rules of grammar, or of any other kind of usage, are sentences which are of course not *in* the language we speak but *about* it: they belong to the meta-language. And as anyone knows who ever tried to learn a foreign language by studying merely its grammar, the rules are not needed for speaking a language. Though it is useful to know *that* there are rules and *what* they are, to know *how* to apply them, that is, to speak the language, is a different matter. The rules are needed for *explaining* the use of an expression whenever we are doubtful about what the expression means. For the rules are invented by the grammarian, or by the logician, or by the scientist, so as to reproduce as closely as possible a standard usage for the main expressions in the language used; and so we can appeal to them if we want to make clear what we mean. To show that we include the meta-linguistic scheme of grammar, or of any other set of rules, we often employ the terms 'language system' or 'formalised language'. But here, again, there are degrees of formalisation to be considered. Certainly, grammar is not a complete and exhaustive system of rules, even for ordinary usage. Though such systems exist for special, and very restricted, disciplines, e.g. of mathematics, we shall have to be content with giving only some rules for the main expressions, say, of a certain theory of physics.

It is good policy to set out clearly these distinctions in order to avoid misunderstanding. But one need not be too pedantic, since the context will show what sense of the term 'language' is employed in a given instance. No great harm is done if we are less cautious. We may say, for instance, that when learning French we speak in English about French, and then French is our object-language and English the meta-language. It is true that natural languages are not formalised. But, from the semantic point of view, they are capable of formalisation at least to some degree, otherwise we cannot make them precise enough for the purposes of scientific discourse. Any language whatever may be taken as object-language, and any language which contains expressions designating symbols or sentences of the object-language may be taken as meta-language. And we may use parts of the same, natural, language to represent the two languages. Indeed, we normally speak in English about English, taking a part of our vocabulary as object-language and our total vocabulary as meta-language; in this manner the meta-language is a mixture of the first and second level but becomes impure as to type, which requires caution. Ordinary language anyway does not discriminate between levels of language, and this is the reason why certain paradoxes arise. But the distinction must be made, at least for a limited purpose, within a specified context. It is only, for example, in this manner that we can define, clearly and unambiguously, the concept of truth.

The *semantic conception of truth* has arisen from the investigations into the logical foundations of mathematics and was first formulated by A. Tarski. This conception represents a great achievement. It makes obsolete the two theories of truth—the so-called correspondence and the coherence theory—which stem from traditional epistemology. And it represents a re-construction of the concept of truth that is closer to both the ordinary and the scientific usage of the term 'true' than the previous theories. Indeed the semantic conception of truth is very close to the classic concept first formulated by Aristotle in

$Περὶ Ἑρμηνείας:$ " εἰ γὰρ ἀληθὲς εἰπεῖν ὅτι λευκὸν ἢ ὅτι οὐ λευκόν ἐστιν, ἀνάγκη εἶναι λευκὸν ἢ οὐ λευκόν."

(For to say truly whether something is white or not white, it is necessary that it be white or not white).

To give a brief indication let us see how the concept of truth is made more clear by the distinction of levels of language. When we say, It is true that snow is white, we mean to say that, in fact, snow is white. (The phrase 'in fact' has no function save emphasis). Or, the sentence 'snow is white' is true. We wish to *assert* this sentence by using the word 'true'. And 'snow is white' is true if, and only if, snow is white. The expression 'snow is white' occurs twice: as itself and, between quotation marks, as its name.

This is necessary from the viewpoint of ordinary grammar. Whenever we speak about a thing it is the name of the thing which must be used, and not the thing itself. Thus, when we say something about a sentence, for instance, that it is true, we must make use of the name of the sentence, and not of the sentence itself. The two sentences " 'Snow is white' is true" and 'Snow is white' are equivalent; they differ only by their emphasis, by the pragmatic aspect of their formulation, and not in truth-value. To assert that a sentence is true is the same as to assert the sentence itself. Truth, thus, is not a relation between an expression and a physical thing as is often mistakenly believed. Rather, the word 'true' is of different logical character, for it denotes a property of a sentence and so is used as term of the meta-language. And it is a particularly pleasing aspect of the semantic conception of truth that it combines, in this way, the two features of the traditional theories that we normally feel to be of import in the meaning of 'true'.

We preserve the correspondence with fact since we assert a sentence as true if, and only if, the sentence holds. And we show up the coherence of our system of knowledge since only language formalised as a system permits a complete and adequate definition of the concept of truth by stating precise rules for the usage of this word. For a natural language, though in some sense open (i.e. more flexible than a language system), is semantically closed. It contains, apart from its expressions, also the names of these expressions as well as semantic terms such as 'true', and we assume that all sentences containing this term can be asserted in the language. At the same time we also assume that in this language the ordinary laws of logic hold. But this allows us to construct antinomies such as the Liar, and so natural language is inconsistent. An adequate definition of 'true' can be given only for a formalised language, or language system.

The concept of truth, then, can be strictly applied only within a formalised language; and to be precise we must say that a sentence is true *in a language system*.

But here an objection has been raised. Truth is said to be linguistically neutral: whatever is true is true in any language. And do we not speak sometimes of true facts or true propositions? This would indicate that the concept of truth is not always used meta-linguistically, and so the semantic conception seems to be not universally applicable.

Indeed, we do speak in the object-language normally, both in science and in every-day conversation. This use of the word 'true' has been called the *absolute* concept of truth. The semantic conception does not require that the concept is always used in the meta-language, though it often is, e.g. in 'It is true that . . .'. When giving a logical re-construction of a concept we must speak about it and so cannot help using a meta-language; only then can we make clear the usage of a word. It is a serious mistake to believe that semantics always forces us to speak in the meta-language; hence the strange idea that semantics is concerned only with words. Not at all—semantics is the logical analysis of meaning; and to know the meaning we must also consider to what our sentences refer. I use the word 'tree' to refer to something in the garden; but when I want to find out whether the word is correctly used, I must speak *about* it. We use words to refer to something extra-linguistic, at least sometimes; for example, scientific theories are usually in the object-language since they are intended to describe physical events.

We can always use any word, including 'true', in the object-language; but we may also use it in the meta-language. The two concepts (or, better, usages) correspond: they represent *two different ways* of speaking. So when we speak in the object-language *alone* (without the help of a meta-language), e.g. 'This is true', we have no means of speaking *about* our expressions. Hence no *explicit* reference can be made to the language system in which the sentence occurs; and this is the absolute usage, or linguistic neutrality.

The objection is based upon a double confusion, between mention and use of expressions, and between mentioning a

sentence and designating what it refers to, e.g. the thing or proposition. The absolute usage is implicit and incomplete; the use
of 'true' in the meta-language is explicit and complete. The
semantic conception states all the conditions under which the
concept of truth is explicitly used; so both usages are re-constructed by it, and it is the same concept. For to say '(A proposition)
p is true' is the same as to assert the sentence which expresses the
proposition ; and by saying 'It is true in the language system L
that . . .' everything is openly said that needs be said.

A natural language is semantically closed, i.e. admits paradoxes.
When re-constructing the concept of truth (which is not giving
another epistemological theory about the 'nature of truth') we do
not imitate natural language but avoid the paradoxes by suitable
formalisation. In this sense, the semantic conception of truth may
be said to disagree with ordinary usage; but surely it agrees with
our intention, since otherwise we cannot use the word 'true' unambiguously. At least in science we want to be able to do so: we
want not only to speak the truth (which we can always do even
without formalisation) but also to *show* that our statements are
true. The semantic conception of truth demonstrates that this
can be done, strictly, only for formalised languages. We therefore
need formalisation so that we can speak *about* our statements and
explain their meaning. The semantic conception is basic and
indispensable: without it we cannot give an adequate account of
the theoretical methods of science.

The distinction of levels of language then shows the antinomy
of the Liar to be capable of solution. This is seen to involve a
meaningless sentence, a proof that is of great import to logical
theory.

When Epimenides the Cretan says that all Cretans are liars, it
is the self-reference which violates logical rules and makes the
sentence meaningless. If we use instead of 'that' the quotation
marks which are in place here we see that two different levels are
involved. The Cretan says 'all Cretans are liars'. The words
included in the quotation marks represent a single sign of a higher
logical type; it is a sign of a sign and so an expression of the
meta-language. If we had at our disposal a special sign that
designated the expression 'all Cretans are liars'—say 'acal'—then
no more is meant here than that Epimenides the Cretan says
'acal'. It is a mistake to speak *about* a linguistic expression *in* the

language to which it belongs, and this mistake produces the anti-nomy. So when we say, It is true that London is large, we must not forget that, in this instance, the term 'that' has a special function. Fortunately grammar does not allow us to say, It is true London is large; we feel that a distinction which is indispensable is obliterated.

In 'abstract', and unfamiliar, discourse we are often tempted, unwittingly, to make this mistake: we fail to separate use and mention of expressions, but this can only end in confusion and error. Traditional philosophy provides ample illustration. When a metaphysician asks, for instance, about the nature of the universe, he believes he is asking a question of fact. But the 'universe' is normally taken to denote the class of all physical events and is used, therefore, as a term of the meta-language. To ask, What is the nature of the universe, is to ask for the use of a name—it is a question regarding grammar, and not a question of fact.

Of course, it would be strange if, in ordinary life, we would continually endeavour to maintain this distinction of levels. It would in fact be utter pedantry, since the context usually clarifies the usage of a word in question. But we can adopt an attitude of tolerance only after we have understood what to be tolerant about.

We do use language elliptically, and we confuse use and mention of words; but in scientific discourse this ellipsis is in-tolerable since it engenders paradoxes. Science, historically speaking, was built up with the explicit use of Aristotelian logic, a system which is faulty not only for the reason that it overlooks the distinction of types and levels of language. True that, impli-citly, better notions and methods were used in science. Modern logic, after all, is a direct outcome of mathematics and physics; it represents the methodology of modern science. It is now the task, however, to apply, openly and directly, the tools mathematical logic and semantics put at our disposal.

The account of modern logic given in this section is not com-plete and, for this reason, neither very adequate nor entirely accurate: it is a rough and ready account, a first approximation. But it will suffice to guide our analysis of the theory of physical science; the necessary refinement and adjustment of our termi-nology will be introduced as the need arises.

2. *Mathematical terms*

Einstein once described science as 'an attempt to make the chaotic diversity of our sense impressions correspond to a logically uniform system of thought'.

What, then, is a system? Historically, it was Euclid who, with his axiom system of geometry, first demonstrated the advantage of ordering our statements in a definite manner. The clarity so obtained, the apparent certainty of the statements derived, and the simplicity of the method of derivation, were a great attraction to philosopher and scientist alike. To philosophize, *more geometrico*, became the aspiration of many philosophers.

But there is a world of difference, in method and in purpose and in content, between a philosophic system and the logical systems of science. This is necessary to emphasize even to-day, since there is often so much talk about First Principles.

Historically, science does not start with first principles, but the system of science evolves in a slow and painstaking way, with many difficulties and détours. The history of science is not science itself. The study of the development of science may be of interest for this purpose; but it cannot solve the problem of finding these principles. For the assumptions underlying a given branch of science, and the requirements a scientific theory has to satisfy, are not clear at the beginning when a new science is founded. The discovery of scientific theories, interesting as it may be, must be distinguished from their logical justification. And first principles come last, if ever: it is certainly of no use to start with preconceived notions. The indirect attack is more likely to produce results. First principles are not what traditional philosophers have believed them to be: there are no statements about experience that are unalterable and eternal, not even in science. When we sometimes speak, loosely, of principles, we merely mean to refer to some postulate or general sentence which represents, at any given stage of development, a convenient and short summary of some important results, e.g. the principle of conservation of energy. But new experiments may lead to new results and, therefore, to new principles. Such principles are, actually, often used as definitions and so say nothing about the world. But if they are used as postulates, i.e. as empirical sentences, they are accepted only if we can build up with their help a logically consistent system that can be tested by experiment.

The quest for certainty has often animated philosophers but is pursued too far. It is necessary to separate the psychological from the logical component in our intellectual activities. There is no doubt that the desire of human beings to systematise, to create order, springs largely from a psychological need. We wish to reduce the wide and bewildering variety of experience, and so want to derive from a small number of fundamental assumptions all the sentences that embody actual and possible knowledge. We seem to be unable to keep in our heads all the facts we have accumulated, and it appears that our limited brain capacity leads us to construct systems.

This psychological desire is only one aspect that shows up in the process of system construction: it is a motive for, rather than a justification of, the system of science. Naturally, psychological need is prior, in the order of time, to the logical requirements a theory has to satisfy. And what is logically fundamental comes later—but it is this logical character that is of import to the analysis and methodology of science, and it safeguards the results of science.

After all, when we wish to develop a theory, when we set up a system, we have to start with something: we must make some assumptions. In order to construct a system we start with primitive sentences—axioms or postulates—that give the subject-matter to be systematised: they represent what we consider to be the most relevant knowledge of the field in question. This shows that we must know already something before we can attempt to re-construct our knowledge as a logical system. Further, we need definitions stating in familiar words what we wish to understand by a new term we require, or giving explicitly the implicit meaning of a word. For instance, 'mathematical point' is defined as 'intersection of two straight lines'. By this verbal definition we introduce new words into the vocabulary used in our system. It presupposes of course that we have knowledge outside the field to be axiomatized, and that we possess a stock of known words we can use for this purpose. Finally, we need rules: rules that tell us what form of definitions and sentences are to be admitted to the system; and rules of inference or proof that allow us to infer one sentence from another, or to derive theorems. In this manner the axioms become sentences that contain implicitly the knowledge the system as a whole will provide explicitly. For from the axioms, together with the definitions, we derive formally the theorems; and the theorems state explicitly what appears at first sight to be new knowledge.

The system of Euclid has remained a model of an axiom system until to-day; but a radical change has occurred in our understanding of the nature of the axioms and, also, of the rules. The truth of the system, it was argued, must lie in the truth of its axioms; since the theorems are derived from them, and since the theorems turn out to be valid, we must ascribe absolute certainty to the axioms. But how can any statement be certain? Some philosophers have answered that the axioms—say, of mathematics—are self-evident, and they are supposed to be so because they represent the very principles of thought.

Mathematics is a formal system; by itself, without interpretation it says nothing about the world or about human minds. It is like a game of chess, an analogy so often used; the theorems follow formally from the initial assumptions contained in the axioms, by rules of deductive inference. And the axioms are the invention of the mathematician. Of course, as with everything human beings do, it is experience that suggests to us a particular axiom, or set of axioms. But this psychological origin contributes nothing to the logical import and to the justification of the axioms. For mathematical axioms are sentences which are not in a *factual* sense true (or false). The theorems of pure mathematics say nothing about the world, since they are sentences used for showing the relations between symbols. As Bertrand Russell said in a famous *bon mot*: 'In mathematics no one knows what he is talking about, nor whether what he is saying is true'.

In mathematics we make use of symbols invented for a purpose; we give rules to govern their use; and we invent axioms which endow a combination of symbols with certain properties. From the logical point of view, it is an arbitrary invention. Psychologically, it is true we would not speak about numbers, or about geometrical figures, if experience did not suggest such notions in some sense. It is well known that the Egyptians invented geometrical concepts in order to cope with the periodic floodings of their land by the Nile. But, logically, the system of pure geometry is empty so far as knowledge of the external world is concerned. It is by logic, through the formal application of rules, that theorems are derived; and only when we misapply a rule, or miscalculate, must a theorem be rejected. But it is rejected on formal grounds, and we need not appeal to experiment to do so.

However, we must be careful to retain a critical attitude; otherwise it becomes a slogan when we say that mathematics is empty. Tarski pointed out this danger of over-simplification. When constructing a deductive system we need not make use of the meaning of the terms, but this is not the same as denying all meaning to them. We treat the primitive terms as variables, and in this way the theory functions as a formal system. But it is always possible to give various interpretations to an axiom system, and indeed that is the reason why we are interested in it. The interpretation may be of two sorts. We may interpret a formal axiom system by special, technical terms, that is we set up a certain mathematical system. Or we may apply the system, say to physics, that is, we interpret it in terms of a certain kind of experience. When we insist on saying that an axiom system is formal, we merely assert that we wish to treat the symbols of the system according to rules we have arbitrarily specified. So when we say that a mathematical formula is a tautology we mean that, provided we replace the symbols according to given rules, the formula always holds. Or when we say that the sentences occurring in mathematics are *analytic* we mean to say that they are used according to *syntactic* rules, i.e. rules that refer only to the shape of the symbols and the logical character of the expressions. We use mathematical terms according to their *logical* meaning, but need no knowledge of the external world to do so. But we do know a logical meaning. We know what 'variable', 'constant', etc., mean, for we define these terms by a known meta-language, or give a special, mathematical, interpretation. We define what 'point' means in pure geometry, but we need not know what 'point' means in physical geometry, i.e. in experience.

It is for this reason that pure mathematics says nothing about experience and that it can be used to describe experience. Since mathematical systems say nothing about the world, we can interpret them in terms of experience, for they fit all and any experience. It is often said that a system represents an empty shell or form, and we can give it a content; or, the skeleton can be covered by any kind of clothes: but it is true that the fit may be better or worse. If we *apply* mathematics, we are free to choose the kind of mathematics by which to describe a particular kind of experience:

but the choice is so made that we can describe as simply and as completely as possible all the experience we have in the field in question. Thus, both matrix algebra and differential equations may be used to describe quantum mechanics. And at any time we are free to introduce still another kind of mathematics, e.g. group theory, if experience makes it advisable to do so.

It is the order that a formal system can give to our arrangement of symbols—whether interpreted or not—which provides the great advantage. The interrelation of sentences is made clear and the logical structure of the theory can now be seen. An axiom system is, in principle, acceptable if it fulfills three conditions: the axioms must be mutually independent, the system must be consistent, and it must be complete.

The *independence* of axioms is mainly demanded for reasons of economy. We want to construct a system that does not contain superfluous axioms, i.e. an axiom that can be derived from the remaining set of axioms of the system, for it could then be regarded as a consequence of the theory. The demand for an independent axiom system need not be strictly maintained. Often we admit superfluous axioms to a given system since it makes the system as a whole less complicated and so gives a practical advantage.

The system is *consistent* if it does not contain contradictions. It must not be possible to derive two theorems, by correct application of the rules, which contradict each other. Or, of any two contradictory sentences at least one *cannot* be proved.

A system is *complete* if it allows us to derive all theorems that can be formulated exclusively in terms of the theory. Or, of any two contradictory sentences at least one *can* be proved.

This terminology may be applied to the primitive terms, the axioms, and to the theory as a whole. To quote Tarski 'a deductive theory is consistent if no sentence can be both proved and disproved in it; a theory is complete, if every sentence formulated in the terms of this theory can be proved or disproved in it'. Thus, the demand for consistency is made by the logical law of contradiction—not both a and non-a—and completeness by the law of excluded middle—either a or non-a. The consistency and completeness of a system is required for the full formalisation of a theory: a theory being consistent allows us to decide any problem by at most one answer, and being complete by at least

c

one answer. It is clear that completeness creates the greater difficulties. And the problem arises to find a general method so that we can decide whether or not any sentence formulated in terms of the theory can be proved within this theory. This is the famous *decision problem* first stated by Hilbert when he investigated the foundations of mathematics.

To quote Tarski once more 'by a decision *method* for a class K of sentences (or other expressions) is meant a method by means of which, given any sentence θ, one can always decide in a *finite* number of steps whether θ is in K; by a decision *problem* for a class K we mean the problem of finding a decision method for K. A decision method must be like a recipe, which tells us what to do at each step so that no intelligence is required to follow it . . .'.

There are few deductive theories that can actually be shown to satisfy the ideal of being both consistent and complete. One example is given by elementary geometry. But when we wish to extend our investigations, say, to advanced geometry or to arithmetic, we encounter insuperable difficulties. It will never be possible to construct a consistent and complete theory of arithmetic containing as its theorems all true sentences that can be formulated; nor is it possible to provide a *general* method which would enable us to separate the sentences provable within this theory from those which cannot be proved. This is, in brief, and in non-technical terms, the content of the famous theorem of Gödel.

Gödel's theorem, when first published in 1930, plunged many logicians and mathematicians into the pit of despair. The hopes for a complete axiomatisation of mathematics which had been raised by Hilbert's successful research into the foundations of geometry were dashed. Even to-day, twenty years later, there are still people who believe that Gödel's theorem represents the ultimate failure of logic and mathematics. But, to paraphrase Mark Twain, the reports of the early demise of logistic are greatly exaggerated.

What does Gödel's theorem mean? It does *not* mean that there *are* definite theorems for which we can prove that we cannot decide upon their validity. Such a proof would suffice to show that the theorem is not derivable from the axiom system in question, while the completeness of the system would allow us to prove the contradictory of the theorem. Thus the validity of the theorem *can* be decided, and the answer is in the negative.

It is necessary to understand that the problem of decision is a semantic problem, and so we must distinguish the two levels of language that are involved. We cannot make general statements *about* the theorems of a theory *within* the theory itself. When we speak about the theory—that is the object-language—we need another, and richer, theory, a meta-theory—that is a meta-language.

That we require a meta-mathematics in order to prove the consistency and completeness of mathematics, or that we need a meta-language in order to formalise an object-language, does not mean that we are confronted with the final break-down of logic and mathematics. This misunderstanding appears to rest upon a strange conception of what we consider the formal character of a theory to be. We formalise an object-language relative to a known meta-language. The fact that the meta-language is usually not itself formalised, and that it contains among its expressions also the sentences of the object-language, does not invalidate the formalisation of the object-language. We can, if we wish to do so, formalise the meta-language also by introducing a meta-meta-language; and so on. The fact that the meta-language is not formalised, i.e. that we do not know whether it is consistent or not, does not affect the consistency of the object-language. It is only when we set up, perhaps unwittingly, an impossible, absolute standard by which to measure the formal character of a system, that we are disappointed. When we speak of the logical hierarchy of languages, this does not mean that the language of higher level must be, so to speak, logically better, i.e. more formalised.

Formalisation is a technique to make the meaning of our sentences clearer within a definite context. For example, a child learns elementary arithmetic by being told in ordinary language how to manipulate the symbols and to apply the rules. We speak about the symbols '2', '4', and about multiplication in terms of what the child knows, and so it learns that twice two makes four; finally, it understands the equation '$2 \times 2 = 4$', and the multiplication table, as a formal procedure and can make use of the machine-like functioning of the calculus. In this way elementary arithmetic is made more precise by talking about it in ordinary language. It seems natural that we can treat an object-language in a formal manner, or that we can regard the symbols as marks on paper, only if we know that they *are* marks on paper. We must understand the meaning, for instance, of the sentence 'there are two parallel lines between two letters' in order to know that we deal with an equality.

Gödel's theorem, far from being a catastrophe, has emphasized the semantic character of scientific theory, and so provided a better insight into the formal structure of a system. And it shows up what we may call the 'piece-meal method of science': we can never set up a single, universal, comprehensive system of knowledge which contains all the knowledge there is. For the meta-language required to formalise it (to show that it does not contain any contradictions) must be richer than the object-language, even if this additional knowledge consists only in one sentence more than the object-language; and so the system would not be comprehensive. In other words, we cannot solve all problems at the same time. As Ramsey said, we can make several things clearer but we cannot make anything clear.

3. *Physical terms*

While mathematics may be regarded as a formal system which says nothing about the world, physics does describe experience. And since a physical theory is usually formulated in mathematical terms, we see that it must contain, apart from mathematics, another component referring to the physical world. A physical theory thus consists of at least two parts: a formal calculus and the interpretation in terms of experience. The calculus itself may also contain two parts: the mathematical equations, and logical symbols and rules; for the moment we need not consider this distinction and take both as formal. We then speak of a physical theory as possessing a formal calculus and a system of *semantic* rules that provide the interpretation. The semantic rules establish the meaning of the statements of the theory; ultimately, they provide the link with experience, and in this manner we give an interpretation. It was Einstein who, in his famous essay on 'Geometry and Experience' pointed out the difference between mathematical and physical geometry, and this difference demonstrates the semantic character of a physical theory.

In pure mathematics we are interested in working out only the relations between symbols and other expressions; we have *syntactic* rules which refer only to the formal properties of the expressions, and the resulting sentences are *analytic*. In physics we wish to describe the world, and so the *semantic* rules must in some way have extra-linguistic reference, for the sentences are either analytic or have factual import, i.e. are *synthetic*. This distinction between analytic and synthetic sentences goes back of course to Kant and has such wide currency even to-day that it would be odd not to use it; but its employment here differs significantly since no epistemological assumptions are implied. The terminology is merely a convenient classification and applies only to *declarative* sentences; and no sentence is inherently either analytic or synthetic but becomes so solely by its use in a given context. There are only two ways in which declarative sentences are used, either as referring to symbols or to experience; and the distinction is merely a logical re-construction of actual usage, within a semantic system. For example, when we say, Roses are red, we may take the sentence as synthetic, i.e. announce the genuine discovery that there are in fact red roses. Or, it may be an analytic sentence, i.e. state our decision that we count only red flowers as roses (apart from whatever other properties they may have). It all depends on what meaning we wish to give to a sentence, or on the rules according to which we use the sentence, and so the distinction holds strictly only within a formalised language.

It is unfortunately true that there is no part of physics that can be said to be completely formalised as a system. At best, we find a 'mathematization'. The mathematical part is presented properly in terms of axioms, definitions, and mathematical rules. But the logical part is tacitly presupposed in the usage of the terms; and the interpretation is not given as a semantic system but is expressed, usually, in the context.

Physics is formalised only to a limited extent and has not yet received the complete formalisation that the demands of logic make advisable. For in spite of this lack, physics has been so successful up to now that physicists did not bother to follow this line of development. Rather they concentrated—understandably —on making new experiments, and on inventing new theories to account for these experiments. However, we have arrived to-day at an impasse: existing theories have become very complicated, and the wealth of new experiments can no longer be described adequately by them. We must revise our old theories and so recast them, as much as it is possible, in a logically improved form, as semantic systems. For we want to give a better analysis of our concepts and find out which concepts have to be changed and what new concepts have to be introduced.

Physicists have always tried to present their theories in terms of definitions, axioms, and theorems; and thus the theorems are the laws that state the content of the theory in terms of experience. Newton himself wrote down his system of mechanics in this manner. However, his system of definitions and axioms falls short of the requirements of logic: it is very difficult to formulate even a simple theory like Newtonian mechanics as a strict deductive system, and all attempts to do so have, so far, ended in failure. Nevertheless, much has been learnt from these attempts.

After all, science grows slowly. A logically adequate representation of a theory can be expected to be found only after all the facts are known, and the theory is completed. Then we can re-arrange the theory so that it acquires the correct logical form, i.e. give a logical re-construction. But it must be emphasized that all system construction in science is provisional. We can never know —even for the most developed part of classical physics—whether there will not be new facts that cannot be described by the system. No dogmatic attitude will do; but this should not discourage us from attempting to re-construct physics as a semantic system. The fact that we present a theory as an axiom system—or, rather, that we try to do so—does not mean that we are not allowed to change the system. We still have the advantage of the orderly arrangement that a theory possesses only in this form, and this permits us to see more clearly whether or not the theory is satisfactory.

For this reason it is not a serious objection that, in the early stages of development of a theory, our data are usually insufficient to construct an adequate system. If in spite of this we endeavour to cast a theory in an axiomatic form, it does not mean that we are obliged to stick to it, come what may. Psychologically, perhaps, we may feel some disinclination to give it up; but the warnings often uttered against trying to systematise our knowledge too soon are hardly justified. There is no logical reason for believing that, by a premature formalisation, our ideas may be misdirected. Aristotelian physics, though not formalised, is of course a good example of petrification: but it was imposed by external authority.

The recent Lysenko episode is still fresh in our minds, and the encyclical *Humani Generis* (1950) states that discussion on evolution may proceed only provided 'that all are prepared to submit to the judgment of the church . . .'. But politics apart, it is always of logical advantage to try at least to separate more general from less general statements, and to endeavour to find axioms, so that we become a little clearer about fundamental assumptions. There is no danger as long as we understand that all theories of science, and all systems, are tentative, however well confirmed they may be. We must be ready to change them if experience requires it and, in an extreme case, to abandon them altogether. The history of physics gives many examples of theories that were totally abandoned: Newton's corpuscular theory of light, Neumann's vortex theory of electricity, Fresnel's elastic theory of light, and the aether theory. The psychological danger which lurks behind a premature systematisation of science is compensated by the logical clarity we obtain by it.

A physical theory is to be re-constructed, logically, as a descriptive semantic system, that is, as a deductive system, with axioms, definitions, and rules, and in which the formal calculus (e.g. the mathematical equations) in the object-language is separated from the interpretation in the meta-language. And again the question arises, What is the character of the axioms and how do we obtain them? This appears to be more difficult to answer than the corresponding question in mathematics. For mathematics is a formal system of symbols, but physics is a descriptive system: it begins, and it must end, with experience. The axioms chosen for a physical theory must contain some knowledge of the external world, and the theorems that are derived must describe past experience and predict new experience.

There have been many philosophers who asserted that the axioms of physics represent some sort of special knowledge. The key concepts expressed by the axioms are assumed to be of synthetic *a priori* character, in Kant's terminology. For the theories of physics do describe nature, and how can we expect the theorems derived from them to apply to experience unless the axioms do? After all, derivation is a formal method, and it does not add to or subtract from knowledge, but merely makes our knowledge more explicit. Of course, no one will deny that the interpreted axioms of a physical theory are sentences that do represent genuine knowledge and so say something about the world. But we can no longer uphold Kant's view, or the view of transcendental idealism, however attractive it may have been 150 years ago. Kant's system as given in the Critique of Pure Reason was in some ways an attempt to give a re-construction of Newtonian physics. But his epistemology introduces ontological assumptions about what nature and mind must be. We cannot accept to-day that the concepts of space and time, for example, are given by Pure Intuition and expressed as synthetic *a priori* judgments. Relativity theory has shown this view to be wrong: for we would not be able, otherwise, to describe the world in terms of non-Euclidean geometry. It was a decisive answer to Kant, and an answer given by science. This situation is described by Einstein: 'I am convinced that the philosophers have had a harmful effect upon the progress of scientific thinking in removing certain fundamental concepts from the domain of empiricism, where they are under our control, to the intangible heights of the *a priori*. This is particularly true of our concepts of space and time, which physicists have been obliged by the facts to bring down from the Olympus of the *a priori* in order to adjust them and put them in a serviceable condition'.

On the other hand, we can equally not accept the view occasionally proposed by scientists that we read off, so to speak, our fundamental assumptions, or axioms, from experience. They are suggested by experience, it is true; but they are not given by experience. Many different axiom systems are possible, and various theories can be constructed to describe the same set of phenomena. Quantum mechanics, with its duality of theories, is one example: at least two different but equivalent descriptions are given. And it is a matter of choice which set of axioms we take to frame a particular theory. The sentences we put at the beginning of our theory as axioms are not directly subject to the test by experience. It is the success of the theory as a whole that decides whether or not we accept the theory and, with it, the axioms that are its foundations.

In modern physics the basic assumptions, the axioms and key concepts given by them, are very 'abstract', that is, they are so far removed from actual experience that no one could possibly take them to be directly given by experience. Rather we must say that the axioms and fundamental hypotheses of physics are the invention of the scientists which are, in a psychological sense only, suggested by experience. We see here the beginning of the semantic conception of induction, and of scientific method, in contrast to the epistemological view of the Bacon-Mill school that has dominated most philosophers, and many scientists, until today. This change in attitude has been created by scientific practice itself. We must agree with Einstein when he describes the methods of theoretical physics: 'The conception . . . of the purely fictitious character of the basic principles of physical theory was in the eighteenth and nineteenth centuries still far from being the prevailing one. But it continues to gain more and more ground because of the ever-widening gap between the basic concepts and laws on the one side and the consequences to be correlated with our experiences on the other . . . On the contrary, the scientists of those times were for the most part convinced that the basic concepts and laws of physics were not in a logical sense free inventions of the human mind, but rather that they were derivable by abstraction, i.e. by a logical process, from experiments. It was the general theory of relativity which showed in a convincing manner the incorrectness of this view. For this theory revealed that it was possible for us, using basic principles very far removed from those of Newton, to do justice to the entire range of the data of experience in a manner even more complete and satisfactory than was possible with Newton's principles . . . the fictitious character of the principles is made quite obvious by the fact that it is possible to exhibit two essentially different bases, each of which in its consequences leads to a large measure of agreement with experience. This indicates that any attempt logically to derive the basic concepts and laws of mechanics from the ultimate data of experience is doomed to failure . . .'.

There are two points here. First, that we take Euclid's system as a model, and even as an ideal, for a scientific theory; in physics, this works well enough, and we can arrange our sentences there in a hierarchical order; but it need not be always so (especially in other sciences). Second, that a modern theory allows a freedom of interpretation that is not generally acknowledged.

4. Semantics

In the logical re-construction of a scientific theory three steps can be recognised. First, there is *mathematization*. Some of the statements occurring in the theory are given in the form of an equation. But these statements, or laws, are not always connected with one another, except through the context. In order to interpret and to apply the equations, a great deal of explanation in ordinary language is required, and the fundamental assumptions are usually not clearly separated from the other statements in the context. Each new problem poses new difficulties, for no rule is given to show how to interpret an equation in every instance. It requires training and skill to make use of the theory even in those problems that have been worked out already. All the same, the use of a mathematical calculus suitably interpreted is an immense help in making scientific language more accurate. This is amply illustrated by the ordinary type of scientific theory we have to-day which is usually only mathematized.

The second step is *axiomatization*. The basic assumptions are put at the beginning of the theory, as axioms. This allows us to make clearer the formal, or syntactic, relations which may hold between statements of the theory. Apart from mathematics, we can make use of logic (in the wider sense of the word) by deducing theorems from the axioms. But rules of interpretation are still lacking and must be supplied in the context. Many attempts have been made to axiomatize physical theories, but only Carathéodory's axiomatization of the first and second law of thermodynamics is generally accepted.

Finally, there is *formalisation*. Apart from axioms, definitions, and syntactic rules, we have also semantic rules interpreting the expressions of the theory in terms of experience.

A physical theory is then, ideally speaking, a descriptive semantic system which consists of a calculus and of an empirical interpretation. We try to construct a deductive system employing the smallest number of axioms and basic concepts that suffice to provide an adequate description. When we are able to reduce all statements of the theory to a few fundamental sentences, we feel that we have arrived at a psychologically satisfying explanation of our experience. But it is also logically to be preferred since the reduction of theorems to the axioms, or the derivation of theorems from the axioms, proceeds through clearly specified, syntactic and semantic, rules of the system. This, then, approaches the aim of an ideal language which has so often been discussed in philosophy. But this must not be mistaken for a universal language as

Leibniz proposed it. We have an artificial or technical language rather than natural language; and all questions can be unambiguously decided either with the help of the rules or by appeal to experiment. For the purely informative use of language which we require in science, this is not an impossible or unreasonable ideal. Of course, the actual theories of physics do not satisfy it; but they approach this ideal to some, not inconsiderable, extent.

When we speak of an interpretation in terms of experience, what do we mean? The formal calculus of logic and mathematics is used to construct a physical theory, and by virtue of an interpretation physics describes the world. It is usually said that the system of physical geometry, for example, arises from the calculus of pure geometry by interpretation. The primitive terms and axioms are correlated to certain physical objects and situations by giving *coördinative* definitions, e.g. the mathematical point is coördinated to the physical point, the mathematical straight line to a physical straight edge, and so on. However, the procedure is not quite so simple as it appears at first sight: there are two steps before the realm of things and events is reached.

For the coördination is made between two languages. The coördinative definition relates the concept of mathematical length to that of physical length. And 'physical length' is not something immediately given but is a term of a definite language, in this instance the language of mechanics. Other definitions are presupposed specifying, for example, the unit, uniformity, and congruence, of the length measure; and these definitions, in turn, rest upon the definition of 'rigid body' and of 'closed system' (see section 3.6). That is, a whole language-system is presupposed, a meta-language by which the mathematical calculus is interpreted. Ultimately, it is true that the expressions of a language must be related to experience, for instance by what has been called *ostensive definitions*. We may coördinate 'physical length' to 'length' which we may take to be a term of every-day language; and, finally, we point to a stick and say 'length'.

Perhaps this is how we bridge the gap between formal calculus and experience; but the terminology is, I think, misleading. What is wanted here is to re-construct in logical terms the *referential* use of language. How, and how far, can this be done?

There are no ostensive definitions. Defining is a linguistic and logical task. A definition states the equality of meaning (or synonymity) of two expressions, e.g. 'staphylococcus' equals by definition 'a germ having a certain shape'. We cannot define things or events, but we do define words: a new, or unknown, expression is defined in familiar terms. When we point to something, e.g. 'This is a zebra', we do not define the animal but introduce a name for it. Pointing-to is however not a linguistic matter. It is by practice that we succeed in making our expressions refer to the physical world, and sometimes we do not succeed very well or not at all. In this sense of pointing the referential use of language is not amenable to formalisation but rests on a practical procedure. In order to be able to give rules of usage, we must speak not only about things but also about their names. An explicit analysis of the referential use requires a meta-linguistic formulation.

The referential function of language is so taken for granted in every-day discourse that we forget the difficulties in establishing it. And in practice we are hardly ever called upon to give rules for this purpose. Perhaps we need it only when learning a completely unknown language, e.g. an obscure native dialect. We may remember the story of the missionary who, when pointing to a table, found that the natives used a half-dozen different words. In ordinary life the extra-linguistic clues, the gestures, and other help in referring are understood through familiarity. And in the language of every-day life, or to some extent in the language of Newtonian physics, we have a meta-language that is known to us directly in terms of experience. So we can use it for interpreting a semantic system. Then we can state explicitly the relation between uninterpreted symbols and experience, by introducing a rule of *designation*. But this requires the use of a meta-language, naturally.

We say, e.g. 'Mars' designates the planet nearest to the earth. The term 'Mars' is treated as unknown, or as belonging to the object-language we want to interpret, say, when we explain the theory of astronomy. We assume that the expression 'the planet nearest to the earth' belongs to ordinary language and so we know how to use it correctly, that is, how it refers to experience. While a definition states the synonymity of two expressions in the object-language (the definition as a whole being of course in the meta-language), a rule of designation relates an expression in the object-language to another in the meta-language and so gives, *in part*, the meaning of the object-term.

We could have formulated the rule of designation also, e.g. 'Mars' designates Mars, provided we know that the word 'Mars' in ordinary language refers here to the planet and not, for example, to the Roman god.

The rule of designation states to what thing or event a symbol is to refer; and so, in its verbal formulation, the thing or event is mentioned by using its name. The planet Mars is mentioned by using its name 'Mars'. This is necessary merely because we must distinguish, in logic, between use and mention of expressions. It does not mean that designating is the same as mentioning: we can't help mentioning something when we speak about it; and we must speak about a thing when we wish to refer to it. This is of course quite trivial. But there have been objections to the use of designation which are based on this confusion.

Nor is it correct to say that to designate is the same as to name. 'To name' in ordinary language means to label something which, consequently, must be said to exist, in the usual sense of this word. But we may introduce by a rule of designation terms which do not refer to a physical thing or event, that is, we may want to speak about so-called abstract, or even fictitious, entities. For example, 'electron' designates a small particle possessing certain values of mass, charge, and spin. And surely electrons do not exist in the same sense as chairs and tables, although we may, and often do, use the word 'to exist' in this connexion. This is, so to speak, a matter of taste. Or we may say, e.g. 'unicorn' designates a deer-like animal with a single horn on its forehead. And this does not commit us to the belief that unicorns exist in the same sense as chairs and tables. To say that a certain term refers to an entity or situation (physical, abstract, or fictitious), or to give a rule of designation, does not presuppose any ontological assumptions. We must not be misled by an unwarranted analogy from the thing-language of every-day life. However, in deference to this sort of usage we sometimes take *denotation* as a sub-class of designation, whenever the entity, or *designatum*, does exist, in the normal sense of this word. In any case, as far as science is concerned there is no problem. Words such as 'existence', 'reality', or its cognates need not, and usually do not, occur within scientific theories. It does not matter whether the concepts used in the theory are 'abstract' or not: what does matter is only the success of the theory in practice.

But to establish descriptive terms by definition or by designation does not suffice for constructing a system of physics. In this manner we merely build up a suitable vocabulary. This is not enough to show us how to *use* the words. Indeed, when we construct a theory we tacitly presuppose much more. We select a definite set of phenomena, an actual or hypothetical universe, that illustrates how to use our words for the adequate description of the events. We assume a universe of discourse and so have, apart from rules of designation, also *rules of truth* to guide us in the use of our expressions.

All sentences out of context are, strictly speaking, meaningless. The context, or universe of discourse, in which we want to use our sentences is specified when we construct an *artificial language system* rather than use natural language, though we may employ expressions of ordinary language within the system. For in normal discourse the context is not explicitly given but tacitly understood, from extra-linguistic clues. But if we wish to make the meaning of our sentences as precise as possible, this context must be made explicit. We must say what possible phenomena we are willing to talk about, or give rules stating the possible (though not actual) truth of our sentences. When we know what possible states of affairs we may expect, then we can find out by experiment which of them is actual, or say what is true. An experiment can give an answer only when it is posed correctly, as a question that allows of an answer. A language system has then a limiting function since it must restrict the truth-possibilities so that we may know what we are talking about. It must also satisfy certain logical requirements, that is, separate the levels of language; we want to avoid the paradoxes arising in natural language.

Only a brief summary of the main concepts of semantics is needed here. For this suffices to make clearer the meaning of scientific theories, and in the discussion which follows in later chapters no serious technical device is used. And it is of course admitted that no example of a completely formalised language rich enough to allow formulation of a modern scientific theory has as yet been worked out. What is important, however, is to show how semantics as far as it is developed to-day can help us in understanding the language and methods of science. We may not be able to give a complete set of postulates, rules, etc. But in actual science it is useful already to formalise language to a certain degree, as best we can, by giving some definitions and rules. A little formalisation is better than none at all.

The terminology of semantics has been developed mainly by Carnap. To construct a language system we first state the subject-matter, e.g. specify the *individuals* about which we wish to speak, and the predicates and relations that are to apply to them. The *syntactic* rules, e.g. rules of *formation*, give the definition of 'sentence' within the system, or prescribe what kind of sentences we want to admit. Thus we state what we take as *unit* of expression, or as *atomic* sentence; this is the simplest sentence from which other, compound or *molecular*, sentences may be built up by means of logical connectives. Other syntactic rules, e.g. of *transformation*, then give the use of these connectives, such as 'and', 'or', and other logical constants. This can simply be done by taking part, or all, of formal logic into the system. In general, an atomic sentence would be formed by attributing to an individual the simplest property (i.e. predicate) about which we want to speak.

Then there are *semantic* rules providing the interpretation. The rules of *designation* specify the *descriptive* constants, e.g. the individuals. Similarly the predicates designate the properties, or relations, belonging to one or more individuals. In this way reference to whatever you want to speak about is established.

Further, we have rules of *truth* stating under which conditions a sentence of the system can be verified. They say, for example, that a sentence is true if, and only if, the entity designated by the descriptive constant has the property designated by the predicate. Whether or not the conditions obtain in a particular instance is, of course, no longer a matter of rules; it is by observation and experiment alone that we can find this out. Only in this way can the factual content of a descriptive semantic system be established.

Alternatively, or together with rules of truth, we may have rules of *range* stating truth conditions for classes of sentences. They show clearly that we must restrict the meaning of the expressions in the language-system, or state the range of possible states of affairs we wish to deal with. We may arrange the sentences into a conjunction (or into a class, in the case of a language-system treating of an infinite number of individuals) containing, for every atomic sentence, either this sentence or its negation. Such a conjunction is a *state-description*, since it represents a possible state of the universe for all the individuals and their properties. The rules of range then determine the class of state-descriptions for which a given sentence holds, that is, whether the sentence is true if the state-description applies to the actual world. So the rules of range give the meaning of the sentence by stating in which of the possible cases it would be true. In this way we know the kind of universe expressed by the predicates of the system.

This makes it possible to give a precise meaning to the distinction between *analytic* and *synthetic* sentences. In ordinary language this distinction is somewhat tenuous, and there is no fool-proof method of showing whether a sentence is used to refer to facts or not. For this we need formalisation. If the given sentence holds in every state-description (in the language system L) it must necessarily be true without regard to facts. Its range is universal, and the sentence is L-true, or analytic. Conversely, if the sentence holds in no state-description (in L), its range is null and the sentence is L-false or self-contradictory. If a sentence is neither L-true nor L-false, it is synthetic or factual. We cannot give general criteria, independent of language system, as to what sentence is analytic or synthetic, or meaningful, or true; this is asking too much. All these criteria can be adequately formulated only for formalised languages.

When we explain a concept, we must speak *about* it so that we can state explicitly the conditions under which it applies. When we use the concept, we need not know these conditions, though it may turn out that we misapplied the concept; just as we can use numbers without knowing the definition of 'number', though of course we may fall into error. We can apply the distinction of 'analytic-synthetic' also to ordinary language, though we may misapply it. Practical difficulties do not destroy the theoretical validity of a concept, as long as some correct applications can be found; and this is certainly true here. We must also not be misled by the unspoken interpretations current in ordinary conversation.

Consider once more the sentence, Roses are red. The predicate 'red' normally designates a property, and we can give a rule of truth for the possible conditions under which it may apply. If we can speak in the same language of other flowers which are not red, then the semantic rules refer to possible facts; and the sentence is synthetic. But we may use it to express a truism, as we might do in order to show that someone has made an empty statement. Or we may take the sentence as defining what we mean by 'rose'; and this would not be so strange considering the etymological meaning of this word; that is, only a red flower is to be called 'a rose'. If the rules of designation and of truth refer here to all individuals and to all possible states of affairs that can be described in the language, then the rules are *used* syntactically; and the sentence is analytic. For we can use a word that is ordinarily descriptive so that it applies without exception, and then it no longer describes anything. Certain universal sentences are of this sort, e.g. 'Everything happens according to fate': they look like factual sentences but they do not provide any information. In order to give the meaning of an expression we need to know not only the rules according to which it is used, but also the language system in which it occurs, i.e. the individuals, properties, etc. Otherwise, the usage of the expression is not completely determined.

A syntactic rule enumerates formal criteria for asserting the analytic sentence, e.g. 'Every sentence is to be constructed in the subject-predicate form'. We specify the grammar of the sentence, and if the sentence conforms to the rule it is admitted as meaningful. No factual knowledge is needed to see whether this criterion is satisfied; all we need consult is our previously given catalogue of admissible sentences, or the rules of syntax just mentioned.

A synthetic sentence is intended to describe experience, and so is used correctly only if the semantic rule refers to (possible or actual) experience; but whether or not this criterion is satisfied, will depend on observation and experiment. Such a rule may be giving a truth condition, e.g. 'Rain is wet' is true if, and only if, rain is wet. This is a trivial example since meta-language and object-language are drawn from the same vocabulary. In physics this is usually not so. We may say: 'An electron has a specific charge e/m' if, and only if, a certain track in a Wilson chamber exhibits the appropriate curvature under the action of a magnetic field. We speak in a known meta-language about the experimental conditions and so give a semantic rule for the meaning of the sentence in the object-language.

To employ terms like 'analytic-synthetic', or 'syntactic-semantic', is not a matter of prescription, but merely of classification. It is not a question of truth and falsity, but only of adequacy; and there is no doubt that these terms, at least sometimes, serve a useful purpose.

D

The use of symbolism, and of technical terms, always appears formidable to the layman; and no doubt the terminology must look somewhat far-fetched. But in fact the logical re-construction offered by semantics is much closer to actual science than might appear at first sight. This, I hope, will be shown in the later chapters.

But the semantic method is also not so far from our ordinary attempts of solving problems. When we ask in every-day discourse, What do you mean?, we expect examples; and these examples illustrate the usage of our terms. So they indicate the context, and the rules, according to which we wish to employ the disputed expressions. This is, in a non-formal way, what semantics does with the help of formal logic.

Again, I wish to emphasize that semantics is not a fully developed discipline as yet. Logic grows with science. Only by applying the techniques we have, and by trying to develop them through application, can we ever hope to make progress. Just like science itself, the analysis of science is never final but in a continuous development.

Here, we have only the modest aim of applying some concepts of semantics, without the symbolic technique. This suffices to show how much we can learn through logical analysis, and that semantics represents the logical re-construction closest to the actual scientific method that we know to-day.

5. *Observables*

All scientific theories begin, and must end, with experience. However far-fetched the postulates and definitions of a modern theory may appear, they must permit of an interpretation in terms of experience, or we would not know how to apply the theory. And however abstract, and even abstruse, the solution of an equation may be that is given as the end result of a theory, it must be possible to correlate the symbols which occur in it with experience; otherwise we could not test the theory. We must follow Poynting's dictum that, ultimately, we 'must describe the sensible in terms of the sensible'.

The demand that physical quantities must be observable is of course, in a sense, trivial. If science is to describe experience, surely terms or statements (directly or at least indirectly) accessible to experiment must occur somewhere within a scientific theory. But the question is whether all or only some terms must be so related to observation; and what do we mean when we ask 'what is observable?'.

As with all problems of this kind, the question 'what is observable?' must be interpreted as 'what do we mean by the term "observable"?'. For we do not wish to find out what specific things or events are observable, nor do we intend to write out a catalogue of observable things. We merely want to say under what conditions we call something an 'observable'. This is not a question of fact but a question about the meaning of a word. Only by using a meta-language can the meaning of this question be made clear: it is a problem of the meta-theory of science, or of methodology.

Now, it is by giving examples that we usually establish what we mean by a certain word when we use it in ordinary language. We give first the usage of the term in an instance where we are reasonably certain to understand its meaning. Then, by analysis, we try to find out the conditions which, in fact, must hold when the term is used significantly. And, finally, we extend this use of the term to scientific discourse. For we prefer to keep its meaning within science the same as in ordinary language, if this can be managed without leading to misunderstandings. We certainly call a chair or a table 'observable'. Is this true of other things—in particular, of electrons, atoms, and so on, i.e. of the so-called scientific objects?

If we adopt traditional terminology we may say that the things of every-day life possess what have been called secondary qualities: colour, smell, etc. These qualities cannot be predicated of scientific objects. Granted that they are a condition for *direct* observability, are secondary qualities always needed if we wish to observe something?

Clearly, even in the most direct act of perception, in every-day life, inference and theories have to be relied upon: certain conditions under which the observable thing is perceived are tacitly assumed. For the possibility that we deal with hallucinations or a dream can never be excluded. We assume normal conditions to be present. To say that we observe a chair implies the condition, among others, that there is normal lighting, and so on.

Like most words ending in '-able', the word 'observable'

expresses modality. It is then necessary to distinguish the various sorts of possibility (or impossibility) of observation. Logical, physical, and technical possibility are the three terms ordinarily used. Logical possibility has the widest range, or logical impossibility possesses the null-range. When a logical contradiction arises a misuse of the rules of usage has occurred. It must be logically possible to observe everything that is said to be observable, in the sense that the sentences expressing observation must be correctly formulated. Physical possibility has an intermediate range. So long as no known physical law is violated, we are entitled to say that it is physically possible to observe a given thing or event. Technical possibility has the narrowest range. For instance, it may be technically impossible at this time to fly to the moon; but it is physically possible since no law of physics would be violated if we carried out such an enterprise. It is a mere technical impossibility that can, in principle, be overcome. Here the usage of 'observable' in science may differ somewhat from its use in ordinary language. But in physics we need not be limited by technical difficulty. If it is physically possible to observe a thing or event, we say that the thing or event is *in principle observable*. It is in this sense that the term 'observable' is used in science. A wider range of possible observations is therefore admitted in physics than in every-day life.

Moreover, we have to distinguish between direct and indirect observability. No doubt we must take some things as being directly observable, or we could not begin to do science. But the more science advances, the more indirect observation comes in. No one has ever seen the other side of the moon, but we would call it observable, though indirectly. Inferences of various, relatively simple, kinds are needed to verify statements about it. In principle, this does not differ from the situation when speaking about electrons.

It is logically possible to observe electrons; but they cannot be said to have the secondary qualities needed to make them directly observable. The back of the moon is assumed to possess them: yet there is no essential difference. The mistaken belief in the importance of secondary qualities has led people to say that atoms are not observable, or that electrons do not exist, and that they are scientific constructs or fictions. It is merely a different chain of inference that is involved when we describe every-day experience and laboratory experiment. And we might conceivably have more reliable knowledge about electrons than about the other side of the moon: it depends on the inferences used.

Thus electrons are only indirectly observable. The pointer reading, the flash on the screen, the track on the photographic plate, and the click of the counter, require interpretation; but the hypotheses that permit us to infer the existence of the electron are well confirmed. Although, by definition, the electron cannot have secondary qualities—being invented, as it were, just to 'explain' those qualities—the electron is still observable. To deny the use of scientific instruments as means of observation while, say, accepting human eyes for the purpose, is not defensible. To ascribe existence to electrons is compatible with a consistent usage of the term; indirect observability must be accepted. True that, in the end, we must have some directly observable event that may serve as stimulus for human response. But the use of scientific apparatus not only increases the range of observation, it also provides a check on our perceptions. And so indirect observation—through 'inductive' inference by means of confirmed hypotheses—may even be more reliable than direct observation; just as in court, testimony by a concatenation of circumstantial evidence may be more trustworthy than a single eye-witness account.

Electrons are not arbitrarily invented to 'explain' secondary qualities, although the concept of electron is invented for the purpose of describing experience more accurately. 'Electrons' and 'atoms' are terms used in a more 'abstract', i.e. technical language: the language of physics differs from ordinary language in which we use terms that designate secondary qualities. We shift from one language to another language of different *semantic type*. And we can, if we want to, extend the use of terms such as 'observable' to scientific language in a perfectly consistent manner.

Since science does not make use of secondary qualities, we must give the conditions for observability in a different way. A technical explanation, or explication, in more logical terms is wanted. A thing or event is observable, directly or indirectly, if we can devise tests for the observation-sentence which refers to the thing or event. Experience remains a necessary condition for observability. But since we equally experience dreams and hallucinations we must give another, and sufficient, condition. A thing or event is observable if sentences about them can be tested by the theories and procedures of science.

This does not mean that we forbid new methods. On the contrary: a new method is a welcome extension but cannot be such as to abolish *all* previous theory and practice. Methods of this sort would involve us in a contradiction. For a new hypothesis, however revolutionary it may be, can be tested only if there are other hypotheses and procedures that are not, at the same time, being tested. In other words, we can speak of testing only with respect to a given theory, method, and practical procedure. A sentence can serve as observational report only for a certain hypothesis. Observation or experiment and theory or hypothesis are joined together in science.

Observable things are often said to exist. The ontological problem however has no place in science. But the mediaeval dispute about *realism* and *nominalism* has recently broken out again between philosophers and found an echo among scientists. This shows in the discussion whether or not there is, and what constitutes, a single language suitable for all science, i.e. a basic, or empiricist language.

Now, 'to exist' is not a predicate like 'to fly'. To say 'the table exists' is not similar to saying 'the bird flies'. For the last sentence may contain an adverb, e.g. 'the bird flies swiftly', while 'the table exists' is a sentence that cannot be qualified. To assert that the table exists *really* does not introduce any qualification but merely adds emphasis. In other words, existence taken in this *universal* sense is not a property. When we ask in this comprehensive manner, e.g. 'Do electrons exist?', or 'Are there abstract entities such as numbers?', we do not present a question but advocate a usage for the word 'to exist', or recommend a special language. The choice of a suitable language to be used for formulating a theory, of electrons, or of numbers, is however not to be decided by logic alone. There is no genuine logical issue between realism and nominalism: it is merely the question which way of speaking is more useful and convenient for whatever purpose we have in mind.

But once a language system has been adopted, then we ask a similar question about existence once more, though in a different sense. Instead of the question 'Do electrons exist?' we ask 'Does *this* electron exist?'. We mean whether a particular electron can be found at a certain place and time. But in this context the word 'exist' can always be eliminated: we merely want to know whether, in an experiment, some electrons occur, or are observed. Obviously, we can answer this question only after we have decided whether we can speak of existence in connexion with electrons. It makes no sense to test for the existence of electrons in an experiment, unless we have previously admitted that electrons are entities that can be localised in space and time. In other words, we first have to accept the language of atomic physics and so presuppose that the word 'to exist' may be used when we speak about electrons.

Modern philosophers are so frightened of so-called 'abstract' entities that they have searched, desperately and in vain, for a way of avoiding any mention of them. This is understandable when we look at the history of philosophy. Empiricists, for example, sometimes say that we may speak only in terms of sense-data, i.e. refer to what is immediately given in sense perception. Thus *phenomenalism* is supposed to be the language we must adopt, since experience is taken as consisting in having sense-data and expressed in protocol-sentences, e.g. 'This here blue now'. Chairs and tables then become logical constructs of such sense-data.

Obviously, this attitude implies an ontology. It is assumed either that sense-data are the ultimate stuff of which the world is made, or that the world is such that it can be described only by a sense-datum language. But do we not have experience of chairs and tables? Of course we do—but we are sometimes mistaken about them. Therefore, it is said, we must go back to what is more certain and even indubitable, and this is an account in terms of our five senses. I see the stick bent when it is half submerged in a glass of water but it is, in fact, straight; I observe the penny to be elliptical though, actually, it is round. We are then told that the mistakes arise from referring to things, like sticks and pennies; but sense-data never lie and are only put together wrongly, so to speak, in the story told in the thing-language. Of course, no one denies that the phenomenalist language is useful in describing experiences of this sort. But it is due to the mistaken quest for certainty that the sense-datum language is advertised as basic: what is more certain is supposed to be more real.

By definition the expressions of a phenomenalist language refer to immediate awareness. We cannot speak of a mistaken sensation.

And if we can never be mistaken in sense-perception, then of course we can never be *not* mistaken: it makes no sense to use words like 'mistake' in this sort of language. But this grammatical fact does not imply either that the sense-datum is basic (as being 'free of mistakes'), nor that the use of the thing-language always incurs mistakes.

To *have* a sensation, to *make* an observation, to *see* a thing are three different ways of speaking about the same happenings, and not three different kinds of knowledge. And it is certainly not true that one 'kind' of knowledge is better than the other, though one way of speaking may be more appropriate than the other, in a given instance.

That we can make use of the sense-datum language rests on the fact that, sometimes, we can speak veridically about seeing sticks and pennies. Otherwise we could never connect the sense-datum account with ordinary thing-language. The situation is slightly improved by admitting that, though sense-perception is never wrong, we may be mistaken in our use of the language describing it. But how can we misapply words unless we know, at least in some instances, how to apply them correctly? A pure sense-datum language could never help us here, and phenomenalism cannot provide us with a basic language. If we could not speak about the same experiences in some other way, i.e. in another language system, we should not have much success. It is an empiricist prejudice to assume that there is a basic language of this sort and that sentences formulated in other ways must be reduced to expressions in this basic language. Rather the opposite seems to be suggested: that we need a *multiplicity* of possible interpretations, or language systems, in which to speak about the experiences we have.

Many scientists to-day tend towards phenomenalism, just as they seem to prefer nominalism to realism. We are told that only particulars exist, e.g. this or that object, but not universals, and that the logical term 'class' must be shunned at all costs. This is again the bugbear of 'abstract' entities. Both concepts are useful, obviously; and no ontology need be implied when we use them. The only issue is to construct a technical language that can do the job for a given purpose. In biology, for instance, it is said that only individuals exist but the genus, or species, does not; and certainly the word 'existence' is used here in two different senses.

To construct a language in which expressions referred to individuals only might be of great interest and advantage. But in mathematics we like to say that numbers exist, i.e. classes of classes. That is, we have accepted a different manner of speaking as suitable, or adequate, for mathematics; and only then can we ask, e.g. 'How many prime numbers exist among the first ten numbers?' This is then a question that can be decided, by counting or otherwise, after one has specified the language system in which the question is formulated.

The choice of a vocabulary, however, does not necessarily commit us to any view about the world. The language we use does not coerce us to adopt any ontology. Because the thing-language of ordinary discourse is *psychologically* connected with an ontology, owing I suppose to our 'robust sense of Reality', we assume that there is a *logical* connexion, and that is so for all languages. But to test for the existence of an entity presupposes a language in which the sentence ascribing existence to the entity can be meaningfully asserted.

After all, sometimes we wish to refer to physical things and sometimes to 'abstract' entities. The point is to make the language do the job we want it to do. So when we refer to unfamiliar entities like electrons, or to 'abstract' entities such as numbers, this does not commit us to say anything about their existence. Indeed, it is best to banish this word, and its cognates, from our vocabulary. We can still distinguish between fact and fiction, within a given context, or between dreaming and being awake, e.g. in the ordinary language where chairs and tables provide the standard. The use of 'existence' does not help at all and the word is always eliminable.

Historically, the traditional theory of knowledge, or epistemology, introduces ontological assumptions and, with them, the various philosophic theories. Logically, the difference between such theories is purely verbal, at best. It is a merit of the semantic method that it does away with all -isms.

6. *Meaning and verifiability*

Language consists of signs that are grouped into words, and words are arranged into sentences. One and the same word may have many different meanings depending upon the context, that is, on the sentence in which it occurs and on the universe of discourse to which the sentence belongs. Thus words have meaning only in an indirect manner; they have a *sense* that is derived from the usage within a sentence. It is, I hope, no distortion of ordinary language to say that even cries like 'fire', say, are in fact an abbreviation for the sentence 'here is a fire', or something of this sort. We would certainly never say that a word is either true or false—and this suffices to show that word-meaning or sense is derived from the meaning of a sentence. The property of possessing a truth-value, and therefore meaning, must be restricted to sentences.

But not every combination of words is a sentence. Language prescribes rules for arranging words into sentences, and a necessary condition is that the words are ordered according to the rules of grammar. This condition holds even if the words have no sense, i.e. for non-sense words. For the rules are concerned mainly with the formal characteristics of a sentence; nouns, verbs, and so on, must follow each other in an order and, moreover, nouns and verbs are usually recognised by their design. 'It was brillig, and the slithy toves did gyre and gimble in the wabe.' So it is not a sufficient condition; for the grammatical rules of any natural language permit a good deal of latitude. Sentences may be formed that satisfy the demands of grammar and contain words having sense, but that are meaningless all the same. 'Socrates is a prime number' is an example.

Grammar is a rudimentary logic, historically grown; and for this reason, though sufficient for many purposes, its rules are not restricted enough. They suffice when we deal with familiar experience; but in more 'abstract', i.e. technical, discourse, as in science, we want less latitude so that we can give a more precise meaning to our statements. The word 'force', for example, is used in many different ways in ordinary life; but in physics its sense is more restricted since we use the word there according to fairly definite rules. Otherwise we should be hard put when we want to test experimentally sentences containing this word.

This is another reason why mathematics is so useful a tool in science: the rules according to which one equation is derived from another, or a solution is obtained for an equation, are very restricted and clearly defined. Or, we may take it as a *necessary* condition for a sentence to be meaningful that it is constructed according to the rules of logic. By this formulation we take into account those refinements of modern logic, e.g. the theory of types and levels, that we need to make language a reliable instrument for communication.

But we require also a *sufficient* condition for deciding whether or not a sentence is a statement, that is, when a sentence is true or false. This is not difficult to state for analytic sentences. For analytic sentences are used, in a given context, according to logical rules previously prescribed, and so are true if they are constructed correctly according to these rules. The necessary condition for an analytic sentence being true is also sufficient. But synthetic (factual, empirical) sentences are used, within a context, to say something about the world. When we wish to give a criterion of meaning, it is about factual sentences alone that we are concerned.

There is no doubt that, in science, we accept as factual only sentences that, either directly or indirectly, are amenable to verification (or falsification) by experience, that is, by experiment. Indeed, this idea has been one of the motives that gave rise to quantum mechanics. For modern physics is so unfamiliar that it is difficult to find out how its expressions apply to the actual world. The suspicion arose that, even in physics, we had accepted sentences that must be regarded as meaningless, since they could not be found true or false by any actual, or possible, experiment. Relativity theory, with the problem of the aether, or of simultaneity, first demonstrated that meaningless sentences had been admitted, unwittingly, into physical theory. That is to say, questions were believed to be about experience that could not be given an answer in terms of experience. Quantum mechanics, in the formulation of Born and Heisenberg, explicitly states that only such sentences are acceptable which, at least in principle, can be decided by observation and experiment. The success of modern physics testifies that this view is, to say the least, fruitful.

The demand for *verifiability* is usually formulated in terms of epistemology, as a thesis which is part of the doctrine of empiricism. It has long been known in the history of philosophy. If we restrict ourselves to scientific discourse, not many will dispute this thesis. But the import of such a criterion of meaning, even within this limited domain, is considerable: aprioristic, and other types of metaphysical, theories are automatically ruled out. For they purport to make statements about matters of fact that, even in principle, can never be verified by any facts. But such sentences play no rôle in science, whatever their emotional or other import may be. Whether or not we include them in our theories makes not the slightest difference to the information we can obtain from the theories, and so we may safely drop them. It is a methodological decision that is justified by the practice and success of science.

We can then make it a sufficient condition for a factual sentence to be meaningful that it is in principle possible to decide by experience whether it is true or false. This is commonly known as the *verifiability criterion* of meaning. And if we take scientific language to differ from ordinary language only in the stricter and clearer usage of its expressions, we may extend this criterion to apply to any kind of language.

The general use we make of factual sentences in science is indicated by this formulation. But it must be supplemented by showing how, in technical detail, such verification can be carried out. The question arises, What is meaning? And the phrase 'to decide by experience' is much too vague: we must explain what we would count as verification.

Language after all has many uses. We want to arouse emotion, to persuade and to command, as well as to transmit knowledge. Obviously, the simplest, and most straightforward, use of language is to give information about the world; it is *the* function of language that is least distorted by personal and social factors. And we must start with the *literal* interpretation of the sentence, that is, we must take the words in their usual sense and the rules in their normal usage. Assuming that we understand a language, say ordinary English, we investigate the conditions under which a sentence is said to be true or false; we try to find out the physical events that are correctly described by the sentence in its literal meaning. Or, as has sometimes been suggested, to know the meaning of a sentence is to know the conditions under which the sentence is said to be true.

There are, however, difficulties. The criterion of meaning must be formulated more carefully, and the slogan—though in principle acceptable—does not quite suffice, since it is open to misinterpretation. Since sentences have meaning even if in fact the conditions do not obtain that would decide their truth, we must admit that the conditions need not be actual but merely *possible*. In other words, the sentence has meaning when we know under what conditions it *would* be said to be true. We thus widen the criterion, but this introduces the problem of possibility.

We say that the conditions for verifying a sentence are *physically* possible though, in fact, they cannot be realised owing to technical difficulties. For instance, we would allow a sentence to possess factual meaning even if no one had ever succeeded in producing the conditions under which it could be asserted, so long as no known physical law was violated. It must be physically possible to fulfil the truth conditions of a sentence having factual meaning (and *a fortiori* it must be logically possible, since to break a rule of logic necessarily makes the sentence meaningless); but it need not be technically possible to do so. This implies that we accept science in helping to decide the meaning of a sentence. To say that something is logically and physically possible is to say that it is compatible with science as we know it to-day.

This is not a serious difficulty. But it entails that we may reject sentences as meaningless that, previously, we had accepted. In classical physics, we believed sentences about the motion of the aether to be meaningful, and experiments were devised in order to verify them. Relativity theory has shown them to be meaningless; and we have since eliminated from physics all sentences about the aether.

This shows clearly that meaning depends on the theory in which the sentence occurs. The same sentence, that is, the identical series of words, may be meaningful or meaningless according to the context. It is proverbial that two people may say the same words and yet mean something different. Of course, the situation is actually not quite so simple as we might wish. A sentence is meaningless if it violates the very rules which are supposed to specify the usage of the terms occurring in it. Now natural language, or a pre-scientific theory, and even a scientific theory on occasion, are not sufficiently formalised ; and the rules reconstructing a reasonable usage are, in practice, not always uniquely determined. A theory, i.e. a way of speaking (and, with it, the rules of usage), may turn out to be inadequate ; and we may question whether the truth conditions, i.e. the sentences used for verifying the factual sentence, are acceptable. It merely indicates that, with further progress in science, we may change our view what meaning, if any, a given sentence possesses. In other words, with our changing knowledge the meaning of our sentences may change as well : it is exactly in this manner that the cognitive content of the statements of science is safeguarded. There is no *absolute* meaning.

This shows that we must avoid saying that the (actual or possible) physical conditions under which a sentence is asserted *are* the meaning of the sentence. No *causal* theory of meaning is possible, in the sense that the state of affairs referred to in the sentence, or the conditions which cause us to utter the sentence, are the meaning. Among other reasons, it would make statements about the future meaningless, and this is absurd. Nor is a *relational* theory of meaning acceptable. The relation that may exist between a sentence and the fact it describes helps in elucidating the meaning but is not the meaning of the sentence. Otherwise, negative sentences, that is, sentences about whatever is not the case, would be meaningless (unless we re-formulate them in a positive form) ; but this would be contrary to all reasonable usage. Or, abstract, technical discourse, i.e. about entities to which we do not want to ascribe existence (in the ordinary sense of this word), would always consist of meaningless sentences, and this is certainly not so in science. Though the referential use of language has something to do with the meaning of a sentence, it is—to put it in semantic terms—neither the designatum nor the rule of designation that *is* the meaning of the sentence.

The *operationist* theory of meaning, too, is not acceptable. The distinction between *physical* and *paper and pencil* operations is very vague, though they correspond to some extent to the logical distinction of analytic and synthetic sentences. We are told that this operationist difference can only be learned by experience, in the laboratory ; but we require a logical, or semantic, criterion for meaning. For sentences which are tested by different operations need not always have different meanings (although sometimes they do).

Meaning *is not* the use of a sentence but *lies* in its use. Meaning is a property of sentences and so depends on how the sentence is used in a given context ; it is given by *all* the rules according to which the sentence is used and depends also on the whole language system, but the rules are not the meaning. Meaning is not a thing to which we can point, it is neither an entity nor a relation, not even an operation. And so it is better to speak of sentences *being meaningful* rather than having meaning, lest such imputations arise.

Three main proposals have been made to show how facts bear on the meaning of a factual sentence, i.e. what is to count as verifying a sentence. These attempts at giving a logical re-construction of a criterion of meaning, that is, a technical explanation, are well known, and a brief summary will suffice.

It was first proposed that a *deductive* relation must exist between a factual sentence and the observation sentences that verify it. The observation sentences (taken to express directly our experience) are said to entail the factual sentence. Clearly this will not always do, since no finite class of observation sentences can ever entail a universal sentence, and sentences of this sort are indispensable in science. (It is of course possible to deny that universal sentences, that is, sentences of the form 'For all...', have a factual use in science, but it would be rather a strange view to take.) Observation sentences are existential, by definition, i.e. refer to particular things or events ; and we can only have a finite class of observation sentences at our disposal. Of course, the difficulty arises also from the demand for *complete* verifiability, that is, that the observation sentences exhaust the meaning of the sentence to be verified. This demand is not very reasonable, however. Since future observations may show that a mistake was made in the past, it could never be satisfied. But there are other, purely logical, difficulties.

A simple, existential, sentence is completely verifiable by a finite set of (self-consistent) observation sentences ; but such a sentence is logically equivalent to the negation of a universal sentence which is not so verifiable—and this produces a paradox. Finally, if S is a factual sentence and N is a non-sensical one, e.g. 'The absolute is heavy', then the disjunction (S or N) is verifiable by this criterion, and this cannot be allowed. In other words, the criterion as it stands is too lenient. The difficulty is not removed if, with Ayer, we invert the logical relation between factual and observation sentences. It is proposed that the factual sentence, together with a suitable hypothesis, entails obser-vation sentences that are not derivable from the hypothesis alone. Even if the hypothesis is itself previously subjected to the veri-fiability criterion (to exclude a meaningless hypothesis), this criterion still allows the conjunction of factual and non-sensical sentences, e.g. (S and N), to be meaningful. In other words, deducibility between factual and observation sentences can never suffice for re-constructing a criterion of meaning.

Second, then, is the proposal to establish the meaning of a factual sentence by its *translatability* into an empiricist language. An empiricist language is supposed to exclude non-sensical expressions by its vocabulary and grammar. This may be a criterion sufficiently narrow to escape the previous difficulties. But other problems arise in its stead. What is meant by 'translatability'? And what is, exactly, an empiricist language?

It appears that translatability is taken as being able to *define* the unknown terms of a technical, scientific language by the known expressions of the laboratory language, or of ordinary language in which we describe our experiments. For example, a predicate of the scientific language must be definable by one, or more, observation predicates. But a definition states an equivalence of meaning between two expressions : an unknown expression is defined in terms of what we know. So a definition may make the meaning more explicit but cannot give this meaning ; we must know the meaning beforehand.

What can 'translatability' mean otherwise? It is certainly not used here in the sense, say, of being able to translate from English into French. No dictionary is available when we wish to connect the scientific term with an expression of the observation language. We do not know the state of affairs that the expressions in the two languages describe, or rather what the scientific term refers to : this is exactly what is in doubt. And certainly we do not translate any language into another by means of definitions. We do not define 'cheval' in terms of 'horse' but know that both terms *designate* the same thing. In other words, translation is a matter of both syntactic and semantic rules and, moreover, the semantic rules remain the same. We say that we have a good translation if it conveys exactly the same meaning as the original text. It is not translatability but *interpretability* in terms of an empiricist language that can establish meaning.

What, then, is an empiricist language? Such a language is supposed to express experience directly, but this is rather vague : we must specify its key-concepts and principal rules of usage. It is therefore said that a thing-language, or a phenomenalist language, e.g. one taking sense-data as a key-concept, represents an empiricist language. To some extent this is true : we certainly know how to use a thing-language for speaking about experience, at least the sort of thing-language that we employ in ordinary conversation. There is more doubt whether the sense-datum language can do this job. But whatever language we accept as empiricist, we must never take it as *the* basic language, or believe that experience dictates which words we must use. This is another form of the ontological prejudice : not that nature is 'really' like this or that, but that the language in which we must speak about nature is 'really' of this or that kind.

We accept, provisionally and tentatively, some knowledge, that is, we have at our disposal a language in which we can express our experiences ; at least, we understand the meaning of *some* sentences. If we have made an unwise choice and find that the meta-language used to interpret a calculus, or object-language, is unsuitable, we shall have to find another way of speaking that can serve, for the time being. This is character-istic of the self-correcting method of science. We first use one theory to understand another and then, in turn, take the second theory to correct the first. So we use ordinary language for con-structing the language of science whose expressions thereby acquire a meaning ; but we may use scientific language to correct, and to give a more precise meaning to, the expressions of ordinary language. It suffices to say (without going into technical detail) that any language we know how to use for describing experience may be used as empiricist language ; and so ordinary language will in practice serve, though its vocabulary may be enriched by a few, simple, technical terms. In other words, the so-called empiricist language represents no more than the way we normally speak in the laboratory.

In this connexion, one logical difficulty may be mentioned. The thing-language of ordinary discourse may not always suffice for describing experience. More technical terms are needed, e.g. 'electric charge', 'temperature', etc., or so-called disposition terms may occur such as 'soluble'. So we must supplement the thing-language by these terms, and since they do not express direct experience, how can this be done? We want to be able to say 'All salts are soluble in water'. This is to hold for any piece of salt, even the salt that has never been put to the test,

e.g. the salt I spilled yesterday. Carnap has proposed a solution
in terms of *reduction-sentences*. For example, the sentence 'All
salts are soluble in water' is translated into 'If any thing x is
put into water at time t, then, if x is soluble in water, x dissolves
at time t, and if it is not soluble in water, it does not'. Thus
reduction-sentences give only a *partial* determination of the
term 'soluble'; they are said to provide a conditional definition.
Meaning, however, is not a matter of definition only ; it is a
partial interpretation that is given by reduction-sentences. This
is certainly one way of introducing new terms into the empiricist
language ; but it must be admitted that no suitable reduction-
sentences have been found for many terms that we would need,
e.g. 'electric charge'. Another way of dealing with this problem
might be to say that 'electric charge', and similar terms, are
part of a scientific language, e.g. the theory of electricity. This
theory can be interpreted by ordinary language by giving suitable semantic rules. The empiricist language, then, would have
to consist of a system comprising a simple thing-language and
the elementary theory of electricity (assuming that both have
been formalised). This appears to be a feasible proposal : for we
use ordinary language to construct the language system of
Newtonian mechanics, and we use Newtonian theory to construct
quantum mechanics, etc.

The translatability thesis was originally conceived as requiring
that the expressions of the scientific language must be definable
by observation predicates. The thesis is now weakened to
demand only reducibility to an empiricist language, i.e. a partial
determination of meaning is accepted as sufficient. This is one
reason why it is said that *confirmability* rather than verifiability
represents the criterion of meaning for factual sentences. And a
sentence is confirmable if it is, in a general way, reducible to
expressions of an empiricist language. Another reason is given
for preferring the confirmability criterion. It is said that factual
sentences are never conclusively verifiable but are progressively
confirmed with increasing knowledge.

At first sight, it seems to be more in accord with scientific
practice to accept confirmability as criterion. If we know how to
confirm a sentence, even without being able to test it in practice,
this should suffice, and verifiability appears to be too strict. But
the argument leaves the door open to serious misunderstanding.

'To verify' can only mean 'to justify an assertion', or 'to be able to say it is true that . . .'. This does not depend on the difficulties attending the technique for confirming a sentence. To assert a sentence is not to ask for, or to expect, *more* evidence.

Of course, this attitude often shows in empiricist epistemology ; and it is based on a confusion of the concept of truth with that of (inductive) probability. We either can, or cannot, assert a sentence, and this is the issue here. For this we need to know, not the *actual* but only the *possible* truth of the sentence, or what it would be like if the sentence were true. We can confirm a sentence if we know to what extent the *actual* evidence agrees with the *possible* range of conditions which would make the sentence true. To verify or to confirm a sentence are two different tasks. Confirmation is not a partial, or in-between, truth.

This attitude is inspired by the empiricist thesis that all factual sentences must always be regarded as hypotheses, and so they can never be asserted, only rendered probable. It leads to the third proposal, e.g. the *probability* criterion of meaning, that a sentence has meaning only if it is possible to assign a probability to it.

But this again makes little sense, if we take the proposal literally. It may be unfair to do so ; but all the same some awkward questions arise. Does the meaning of a sentence vary with its degree of probability ? Is any degree of probability sufficient to give a meaning to the sentence ? How about zero probability, or at any rate a very low degree ? Is a sentence half meaningful if we can ascribe a probability of $\frac{1}{2}$ to it ?

We can always *assert* any factual sentence. We can *confirm* a factual sentence only if we treat it as hypothesis, and so must have other sentences representing the evidence with respect to which the hypothesis is confirmed. We may treat one and the same sentence (or two tokens of the same sentence) in these two different ways : they are not incompatible.

When it is said that factual sentences are probable only, what is meant is merely that we are always prepared to revise them, if experience requires it. This is the only sense in which we can say so sweepingly that factual sentences are probable, in contrast to analytic sentences (which are revisable in a different sense). To say that *all* factual sentences are probable only, would mean that *none* are. If we could not assert, at least sometimes, some factual sentences, we could never even say that any factual sentence is probable. For we cannot apply the concept of (logical) probability unless we know the range of conditions which would make the sentence true. To construct a criterion of meaning with the help of probability does not seem to work. The semantic conception of truth is always presupposed.

To admit that no criterion of meaning for factual sentences which has so far been constructed is completely adequate, does not entail that it can never be adequately formulated, nor that the criterion as developed to-day is of no use. Both the deducibility and the translatability criterion can be applied in some instances, but not in all. To construct a logically adequate, and comprehensive, criterion is a technical problem of logic. The logical re-construction of the language of science cannot, any more than science itself, be expected ready-made, like Pallas Athene. All these formulations of a criterion of meaning serve as approximations, that are useful, even if they do not cover all the various sorts of factual sentences we are likely to encounter in science. The difficulty here is a purely technical one, i.e. to find a logically adequate formulation for the criterion of meaning that can be applied in all instances. This does not invalidate the demand for verifiability of factual sentences.

But some of the difficulties arising when we try to give a criterion of meaning can be obviated. Historically speaking, the criterion is formulated in terms of an antiquated epistemology, e.g. of empiricism. It seems preferable to make use for this purpose of the semantic method of actual science.

When we wish to propose a criterion of meaning for factual sentences, clearly we cannot omit reference to the context in which the sentence occurs. Sentences are not inherently factual but are so used, within a context. Natural language does not give this context, at best it is indicated by clues, etc. In other words, the problem cannot be solved unless we construct a language system. Without *formalisation* of the language to which the sentence belongs whose meaning we want to establish, we can never succeed in giving this meaning, nor in constructing an adequate criterion of meaning. A criterion of meaning can be adequate only if it applies to a semantic language system and so must be itself formulated in semantic terms.

By definition a factual sentence refers to facts. The referential use of language is re-constructed by the rules of designation. But in order to know that the sentence does refer to extra-linguistic facts, we must be able to assert it, i.e. know its (actual or possible) truth. This applies to so-called abstract discourse as well; it does not matter whether the extra-linguistic entity is physical, or 'abstract', or even fictitious since nothing is said about its existence. The verifiability criterion therefore formulates what we mean by 'the meaning of a factual sentence'.

This analysis agrees with what we ordinarily take as meaning; *both* reference and truth are needed to give the meaning of a sentence. It is also in agreement with scientific method: the theory as a whole must be known in order to state the meaning of a theorem within the theory. *All* the rules together, i.e. the rules of designation and of truth, within a certain context or for a certain language system, are needed to give the meaning of a sentence.

The meaning of 'meaning' is not something we prescribe or invent: we know some sentences to be meaningful in a context, and we reconstruct the logical conditions that hold in these instances. This is then taken as *standard usage*. A criterion of meaning is a logical re-construction of standard usage for factual sentences. If we did not know the meaning of *some* sentences, we could never tell the meaning of *any* sentence, and so could not formulate a criterion of meaning. The criterion of meaning is then neither a theory, nor a thesis, nor a prescription, not even a definition; but a technical explanation, or explication, of what we take as the meaning of a factual sentence, both in scientific and in ordinary discourse.

What are the disadvantages of the semantic formulation? We say that the meaning of a factual sentence is given by all the rules, i.e. of designation and of truth, in a language system.

The first objection is that the burden is put upon constructing a formalised language and this is, in most cases, practically impossible to do in detail. But in science we do construct such languages, in outline at least, and they are reasonably adequate for the purpose. In philosophic discussion we do the same when we give examples in order to make clear what we mean; for to exemplify a term or a sentence is to give a specimen usage for it. We can often indicate the main rules though being unable to work out a complete formalisation.

It may then be objected that, by this criterion, the meaning of a sentence is never fully known unless we provide a language system to which the sentence belongs. Since meaning and truth are closely connected, this is not surprising. The concept of truth can be adequately formulated only for formalised languages; so with meaning. We want here to give a logically adequate formulation of the criterion of meaning and are not concerned with practical application. This does not preclude our speaking meaningfully without formalisation. We learn to *use* a language by practice and skill, even the language of science ; but sometimes there are difficulties in finding out what we mean, and then we need a criterion for solving them. Formalisation is needed not for its own sake but as a tool for meaning analysis ; it is the method present-day logic puts at our disposal.

Finally, does the criterion achieve its aim, that is, cut out meaningless sentences from informative discourse? Certainly it does in science, and relativity theory is an example. How about philosophic, or ordinary, discourse? To answer this we must consider what a criterion of meaning can reasonably be expected to achieve.

The meaning criterion arose, historically, from the desire to eliminate metaphysics. Philosophers hoped to find a device that could determine, for any kind of isolated sentence, whether or not it was meaningful. Obviously, too much was demanded. A criterion is not a gadget, like a pocket-rule, that we need only to lay on to take the measure of a sentence. How pleasant it would be if we could so simply get rid of all meaningless sentences ! There are, alas, a great many ways in which we can, deliberately or accidentally, talk nonsense. Logic cannot cure all linguistic ills, only logical ills. In natural language the distinction between factual and analytic sentences is often blurred and even factual and emotive components are sometimes mixed, if not in the same sentence, certainly in the same context. Since the meaning criterion depends on these distinctions and applies to informative discourse only, clearly our language must be analysed first, i.e. formalised to some extent, before we can discuss meaning. At least we must state whether we intend to speak about facts, or about something else.

This is not always so in what has been called metaphysics. If sentences like 'The not nihilates the nothing', ('Das Nicht nichtet des Nichts') are regarded either as analytic or as having an emotive meaning, we should raise little objection. If, for example, it is analytic, the sentence is of course queer since it violates even the rules of ordinary grammar ; for 'not' is not a noun, etc. This is no accident : for metaphysicians accept customary rules of usage, at least implicitly, and then calmly proceed to break them.

What is objectionable, then, is to take metaphysical sentences as factually meaningful while, at the same time, refusing to give semantic rules of usage or even denying that such rules are, in principle, needed. But if no rules are given to guide us in using the sentence, what are we to do? It is for this reason that we reject metaphysics : it fails to deliver the information promised.

The trouble is that metaphysical sentences are usually cast in the form of an ordinary factual sentence, and so their emotive function is obscured. Moreover, non-cognitive sentences often possess a *derivative* meaning through which we may understand them ; this does not mean that we must be aware of either the emotive or the derivative meaning, since to know a language is a matter of skill and practice. If pressed to say what some obscure sentence means we may find that it has a meaning quite different from what is commonly supposed.

Of course, our normal way of speaking is imprecise ; though we detect obvious nonsense like speaking about round triangles, it is sometimes difficult to recognise a sentence as meaningless. Let us take an example. If someone asserts that he has seen a ghost, it is a *literally* meaningless sentence that he utters. It is, I think, reasonable to say that we reject this sentence not merely because there does not exist a reliable account of the facts ; but we do not know, strictly, how to use the word 'ghost'. We cannot say what it designates, and we cannot state the conditions which, if satisfied, would make the sentence true. Our incredulity concerns this whole manner of speaking, and the underlying attitude which prompts it. It would be equally meaningless to say that I have never seen any ghosts. If both of us claim to have a genuine experience, we are at a deadlock. No communication is possible, each of us has a private experience and a personal meaning for his sentences.

But communication is, at least sometimes, possible, and we all do understand when someone says that he has seen a ghost. The physical behaviour of the person, and possibly his whole life-history, gives some sort of verifiable meaning to his sentence. We say of a man that he does not know the meaning of 'fear' if we have never seen him show it. If there were no overt or indirect effects we could trace, the sentence would indeed be meaningless since it would be useless ; for it would not make the slightest difference to any person or any situation in the world that the sentence was uttered. But we supply *another interpretation* in order to give it a meaning. We take it to refer to a psychological state of the speaker, and this we can test by experiment. So that we can say that, in so far as the sentence has cognitive meaning, this is still decided by the criterion. Many non-cognitive sentences masquerading as factual may be understood in this manner, e.g. in metaphysics or in theology. But it is not the *literal* meaning of the sentence ; it is one of the many possible interpretations in terms of experience that provides the meaning. If the meaning of such sentences is supposed to be communicable we can hardly accept any other analysis. Since there is a practically infinite number of such interpretations for metaphysical sentences, given by psychological, historical, and other associations, we see that metaphysics remains a pleasant game of hide and seek for those who want to play it.

A criterion of meaning decides only *within* a language system whether or not a sentence belonging to it is meaningful. But does this not let in metaphysics by the backdoor ? How can we show that a way of speaking, e.g. of astrology (assuming it to be something like a theory), is to be rejected ?

The choice of a language system is not decided by logic but by extra-logical considerations ; it depends on what we want to say, and only its success or failure can make us adopt or reject it. To demonstrate that astrologers talk nonsense can only be to show that their sentences violate all the (logical and semantic) rules which we may propose on the basis of their theories. And so this way of speaking is useless for information.

But belief in astrology persists. No logical (or semantic) criterion like that of meaning can destroy it. Superstitions are not exorcised by logic. A change in attitude is needed, a scientific attitude—just as we learned to reject witchcraft, not for logical but for psychological reasons. This attitude is not the least that can be learned from science.

III

THE CONCEPTS
OF CLASSICAL PHYSICS

1. *Newtonian mechanics*

Classical physics represents the theories and laws which describe medium-sized phenomena. Historically, it is the part of physics that has been developed first since it is so close to the experience of every-day life. Starting from Newton's mechanics of particles, classical physics has extended mechanics to elastic and fluid media, and it has developed a theory of optics and of electricity and magnetism, as well as a description of the phenomena of heat. Its culmination is found in the theory of relativity through which the main concepts have been re-formulated and, thereby, classical physics has been unified. To-day we cannot help looking at classical concepts with a critical attitude acquired from relativity theory. Unless we are interested in the historical development there is no reason in keeping to an original, rather vague, formulation of the basic concepts which relativity theory has done so much to analyse. When we reconstruct the system of physics to-day, it is from a more logical viewpoint that we approach it, and from a basis given by relativity. This is another example of the self-correcting method of science : a more advanced theory in turn clarifies the concepts of the original theory upon which it is built.

The great achievement of Newton lies in the introduction of the *mathematical method*. And his method consists not only in giving, or attempting to give, an axiom system for mechanics. It is the consistent use of an artificial symbolism—the invention of a calculus, and the power of the differential equation—that is mainly responsible for the success of Newtonian mechanics. For this enabled us to make use of vague and obscurely formulated ideas and still to achieve a precise statement of the laws. It has freed us from the limitations of the verbal formulation for our experiences upon which Galileo and Kepler had to rely.

In becoming increasingly more abstract the language of

physics has been made logically more consistent but psycho-logically more difficult to grasp. To-day modern physics has completely passed from the realm of ordinary language into a mathematical symbolism often incomprehensible even to the physicist who is not an expert in the field the particular theory describes. For this reason the basic concepts of science are so little known and, if known, so often misunderstood. For it is impossible for the layman, and very difficult for the physicist, to state clearly the hidden assumptions underlying the mathematical formulation of a physical theory. Once the technique is acquired the physicist can make use of the nearly machine-like functioning of the symbolism to describe his experiments, without recourse to an explicit statement of the basic concepts. The interpretation of the mathematical equations, usually given by vague and ambiguous expressions in the accompanying text, is tacitly con-tained in the physical theory. What is necessary is to isolate this interpretation and to try to make it clear so far as this is possible by means of ordinary language.

The concepts of classical physics, however, are not all on the same level. The concepts of force, mass, and motion which characterize Newtonian theory are familiar enough from ordinary experience so that they appear to be nearly self-evident. The concept of field introduced by Faraday and Maxwell to describe the phenomena of optics and electromagnetism is, however, somewhat more technical. Finally, thermodynamics which is commonly regarded as the third constituent of classical physics is even more difficult. Although it deals with simple phenomena such as temperature and quantity of heat, the concepts of state energy, and entropy are certainly not immediately clear and, in fact, require much elucidation.

Newtonian mechanics is the beginning of classical physics ; and it is still the foundation of all physics. From this basis all modern physics developed ; and its concepts represent more closely than any other the experiences of every-day life. It is true that, compared to the naïve ideas of common sense, the concepts of Newtonian mechanics are somewhat more technical. But since even the most advanced, the most 'abstract', theory must ultimately, in its results, link up with ordinary experience, classical physics—and, in particular, Newton's mechanics—remains the cornerstone upon which the edifice of modern physics is built.

Obviously, the origin of Newtonian theory from simple mechanical experience shows that it possesses limitations. But the attempts to improve our grasp of the concepts of mechanics by constructing an axiom system have not been very successful (though work on such systems continues and, recently, some progress was made). Although Newtonian mechanics is the simplest kind of theory physicists have ever created, it is a theory that, so far, has defied all attempts at a complete analysis. It is only on the level of relativity theory, that is in a theory in which the concepts are more refined, that a better understanding of the foundations of mechanics is reached. The concepts of mechanics, taken by themselves, are rather vague and obscure just because they are so close to ordinary experience.

Moreover, Newton's original formulation is open to serious criticism. The three laws of motion, together with the definitions, are given as a postulational system ; but it is a system that does not comply with the demands modern logic must make. The concepts of absolute space and time have been found inapplicable in experience ; however, relativity theory brought about the necessary corrections. But it is the concepts of force and mass that present the greatest, and perhaps insurmountable, difficulties.

I do not wish to give here a historical or systematic treatment of Newtonian mechanics. It will suffice to remind ourselves of the main concepts.

First, there are the concepts of time, space, and motion which Newton took for granted as he explains in the first *scholium*.

Absolute, true, and mathematical time, of itself, and from its own nature, flows equably without relation to anything external...

Absolute space, in its own nature, without relation to anything external, remains always similar and immovable. Relative space is some movable dimension or measure of absolute spaces . . .

Absolute motion is the translation of a body from one absolute place into another ; and relative motion, the translation from one relative place into another . . .

These statements, then, are not to be taken as definitions, but they explain what is supposed to be the intuitive conception of space, time, and motion.

Second, there are some explicit definitions.

The quantity of matter is the measure of the same, arising from its density and bulk conjointly.

The quantity of motion is the measure of the same, arising from the velocity and quantity of matter conjointly.

The *vis insita*, or innate force of matter, is a power of resisting, by which every body, as much as in it lies, continues in its present state, whether it be of rest, or of moving uniformly forwards in a right line.

Third, we have the three laws of motion.

Every body continues in its state of rest, or of uniform motion in a right line, unless it is compelled to change that state by forces impressed upon it.

The change of motion is proportional to the motive force impressed ; and is made in the direction of the right line in which that force is impressed.

To every action there is always opposed an equal reaction ; or, the mutual actions of two bodies upon each other are always equal, and directed to contrary parts.

The criticism of Newtonian mechanics as the science of motion is, of course, earlier than relativity theory ; and the concepts of force and mass were subjected to analysis even before the concepts of absolute space and time were doubted. We may assume that the kinematic concepts are understood immediately if we know the meaning of 'space' and 'time'. Thus, 'velocity' designating the ratio of space over time, and 'acceleration' as the time rate of change of velocity are concepts that do not raise difficulties.

But it is different with the dynamic concepts. Newton's definition of 'mass' in terms of matter and density appears to us to-day to be circular. We do not know what 'matter' means except by reference to mass ; and the same is true of 'density' (though in Newton's time density was regarded as an immediately recognisable property). And to define 'mass' with the help of 'a power of resisting', or by 'weight', is equally objectionable, for both proposals imply that we understand the concept of force. Thus, the condition a good definition has to satisfy, i.e. to define one word in terms of others already known, is certainly not fulfilled.

The usual criticism is to point out that it is undesirable to take 'force' as an undefined, primitive term and to rely on an intuitive understanding of what it means. It is just this anthropomorphic interpretation of 'force' as suggested by daily experience that seems to be against all scientific experience. To interpret the force of gravitation in terms of muscular effort, by push and pull, is not acceptable. Most attempts at reformulating Newtonian mechanics were therefore directed towards eliminating this concept.

How can this be done? It is impossible to take the three laws of motion as supplying a definition of 'force'. For instance, the first law if so used can only define 'zero force', as Eddington pointed out. The second law can provide a definition only if we know already what we mean by 'mass' and 'acceleration'. We are then left to define 'mass'—and this cannot be done with the help of 'inertia' or 'weight', for both terms re-introduce the concept of force. The third law, by stating that forces always occur in pairs, makes the concept of force more clear, but it does not contribute directly to its definition. Since we can derive from the third law a statement about the conservation of momentum, we may try to define 'force' as 'time rate of change of momentum'. This means that we have to define 'momentum' for which purpose we require the definition of 'mass'.

It is impossible to find a satisfactory solution, from the logical point of view. To-day, Mach's proposal to define 'mass' in terms of 'mutual acceleration of two bodies' is considered to be the most acceptable; but this definition, again, involves reference to an *inertial system.*

In Newtonian mechanics we have to refer all measurements of displacement, and therefore of acceleration, to a special coördinate system, the inertial system in which the second law holds for all motions, and this represents the preferred system among all the possible ones. It thus expresses the absolute character of space and time and shows that force is equally something absolute. The fixed stars may be taken as an approximate example of such a system. To define 'mass' by means of 'acceleration' within Newtonian mechanics therefore entails that we already know the second law, and so on. Only on the level of relativity theory, that is when we are permitted to use any arbitrary coördinate system for the description of mechanical phenomena, can we avoid this difficulty. But then the whole conceptual basis is changed.

This traditional critique of Newton's mechanics is of course somewhat old-fashioned ; for it springs from the belief that we must always define our terms. There is no need, in science or anywhere else, to insist on *explicit* definitions. This demand arises from the mistaken view that language is made precise by means of definitions. This view, I suppose, derives from the vulgar use of 'definition' in everyday life where we mean not the technical, logical concept but something closer to explanation. In fact, definitions are nearly irrelevant ; they do not tell us how to use the term which is defined, that is, they do not give its meaning. What we do need are the rules of usage of a term, i.e. the semantic rules, and a language system in which the term occurs. And this usage gives us an *implicit* definition. We do not find anywhere an explicit definition of 'electron', for example ; but there is an electron theory.

If, however, we insist on explicit definitions, then we can do no better than to define 'force' by the concept of mass, and vice versa, provided we also know independently the meaning of 'inertial system'. There is a close connexion between these two concepts ; we may use either as the primitive term. And it has been said, occasionally, that this interrelation of the fundamental terms indicates the very content of Newtonian mechanics. In one sense, this is true ; but it is making a virtue of the necessity arising from an incomplete analysis of the concepts.

On the one hand, it appears to be a physical discovery that we find—on the assumption that we know the concept of force— that the mass of a body shows up as coefficient in the equation for inertial motion given by the second law ; that, moreover, this coefficient is numerically equal to the one occurring in the force law of gravitation. That is to say, it seems to be an experimental fact that 'inertial mass' and 'heavy mass' have the same denotation. On the other hand, it is a physical discovery— assuming the concept of mass to be known—that force has the magnitude and direction of the product of mass times acceleration ; and that it is the change in motion rather than motion itself which characterizes what we call 'force'. It was exactly this usage of the term 'force' which is against all common sense that marks the beginning of the science of mechanics. It reveals the difference from Aristotle's definition of 'force'; the wide range of experience in which earlier scientists have used, and we sometimes still do use in everyday life, the concept of force, e.g. weight, energy, work, momentum, etc., is reduced in Newtonian mechanics. The concept of force has become meaningful in this way, not by an explicit definition but by constructing a theory. The lack of independence of the primitive terms, however, remains a logical fault that makes it impossible to set up a consistent axiom system for mechanics.

It has also been asserted on occasion that Newton's laws are self-evident. But the circumstance that we are so familiar with them must not mislead us into believing that these statements need not be analysed or that they are devoid of physical meaning. The very opposite is true ; and that by using one or the other concept as primitive we can set up different systems of interpretation, illustrates a feature important to all scientific theory.

Indeed, there are many other ways of formulating the fundamental laws of mechanics. Since the Newtonian system is logically so unsatisfactory, physicists have always tried to improve upon it by stating a unifying principle—expressed by a single mathematical equation—from which the whole of mechanics can be derived. These principles usually introduce more comprehensive and technical concepts, with the resulting economy in symbolism and in assumptions that are otherwise needed ; and, in particular, the explicit use of 'force' and 'mass' is modified, if not completely avoided. It is impossible to do justice to these principles without giving their mathematical formulation ; they have been, and they still are, of the utmost import to the whole of physics. A brief indication must suffice here.

In Newton's original treatment, if we want to solve a problem, it is necessary to find the forces acting on any given particle. Forces possess both a magnitude and a direction : mathematically, they must be symbolised as *vectors*. The law of motion is a vector equation containing, as components, the three directions and magnitudes of the force that determine motion in ordinary space. It is obviously of advantage if we can describe motion by one, or more, *scalar* quantities, that is, by something which is uniquely characterized by one value only. The mathematical formalism which makes this *analytic* treatment of mechanics possible is based on the idea of *variation*.

Let us illustrate this idea by the principle of *least action* (first discovered by Euler and Lagrange and reformulated, or re-discovered in another form, by Jacobi, Hamilton, and Monge). The actual motion of a particle may be represented by its path between two points. Let us imagine all possible paths between these points that are compatible with the given constant energy of the motion. The mathematical principle, then, tries out all these *virtual* variations of the actual path ; it computes auto-matically for each path a certain mathematical expression called '*action*'. There is one path for which the action is a *minimum* (or, in general, an extremum). The principle of least action shows that this particular path is the actual path of the motion as it occurs in nature.

This method of variations—which may be traced back to Leibniz's possible worlds—can be applied to many different concepts. D'Alembert's principle of *virtual displacement*, for instance, reduces dynamics to statics, and so is an attempt to overcome the difficulties concerning the concept of force. A system of moving particles is imagined to be in equilibrium ; the equilibrium is slightly disturbed or varied ; this allows us to derive the equations of motion for the particles. The principle was used by Lagrange—the 'Shakespeare of mathematics'—in his 'Mécanique analytique' in which, as he emphasized proudly, no recourse is had to diagrams or pictures for the proof of theorems. Hertz, in his 'forceless' mechanics, made use of a principle of the *straightest path*. Hamilton's principle states that the *energy* (or, rather, a certain kind of energy) must assume a minimum (in general, a stationary) value ; and so on.

The most important concepts which these various formulations introduce into mechanics are : action, energy, equilibrium, path, and work ; and they are more 'abstract' (i.e. unfamiliar or specialised) than the concepts of force and mass. Moreover, this approach brings with it a generalisation of the Cartesian concept of coördinate. Any set of *parameters* which can characterize not only the position of a mechanical system but also its momentum, energy, etc., may be used as coördinates. They are the *general-ised* coördinates of the mechanical system. In this way we make use of the pictorial language of n-dimensional geometry to reduce the mechanics of a complicated system of many particles to the motion of a single mass point ; for we replace the motions of n particles in ordinary space by the motion of a single *phase-point* in 3-n-dimensional space. This is no longer ordinary, physical space, of course; it is a mathematical, *configuration* space with as many dimensions as there are independent para-meters, or *degrees of freedom*, which are needed to solve the problem.

The variational approach to mechanics, then, opens a way to many new interpretations. Each system of mechanics so con-structed is mathematically more elegant, but logically not more satisfactory, than the Newtonian system; for the basic concepts are not intuitively clear, and many implicit assumptions are made. Nevertheless, these systems are of heuristic value; and they do contain useful information which is indicated by the name of the various principles. For they suggest a possible interpretation for the mathematical equations, and it is in this way that together, they give us, a better understanding of the foundations of mechanics.

But how is it possible, so we may ask, that Newtonian mech-anics is so successful, if its foundations are logically so insecure, if its basic concepts are so vague and ill-defined, and if so many alternative formulations can be given? It is a source of perpetual wonder to the critical physicist to see how little can be said explicitly about the basic concepts of mechanics and how much can be achieved, in practice, with their help. Where is the power of this method?

2. *The concept of model*

When we want to explain how scientific theories are con-structed and how they function, we must speak *about* them; and this requires a suitable terminology. This meta-theory, or methodology, is as necessary to science as grammar is to ordinary language; and scientists have often spoken of the 'grammar of science'. It is obviously best to follow the scientists here as closely as possible, at least in the first instance; we may hope in this way to avoid forcing science into a pre-conceived scheme, as philosophers have so often done.

How, then, can we explain the power of Newtonian theory, in spite of its lack of logical clarity? The answer is that, apart from the explicit statements which occur in the theory, a number of

F

assumptions is tacitly made. A *model* is presupposed. To begin
with, this is a visual representation that allows us, both psychologically and logically, to make use of exact mathematical
formulae in spite of the inexact meaning of the symbols.

A mechanical universe is assumed which is constituted of
particles in motion ; and it is often said that Newtonian theory
represents the mechanistic world-view. Newton himself seems
to have accepted the picture of moving particles ; and he
described it by saying, in his *Opticks*, '. . . that Nature may be
lasting, the Changes of corporeal Things are to be placed only in
the various Separations and new Associations and Motions of
these permanent Particles'.

The model helps us to imagine what happens in the world by
suggesting an analogy with familiar experience ; but it is not
merely a *psychological aid*. A model also has a *logical function*, for
it shows how the thing symbolised in the equation behaves in a
given situation. The model gives a possible interpretation to the
symbols which thereby acquire a meaning, and we can apply the
equation, or formula, and test it. This interpretation is expressed
verbally in the accompanying text, or is shown by discussing an
example, or by making a diagram : for this reason, the model is
important in science.

What is a model, then? A preliminary, and somewhat general,
description will suffice here ; a more detailed account will be
given after the various theories of physics have been discussed.
The term 'model' was first introduced into science in the 19th
century ; originally, however, it seems to have been received into
the language during the 17th century when it was used for
denoting what, to-day, we call an architectural blue-print. In
modern usage, the word may refer to anything, from a three-
dimensional representation, or replica, to a diagram.

The Victorian scientists believed physics to be impossible
without the help of models, and particularly of mechanical
models which, if need be, could be actually constructed by
means of string and card-board. The task was, then, to build up
a technical language for electricity and optics, and mechanics was
used for this purpose as the simplest theory available for interpreting the electro-magnetic equations. From this stems,
historically, the suspicion with which the model is sometimes
regarded, since there is always the danger that we take the model

as the thing or situation for which it is a model. Present-day scientists decry the use of visual models and they have emphasized the 'abstract', or non-representational, character of the interpretations required for a modern theory. It is alleged, on occasion, that modern physical theory is purely mathematical : we are not told, however, how it happens that such a theory does describe our experiments. The logical rôle models play even in the physics of to-day cannot be so simply denied. The interpretation, say of quantum mechanics, is more 'abstract' since it is in terms of probability ; but it is still an interpretation.

role of models today

It is true that there are usually many different models providing, for the same calculus, interpretations of various degrees of abstraction. This is easily seen in Newtonian mechanics, for example. Indeed, the various formulations of the theory are designed to improve the clarity of the basic concepts ; they are connected with interpretations varying from a simple picture of the phenomena to a rather schematic presentation, say, in terms of action. Once we have learned to work with the 'abstract' model we can sometimes dispense with the simpler model which, in this manner, has been used as an intermediary to a more formal and technical interpretation. The standard textbooks, for instance, start with the simplest formulations of vector mechanics and end with the variational principles. This is also, to some extent, the order of historical development ; but it must not blind us. We must not let psychological and historical factors obscure the logic of theory construction.

then

The model, then, was originally used for interpreting one theory, e.g. electromagnetism, in terms of a simpler, or at least better known, theory, e.g. mechanics. In the same sense, we may say that the calculus of mechanics is interpreted, to some extent, by the simpler conceptions current in ordinary language, e.g. of force, work, body, etc. The model, however, is a simplified interpretation and usually not even completely formulated in words, but pictures, diagrams, and graphs are needed to support it. For the concepts of everyday life do not suffice for interpreting mechanical theory ; new concepts have to be invented ; and even when we keep the same word, e.g. 'force', it is used differently. In a similar way, mechanical concepts are insufficient for interpreting electromagnetic theory. The model is, therefore, an incomplete, or *partial*, interpretation of one theory in terms of another, or of one theory in terms of simpler concepts. For this reason, a derogatory sense sometimes attaches to the term ; for the model is not the same as thing or situation for which it serves as description, or like the theory it interprets. 'It is only a model', we say and so express our wish for a better, or complete interpretation.

But the fact remains that we cannot do without models; for there exists no single theory in physics for which we can give a complete interpretation in terms of suitable rules, that is, a formalised theory. Moreover, apart from the *heuristic*, or *pragmatic*, use the model has a logical function which remains indispensable, as an explanation, that is, an interpretation of a theory in simpler terms.

Models thus resemble *metaphors* in ordinary language. Metaphors are used to give a more precise meaning, or to add an important *nuance*, to our expressions ; when words normally used in a given context seem to fail, we seek help through words which, usually, belong to another context. In this way we extend the usage of our customary expressions ; and this is necessary if we want to build up a technical language for describing an experiment artificially produced in the laboratory. In physics, we speak of a *field* of force, or of the *flow* of heat, and so on. Indeed, technical discourse cannot do without metaphorical language ; and, for that matter, almost every expression in ordinary language (save the most primitive ones) is a metaphor ; it is only that we no longer remember the original meaning. This is exactly the danger : we forget the origin of our metaphors and try to make them do a job they cannot do. It is well to remember that 'no word is metaphysical without having first been physical'.

Models as well are often too simple, and we forget their limitations. For the model arises from the simplest experience in the description of which the expression in question is used. This sets the standard, or is taken as a schema of some sort, and it so prescribes implicitly the semantic rules for the usage of the expression. But ordinary language has a wide latitude for possible interpretation of our expressions, and there may be many different pictures and analogies conferring some sort of meaning on the expression we investigate. For instance, when we say that time flows, we suggest a picture of a river flowing evenly past its banks (as described in Newton's *scholium*) : this may make us believe in a theory of absolute time.

But metaphors are single, isolated expressions embedded in natural language ; when used in more technical discourse, they are apt to carry with them their ordinary usage which may no longer be appropriate. And the rules are never explicitly stated ; it is left to our imagination to see where the similarity (or dissimilarity) lies which gives point to the metaphor.

A model, however, is much more than a metaphor. It is an attempt, not only to extend the use of a single expression, but to build up a whole system of expressions, or a terminology. Though the rules of usage are often not explicitly given in so many words, they are *specified* by making pictures and diagrams, or by a mathematical equation. The picture, or a general, verbal description indicates the possible situations, and so a language system is given, at least in outline. The pictures we draw for a simple experiment—say, a collision between two particles—are not merely used for supporting our limited imagination. The geometry of the situation, the lines representing the forces, the angles between the lines marking a direction, etc., allow us to use the vector calculus in order to solve the problem.

The model, then, introduces *syntactic* rules of usage for terms like 'force', and its import in physics lies in the fact that, by its help, we can set up an equation. Past usage of the equation, or the situation in which the equation is primarily used, suggests a possible interpretation and so specifies some *semantic* rules for the symbols occurring here. For example, whenever we see a certain differential equation of the second order (in the space and time coördinates), we think of waves, and we call it the wave equation. The model provides us with a descriptive *key concept* ; the original meaning of the equation is kept to some extent, though not completely. There are a great many, even if related, senses of 'wave' which occur when we make use of the wave equation.

In Newtonian mechanics, then, a universe consisting of particles in motion is tacitly presupposed, and by reference to such a picture we know how to apply the concepts of the theory. It is a picture with somewhat blurred outlines, for it may be analysed into a number of slightly varying interpretations according to what concepts are used.

The concept of particle presents the greatest difficulties here ; it is taken to designate a small body. In the crudest picture, the particle is the ball Galileo used to find the laws of the inclined plane and of free fall. A particle, thus, must possess mass and position, volume, shape, impenetrability, and permanence. Its behaviour in the experiments illustrates some of the possible situations in which a moving particle may be found. The range of experiences to be expected, and with it the logical range of the concept, is so indicated ; and this suggests, vaguely, semantic rules for the use of 'particle'.

But in Newton's mechanics the particle is a *mass point* ; it has no extension, i.e. volume or shape, but only position and mass (or inertia). Any actual body is considered to be either such a point-particle or an assembly of them held together by internal, cohesive forces which, normally, need not be known since they will not affect the motion. This *idealisation*, or simplification, was very successful ; it enabled Newton to set up a theory of gravitation, that is, a law that can describe by the same formula the behaviour of small bodies as well as of planets.

This model has limits, however, in the sense that it delimits the universe of discourse ; and it must do so, if it is to be of any use. Not all motions that a particle can be imagined as carrying out are possible ; and this restricts the logical range of the concept. It was quite right that Huyghens's wave theory overthrew Newton's particle theory of light. A mechanical particle cannot move like light, and the particle language suitable for describing optical phenomena has different rules of usage for the term 'particle'.

The model must be supplemented now by saying how the motions are produced, i.e. by the concept of force. Newton wanted 'from the phenomena of motion to investigate the forces of nature, and from these forces to demonstrate the other phenomena'. In the simplest picture a ball to which a coiled spring is attached illustrates how a force acts ; a particle is acted upon by a force increasing with the distance to which the spring is stretched. Even to-day this idea is not completely given up since we employ, in nearly every theory of physics, the auxiliary model of an *oscillator*. But the force of gravitation is of a different kind ; it diminishes with the square of the distance between the two particles ; another, simple situation must be found to illustrate it. In this instance, the concept of force is made clear by pointing to planetary motion. The force originates in the particle

and acts along the line connecting the particles (or centres) ;
it is the *central force* model. A difficulty arises since here we do
not know how the force is transmitted through space ; no spring
will act like this. A suitable mechanism has therefore to be found.
In this way, the *particle-force* model of mechanics is constructed.

What serves as model, then, is always something simpler, or
more familiar, than the thing, process, or situation for which it is
a model. So many of our models are therefore taken from
Newtonian mechanics, as it is the scientific theory with which we
are best acquainted and which is most easily related to the
happenings in the laboratory. Similarly, we take simple, and
simplified, situations for interpreting, by model, the calculus of
mechanics. The model so becomes a *link* between theory and
experiment. We explain, and test, the theory in terms of the
model.

With the help of such pictures the laws of motion and of
gravitation make more clear what we understand by 'force' and
'particle'. The concept of motion, by showing what kinds of
motion are permissible, completes the picture ; but it becomes
necessary to introduce explicitly the concept of causality. This is
a vague notion that gains in clarity when we see that a change in
motion, rather than motion itself, requires a cause ; it is, however, only by stating a definite law that we can discuss reasonably
the problem of causality. As we shall see later, it is the inverse-
square law of force that exemplifies the 'dynamical' causality of
classical physics.

Whenever we make a model of physical reality, that is when
we construct a system of interpretation, it is whatever is constant
in the model that is of importance. From the common sense view
of events that we accept in daily life we have learnt to make a
picture of the world which is similar to the familiar situation
found in ordinary experience : we speak of 'things', and things
are impenetrable, have shape, and are permanent. The concept
of particle is a refined version of the concept of thing. We always
search for constants in the description of nature so that we can
attach an interpretation in terms of 'things' to our equations.
The constancy of mass is a characteristic of the particle in
mechanics. Indeed, we speak of a principle of conservation of
mass—a principle which, however, is not of much use even in
classical mechanics. But the conservation of momentum and of

energy are two most important principles : these two statements give us the constants in the equation of motion.

Our interest lies always in finding the constant quantity so that we can construct a model of a permanent thing which is changing only by virtue of its change in space and time. We feel that otherwise we cannot identify the thing as the *same* thing if it were to change itself. This brings with it also the essentially static, or at least stationary, character in our description of events in physics. In every process there is always something that is constant ; we cannot describe a process in which everything changes and, possibly, disappears.

The model we accept in Newtonian mechanics shows how the particle moves in a certain situation ; and we describe it by constructing a universe of discourse which suggests semantic rules for the use of the term 'particle'. By showing the actual or possible situations the model prescribes the *range* for the term 'particle' which thus acquires a more precise meaning. For by giving the range we state the possible states of the world which make the sentence describing the motion of the particle come true. The simplest kind of universe one can imagine is of course one where the individuals are all alike, i.e. points, and have only one, *intrinsic*, property, i.e. mass, while space, time, as well as force, represent the external framework or environment. The language of Newtonian mechanics is, so to speak, the thing-language of every-day life cut down to its barest essentials.

This is, I suppose, one reason why the conceptions of Galileo and of Newton appear to us to be so 'natural'. But it would be a mistake to overlook the difference between the particle-language of mechanics and the thing-language of every-day life. It is, after all, against all *prima facie* evidence of our senses to say that only change in motion, and not motion itself, requires a cause ; it is quite a feat of abstraction to imagine an eternal state of uniform motion which is completely described by one intrinsic property of the particles, i.e. inert mass, without the help of an external agency. Descartes found this idealisation too difficult to accept ; and so he invented a *vortex* language, that is, took the vortex in a medium, instead of the mass point, as the key-concept. This vortex could even be reduced to the more elementary idea of extension. Descartes thought it better for explaining the motion of material bodies since, in fact, the motion does not persist for long due to frictional resistance, as in a vortex.

The invention of a proper, or appropriate, terminology alone enables us to formulate laws. For there are always two problems that must be kept apart if we want to understand the methods of science. We have, first, to find a suitable way of speaking, or a model (since no explicit rules for the usage of the key-concepts can normally be given). And, second, we must test the hypotheses which have been formulated in terms given by the model.

However, whether or not a model is applicable in a given instance, is not a matter of proof but of success in practice. In science, success is a fairly clear-cut criterion ; and we usually find out whether or not we are applying a model beyond its limits, in a field where it is no longer appropriate to speak in this way. The mechanistic model, however, is so powerful that people could not, and still cannot, resist the temptation of 'explaining' everything with its help ; the result is the metaphysics of mechanism.

The particle-force model as an interpretation for mechanics is, however, reasonably clear by now, and a more logical construction of the theory is, at least, approached. The picture allows us to give a mathematical description, even if we cannot formulate precisely the interpretation in terms of semantic rules. But it is not astonishing that the beginnings of science are somewhat 'lost in obscurity'. Indeed, it is exactly this procedure that is so typical of science : to start with vague concepts which are made more precise in subsequent theories. The model, visual or 'abstract', enables us to follow this procedure until, possibly, the concepts are clear enough to construct a more formal, and formalised, theory. It is in this manner that we make use of experience, both to satisfy our psychological requirements and in order to proceed to a logical system.

3. *Maxwell's theory*

The Newtonian universe consists of particles whose motions reveal the forces acting between them. The configuration of particles is first described by geometry, as statics ; their change in time is represented as kinematics ; when the concepts of force and mass are added explicitly, we have dynamics. All sorts of motion are permissible as long as they follow, for a given type of force, the equations of motion ; although at any moment there is only one particular motion which represents the actual world. What kind of universe we have to accept, and the language in which to describe it, is thus determined. We have a picture, or a model, specifying a semantic system ; and by showing the possible states of the world, it prescribes the rule for the description of these states.

The particles are small bodies whose size is negligible compared to their mutual distances : thus, they may be treated as points, which brings out also their character of indivisibility. But what are the forces which produce the motion of the particles, and how do they act?

The forces have to be transmitted through space ; and this suggests the assumption of filling space with a continuous medium, the *aether*. The picture of isolated particles is supplemented ; we invent a medium in which the particles are embedded, and their mutual actions are transmitted by it. Of course it is difficult to state clearly what this aether is : to a large extent, the 'horror vacui' dictates the need for it. In Newton's theory it plays no rôle save to help visualisation : the victory of the Cartesian conception of space as a plenum as against the Aristotelian void. Newton conceived it to be a mechanical medium, somewhat like air : 'It is inconceivable that inanimate matter should, without the mediation of something else which is not material, operate upon, and affect other matter without mutual contact . . .'. In the later development of physics, that is the theories of elasticity, optics, and electromagnetism, there is more need for an aether, as a carrier for action and to explain its mechanism. Many different models were invented attributing the properties of fluids or solids to the aether, and finally the conception of the luminiferous aether was evolved. It is constituted of particles, the aether molecules, but they have no longer the properties which we normally associate with material entities. They must be assumed to penetrate every body and to form a super-fluid medium which however is completely rigid : otherwise the aether cannot maintain the transversal vibrations of light. In short, it is a very strange picture that has lost its main value, for we can no longer visualise the aether in terms of simple mechanics. All that remains is, in fact, that the aether reveals the continuous character of the processes which are supposed to take place in it.

Experiments, particularly in the domain of electricity and magnetism, call for a description in which the concept of continuum, and of continuity, is exclusively used. In Oersted's experiment, the magnetic field in the neighbourhood of current carrying wire is shown by the deflection of a compass needle. The deflection decreases continuously with the distance from the wire : in principle, the whole of space is affected, though most of the magnetic energy involved in the process must reside in the environment. It is Faraday's conception of *field* that becomes the basis of Maxwell's theory of electromagnetism. Indeed, the introduction of 'field' eventually led to the rejection of the concept of aether ; it made possible the unification of mechanics, optics, and electromagnetism which is achieved in relativity theory. For this reason we say nowadays that classical physics is field physics.

A field is said to exist in any part of space, where to any point and at any time a set of numbers can be coördinated unambiguously. No material medium is required to carry it. Though, historically, the concepts of field and of aether were used side by side, we do not need both. In fact, the concept of field represents another stage in the development of the continuum idea, while the aether is an earlier concept found unsuitable in later theories.

The model assumed in Maxwell's theory is thus more tenuous. A field is more of a mathematical construction, while the aether was often thought of as an actual, mechanical, model made up of wheels, bars, and springs. And it is the concept of *energy* which characterizes the processes in a field rather than particles and masses : continuity is in the foreground of the picture. Action is transmitted in a different, less mechanical, manner. While in the aether theories it is represented as mechanical stress and strain of the medium, in the field theory we have energy spreading through space, as waves. The previous, mechanistic picture is replaced by a more 'abstract' model.

Gravitational, electric, and magnetic fields are familiar examples : we have a field of force. A test-body or probe is introduced into the region where the field exists ; and by measuring the force exerted upon it by the field we can assign to every part of space a set of numbers specifying the magnitude and direction of the force. This vector field is, then, visualised as a map in which we have drawn little arrows, and the length and direction of these arrows tell us the force. This graphical representation can be implemented by introducing 'lines of force'. Contour lines are drawn showing the continuous variation of the direction of force throughout the region ; when we take a single line of certain length as unit measure, the number of these lines passing through any point form a 'tube of force', and so we can indicate the strength of the force.

There is some difficulty in field theory when we ask for the origin of the force field. The particle picture and the field model are, to a large extent, opposing one another : it is the contrast of discreteness versus continuity. But ordinarily we say that charged particles distributed over space provide the origin of electric force ; just as mass particles, or bodies such as the fixed stars, are the origin of the gravitational field. These particles however are reduced to playing a secondary rôle. They must be now point particles which are described mathematically, as singularities in the field ; and, in the physical interpretation, the lines of force begin and end in them. Similarly the test-body we require to determine the field becomes infinitesimally small : it would not 'read' the field correctly otherwise. For it has a field of its own, and this must be negligible so as not to disturb the field to be measured. There are of course many different types of field depending upon how many numbers are needed to specify it ; and they may vary in time so that the 'field' may be used to describe continuous processes both in space and time.

To emphasize the continuous character of the field another concept is introduced, and this is 'energy': it replaces to a large extent the concept of force. This is a welcome feature of the field model since the anthropomorphic associations connected with the idea of force have always been found objectionable by physicists. But the concept of energy is somewhat more difficult to grasp. In mechanics where it is first used, energy is in the simplest instance a property of particles, the 'vis viva' which characterizes their motion. We define 'energy' as the 'ability to do work', and 'work' is defined as 'force times distance'; so 'energy' seems to be a generalisation of the concept of force. But we speak also of the 'flow of energy' and this is an idea which is not easily attached to the concept of force, particularly since the direction of this flow need not coincide with the direction of the force. Rather it suggests a substantiation of energy so that there is a subject to the verb 'to flow', and thus this process-language expressing continuity is made to resemble a thing-language. In analogy to what happens in fluids the flow is often represented as a wave. In this way an energy spreading through space as a wave becomes the analogue to the particle moving in a path for describing physical happenings.

In mechanics an individual force can be isolated and considered as acting on an individual particle which is thereby accelerated ; but energy is the integrated effort of a force over a distance : it is difficult to localise it. Moreover, there are two kinds of energy. Kinetic energy manifests itself in motion, and the whole process may be used as help in visualising what we mean by this term. But there is also potential energy as exemplified, say, by a coiled spring. When the coil is released, the ensuing motion indicates the presence of kinetic energy ; before the release the spring is said to possess potential energy that is transformed into kinetic energy of motion. For the energy cannot arise out of nothing ; it is a result of a force previously applied. Thus we arrive at the idea of conservation of energy. The potential energy is, then, again distributed over space, as configuration of particles, or as tension of a spring : but it is noticed only when favourable conditions allow a physical process to take place. Energy is thus contained in the volume of space in which a field exists. In Maxwell's theory, for instance, a simple mathematical expression is given for the energy per unit volume. From it we can easily derive an expression for the force, by means of the latent or potential energy, and so a complete description of the electro-magnetic field is obtained.

By interpretations of this sort the concept of field is made more determinate, and the picture is sufficiently complete to allow of application. Maxwell's theory was the first, great, achievement of the idea of the field : it made possible a unified description of optical, electric, and magnetic phenomena. The continuity of the processes is expressed in terms of energy, wave, and field, and the mechanistic description using the concepts of force and particle is left behind. Moreover, action and interaction is more easily described. The interaction, say, of two waves is simply a superposition. Action proceeds from one point to the next. There is action-by-contact, and we can avoid action-at-a-distance which appeared to Newton, and to most physicists since, as unthinkable. Events are connected by causal chains, and action spreads through space with finite speed. This idea has become most important for the classical interpretation of deterministic causality.

The whole of electromagnetic theory is contained in Maxwell's set of four equations. They are easily set up when we consider the energy balance of all the processes which may go on in the field, and when we impose the condition of linearity so that the resulting equations become as simple as the equation of motion in mechanics.

Linearisation is a familiar trick in physics. In other words, we have always a certain freedom in choosing our mathematics, or in choosing some of the syntactic rules of our theory. The mathematical form, and the logical structure, of a theory is not something unique ; it becomes so only by virtue of an interpretation in terms of experience, that is, when we add semantic rules ; and even then several interpretations may be possible. This is a strong argument against the view, still sometimes heard to-day, that 'nature is essentially mathematical'.

It is, however, true that past practice and application seem to invest a mathematical equation with a certain interpretation. The wave equation is a prime example for this : for Hertz predicted, and found, that electromagnetic waves exist after he had shown that a wave equation can be derived from Maxwell's theory. The 'mathematical' model, then, functions not through its formal, or syntactic, structure but by means of the semantic rules which are customarily associated with such a structure.

This association is not always a reliable guide for understanding a scientific theory. Though a mathematical model, in contrast to a simple picture, at least provides some explicit rules, these rules are only syntactic ones ; and if we want to describe our experiences, we need also semantic rules. An example illustrating this is given by the linear type of equation, as in Maxwell's theory, which we always try to employ in physics if we possibly can.

A linear equation does not contain squares, or higher powers, in the variables—in this instance, the electric and magnetic field vectors. This represents the usual first approximation to a more complicated theory in which such powers would occur. It also normally indicates that no interaction between the two entities is considered since the product of the two vectors (which, mathematically, is of the second power) does not occur in Maxwell's equations. Indeed, a physical argument is sometimes given for linearisation by saying that the two fields are independent ; after all, we can have a purely electric, or a purely magnetic, field.

This is certainly a confusing argument here : for the resulting equations show, as they must if they are to describe our experiments, that the two fields interact. But the interaction is of a peculiar kind. Magnetic fields accompany, or are produced by, any electric current and field ; while electric fields and currents are produced only by certain kinds of magnetic field, that is, when these fields vary rapidly. Electric and magnetic phenomena are not quite on the same footing ; this is shown also in many other ways. Even though the electric and the magnetic fields equally contribute to the mechanical force and to the energy flow of the combined, electro-magnetic, field, there remains an asymmetry between them. In fact, nowadays we regard magnetism as somewhat secondary. We usually incorporate into Maxwell's theory a version of the older hypothesis of Ampère according to which electric *eddy currents* in a material produce its magnetic properties.

There are, then, two points arising from this discussion. The syntactic rules for the usage of a term which a mathematical model may provide do not necessarily coincide with the descriptive, semantic, rules needed to account for our experiments ; as little as grammatical rules (at least, those which we may consider as syntactic) guarantee the extra-logical, factual, meaning of our expressions. It is only within a formalised language, and provided we have a true interpretation, that syntactic and semantic rules coincide. Neither the usual scientific theory, nor natural language are so constructed as to make this the rule ; and so it is vital not to overlook this split if we do not want to fall into error.

The interaction of electric and magnetic fields within Maxwell's theory is an example. We can understand what it means to say that two electromagnetic waves interact, since we can specify how they interact, i.e. by superposition. But to say, in general, that two fields (or, for that matter, two things) interact has little, if any, meaning. 'Interaction' belongs to the cause-and-effect language. If we want to employ this way of speaking, we must give the law of interaction, and even a mechanism to show how the action is transmitted from one thing to another ; and this will vary with the specific situation. It seems advisable to make little use of, if not to drop entirely, this sort of language. The discussion of 'causality', I think, seems to point to the same moral.

Returning now to the main features of the field model, we find that the particles are nearly completely banished from the continuum picture ; they are mere point singularities which may be placed outside the region considered, so that we have a strictly homogeneous field. If we make use of an aether, we can also interpret the action of the field as a system of stresses in an elastic medium ; this, once more, emphasizes the character of continuity and also establishes a link with mechanics ; for electro-magnetic fields sometimes produce mechanical effects, e.g. set small bodies in motion.

However, the discovery of the first, elementary particle, the electron, involved re-introducing an essential discontinuity into the picture. The existence of charges was of course long known. But they can be visualised, in Maxwell's theory, as a continuous distribution over a macroscopic volume, or as a continuous flow of electric current ; this is possibly a relic from the *fluid* theory of electricity. The electron, however, must be taken as an elementary particle having a definite charge and mass ; its charge represents the *minimum* amount of electricity that can exist in nature, and its mass is the smallest ever found. There seems to be some sort of 'natural' unit for both, and the two are some-how connected. While electric (and magnetic) fields may exist *in vacuo*, there are no disembodied electric charges (or magnetic poles). That is to say, 'charge'—like 'particle'—belongs to a thing-language, while 'field' and 'wave', for example, repre-sent a more 'abstract' way of speaking.

This leads to the re-interpretation of Maxwell's theory by Lorentz. The idea of a discrete particle has to be reconciled with the conception of a continuous field. This problem has re-appeared, time and again, in modern physics but, so far, it has not found a very satisfactory solution. And whenever the particle picture is used side by side with the idea of continuity, probability considerations are needed to obtain the continuity as the average action of a great number of particles. The concept of probability, and statistics, is used to 'smooth out' the graininess in the particle picture ; like the heap of sand which, though consisting of individual particles, still gives a smooth appearance. With the help of 'probability', then, we seem to bridge the gap between particles and fields and, possibly, invent a more successful way of speaking than either of the two models. To speak of 'probability' may not be to go very deep into the theoretical foundations, in this instance ; though the idea of field, and of energy, leads to a new interpretation of 'particle'.

On the assumption that an electron is a spherical body endowed with an elementary charge that is the seat of field energy we arrive at the conclusion that the particle must possess finite size : we can compute the radius of the electron. And its mass can be found in terms of the energy ; we find that the mass is variable, a function of the velocity of the particle. In fact, we have the surprising result that the mass increases with velocity, and that there is a limiting speed—the speed of light—at which the mass becomes infinite. The same result is later obtained, on a different conceptual basis and in a more satisfactory manner, by relativity theory.

It is clear that the usage of 'particle' in this theory must differ widely from its use within mechanics. There, particles are solid bodies of fixed size, and their mass is a constant quantity regardless of what happens to the particle. Its actual dimensions may take on any value so long as we may consider it small relative to the distances between particles : mechanics describes the motion of particles regardless of their size. In the electron theory the particle is definitely restricted in size, as a fundamental unit, or elementary particle ; and it seems that it is the concept of unit charge added to the Newtonian conception of particle that imposes this limitation. Also, the particle cannot become very large, or infinite, in mass ; this would mean that an infinite amount of energy has to be applied to it if we want to set it in motion, since its inertia—its resistance to motion—equally increases. And even for the highest speeds obtainable, say 90 per cent of that of light, its mass and volume increases only slightly though to a measurable degree ; the microscopic character of the electron is not changed. Nor can the particle be contracted into a point, an idealisation so convenient for the mathematical description both in Newton's and Maxwell's theory. The electron as a point-particle would possess infinite self-energy : this

G

must occur when a finite charge is concentrated into a point—thus making the charge density, or charge per unit volume, infinite. Infinity, however, is a mathematical concept which is incapable of an interpretation in terms of a physical experiment. But our normal mathematical methods require particles to be points when they occur together with fields, that is, within the continuum picture. This difficulty of the infinite self-energy of a charged particle has been resolved only partially, even to-day ; it is achieved for the domain of classical physics by Born's re-formulation of Maxwell's theory. But the same problem occurs again in quantum physics where the concept of particle is still more modified, and no satisfactory solution has been offered there, so far.

The combination of the continuum and of the particle model produces this change in the concept of particle. In field theory the concept of energy is a main constituent of the picture : the concept of mass is no longer interpreted in terms of simple mechanics. We have the electro-magnetic interpretation in which mass appears to be a concentration, or a 'knot', of energy. Energy is, however, a continuous function of space and time, and not a thing ; and so this interpretation has been hailed as the first blow struck against 'mechanistic physics' which was then finally overthrown by relativity theory. Elementary particles are not miniature replicas of hard billiard balls, and the forces between them cannot be pictured as springs connecting the balls. The idea of an individual, separate, force is submerged in the picture of a field of force. 'Mass' and 'energy' become (near) synonyms : the description of electromagnetic phenomena requires us to change the usage of these terms from that in mechanics. A simple thing-language, and the idea of substance, is no longer applicable ; instead we have the conservation of energy—there must be something constant in the continuous change of nature.

However, in the electron theory, the concepts of mass and energy are not completely identical. There remains the picture of the particle, which is not merely represented as a concentration of energy. When the particle is at rest—relative to a suitable frame of reference—a constant quantity is left over that is called the 'rest mass': the smallest mass the particle can possess. For a while physicists held the view that this rest mass is mechanical, in the sense that it is permanent and indestructible ; and that only the increase in mass of an electron due to its velocity is electromagnetic. But the assumption of two different kinds of mass is not satisfactory, and relativity theory definitely put an end to it.

It is sometimes said that field theory has 'de-materialised' the physical world by explicating 'mass' in terms of energy ; we could equally say that energy has become something like a material substance. Both views are mistaken, however. Science rejects such philosophic theories, i.e. idealism and materialism, as fallacious since they are ontological : it makes no sense to speak about what mass or energy *really* are. A new language is created in which certain words are used according to slightly different rules than was done previously.

4. *Special relativity*

Classical physics consists of three main theories : mechanics, electromagnetism, and thermodynamics. Though certainly classical in character, thermodynamics is however very general in application, and is interpreted either by rather unfamiliar concepts which are exemplified by the various state-functions, or in mechanical terms as statistical theory. Historically, it was the theory from which the quantum idea first arose. We therefore prefer to discuss thermodynamics separately ; and it may even be thought of as the 'missing link' between classical and quantum physics.

Relativity theory which represents the final formulation of classical physics unites, on a higher level, mechanics and electromagnetism ; and thermodynamics enters into it only when interpreted by mechanics. Thus we have some reason to discuss relativity theory only in so far as it revises and re-formulates the basic conceptions of Newton and Maxwell. It is by a field theory, and through the continuum model, that the description of relativity is carried out. This leads to the revision of the concepts of space and time for which relativity theory has become famous.

The theory of *special* relativity rests mainly on the Michelson experiment. This experiment is designed to determine the absolute motion of light, that is, its motion with respect to the aether ; for the luminiferous aether represents a preferred system of reference like absolute space. The result is that no such absolute motion can be found, within the limits of accuracy of the experiment.

The novel, and radical, interpretation which Einstein has given to the experiment is contained in the two principles of special relativity. This is a prime example of modern scientific method, and it illustrates that facts alone do not make a theory, as is often believed ; but that an experiment may be interpreted in many different ways. It depends on the model the physicist wishes to adopt, and upon the fertility of his imagination, whether the experiment represents a successful test of the theory.

Thus Lorentz explained the Michelson result in this way. He assumed that the length of a moving rod (which is part of the apparatus) is shortened when compared to what its length would be according to Newtonian mechanics. This hypothesis permits us to set up the correct equation for the change in length— exactly one half of the equations of relativity theory—and for this reason these equations are still called the 'Lorentz transformation'. But it is clear that the original Lorentz formula has a meaning quite different from that of relativity theory, although the mathematical expression is the same.

For to Einstein the experiment suggested another hypothesis which is given in the two statements : The velocity of light is independent of the motion of either light source or observer (the principle of constancy of light velocity) ; and : There is only relative motion, and no absolute system of reference is required (the principle of relativity). The assumption of an aether as reference system has become unnecessary. Moreover, as a consequence of Einstein's interpretation, certain optical experiments that previously seemed to give contradictory results can be shown now to agree. The concepts of space and time and, with them, of motion undergo a radical change. It was with the critique of these concepts that the problem of 'meaning' was first introduced openly in arguments about physics.

The two principles allow us to construct the equations in a very simple manner, subject only to some general conditions. The first condition states that the transformation must be linear (i.e., mathematically, only the first powers of the space and time coördinates are used in the formulae). For space and time are supposed to be isotropic and uniform, and the events described must not depend upon the point in space or moment of time where they occur. The second condition requires the equations to be homogeneous (i.e., mathematically, they must not contain terms free of the space and time coördinates) : it means that there is no preferred origin of the coördinate system. The third condition requires that the resulting formula for the space transformation be proportional to a simple mathematical expression used in Newtonian mechanics ; this expression refers to the restricted kind of relative uniform motion which is permissible there (the Galilei transformation). The condition ensures that the relativity formulae, for the special case of low velocity, coincide with the formulae established by Newtonian mechanics. This demand for *correspondence* is one of the most important ideas of modern physics. It finds the clearest formulation in quantum theory ; and it shows that the development of physical theories proceeds according to a certain pattern. The new theory contains the old theory (which, after all, is well supported within a limited domain of experience) as a special case. The continuity of science is not merely a historical fact but it is a logical requirement.

The equations of relativity theory represent a transformation ; we are permitted to use any reference system that specifies the position x,y,z, and the time t. Or, there is an infinite number of possible descriptions, and all are *equivalent*, although the equations describing the actual events may differ—that is, the forces, masses, and other quantities may possess different values. The plurality of descriptions shows that nature allows us a much wider latitude than was previously suspected. But there are always some mathematical expressions that are found to be *invariant* under transformation ; and these do not usually refer to simple properties or things but to a more unfamiliar characteristic of a physical situation. Thus, force and mass which are invariant under the classical transformation, e.g. in Newtonian theory, are now *covariant* with the reference system chosen, while the set of Maxwell's equations, or a complex formula stating a space-time interval, are invariant. This shows that a simple thing-language where, presumably, mass would have to be constant, is no longer applicable. But we remain within a language of this sort by speaking of these invariants as if they were things : it is clear that great caution must be exercised. We feel that whatever is constant in the description of nature is 'real', or that invariants represent, or refer to, actual phenomena, while covariant expressions seem to depend on the kind of language we happen to use. But this is not so. In fact, the model, or semantic system, has changed and our way of speaking has become more technical and unfamiliar. We have no longer a thing-language presupposing constant entities, but invariant mathematical expressions which we use to designate certain features of our experiments.

Here is a summary of the results of the special theory of relativity which may serve as a basis for later discussion.

The first, and well known, result states that the length of a physical rod in uniform motion is contracted when compared to its length at rest. And the time interval of a moving clock is dilated with respect to its time interval at rest, that is, the clock is slowed up.

Second, when we wish to compound two velocities—say, of a moving body and a moving reference frame—to find the resultant velocity relative to a rest system, it is not by mere vector addition as in Newtonian mechanics that we obtain the right answer. The Einstein addition law of velocities is more complicated and establishes that the speed of light cannot be surpassed by any motion. It is here for the first time that a 'natural limit' for physical processes is shown to exist.

Finally, it is found that the mass of a body depends upon its relative motion—a result foreshadowed by the classical theory of the electron. It follows, and this is the most striking result, that mass and energy are one and the same property ; or, that the mass of a body represents another form of the energy we must attribute to it. This is stated by Einstein's famous formula of conversion of mass into energy (and vice versa). There is annihilation and creation of mass. Processes of this kind are observed in many atomic (nuclear) phenomena, and the atomic bomb is constructed on this basis, namely, that a great amount of energy is released when a small amount of mass is lost in a process of nuclear fission. But the property of inertia ascribed to mass belongs now to energy, and this is equally confirmed by experiment.

In relativity theory the concept of field is applied without reservation, and so the basic picture is that of continuous processes taking place in the continuum of space and time. The concept of 'mass' which designates the property most characteristic of discrete particles can find no, or only a very limited, application in such a theory. 'Mass' and 'energy' are (nearly) synonymous within relativity theory. The concept of 'energy', however, is wider since it includes, apart from 'mass', also 'kinetic energy' (referring to the motion of the body) and 'potential energy' (referring to the position of the body in space).

In the context of relativity theory, for the first time in the history of physics, the words 'meaning' and 'meaningless' are explicitly used. In what way can there be meaningless expressions in science? Nowadays, I suppose, most physicists would take it as physically meaningless to speak of absolute motion, or of the aether. The Michelson experiment is said to demonstrate, however, that there is no such thing as the aether. And, of course, when this experiment is discussed, it must be at least logically meaningful to speak of the aether ; otherwise, there is no point to the whole experiment. A hypothesis must be logically meaningful before it can be physically meaningful : if the state of affairs is logically inconceivable within the theory to which the hypothesis belongs, we are not able to test, still less to confirm, whether or not this state of affairs is found in nature ; for the hypothesis does not then describe any state of affairs at all. The Michelson experiment, therefore, must be understood within the framework of the original Newtonian mechanics and of the aether theory of light, where the concepts of absolute motion, and of the aether, are logically allowed.

But to-day many physicists would say that the aether, or an absolute reference system, has been abolished by relativity theory, in the sense that these concepts must not be used in modern physics. In other words, sentences containing such phrases *have become* logically meaningless ; and, indeed, we avoid using them, just as we do no longer speak of heat in terms of the *caloric.* We regard such concepts as having no possible application, or as incapable of describing anything : they are relics of a past age in which a superstitious, and perhaps animistic, attitude towards nature still flourished. It is not merely because our theories have changed : it is because our attitude towards nature has changed. Advance in science is brought about not only by factual discoveries, or by more detailed theories, but also by psychological re-orientation.

This tendency to change from the physical to the logical meaning of an expression only shows, after all, that we try 'to

mould our language to fit the facts'. We want to cut out meaningless expressions from science so that it is impossible to misuse
language, however unwittingly ; that is, we propose a new way of
speaking, or a technical language. It is the tendency towards
formalisation which is so characteristic of science. This is a
strong argument in favour of re-constructing our theories in
logical and semantic terms.

But we persist in using a natural language, like English, when
speaking *in* as well as *about* physics ; we cannot help doing so.
In ordinary language it seems to be logically meaningful to
speak of absolute motion, for example, though possibly factually
false. And so a paradox arises ; for physicists sometimes take such
expressions as being factually false (and therefore physically
meaningful), and at other times as being logically (and, *a fortiori*,
physically) meaningless. But there is no serious logical problem
here : it depends on the theory in which a sentence is formulated
what meaning, if any, the sentence may have. The use of natural
language obscures the fact that scientific language is not only
technical (which is obvious), but that we *use* it in a special, and
more precise, way. The formalisation is neither complete nor
always explicit ; but the rules of usage for scientific terms are
sometimes stated, or at least indicated, by the model we use. It is
by way of approximation, and through a succession of small
logical steps, that scientific language is made more precise.

Relativity theory has profoundly changed the whole of physics.
By the analysis of the fundamental concepts of space and time, of
mass and of force, it has given a new orientation not only to
science but also to our approach to philosophic problems in
general. To-day, for a modern physicist, it is virtually impossible
to consider classical theory in its original form. The later development as given by relativity has influenced, and has reacted back
upon, our view of classical physics. We see nowadays classical
physics through 'relativistic eyes', as being a first approximation to a more comprehensive and unified theory. Relativity
theory is in this sense the 'proper' presentation of classical
physics.

5. *General relativity*

The special theory of relativity disposes of the need to assume
the existence of an aether. Or, as Einstein expressed it : '. . . the

whole change in the conception of the aether which the special theory of relativity has brought about, consisted in taking away from the aether its last mechanical quality, namely its immobility ... The electromagnetic fields are not states of a medium, and are not bound to any carrier, but they are independent realities which are not reducible to anything else, exactly like the atoms of ponderable matter . . . Newton might . . . have called his absolute space "aether" . . . '. There are no experiments by which the existence of an aether could possibly be found ; and thus—by Occam's razor—we cut out of physical theory all sentences about the aether. The absolute character of space and time—that is, that they form an immutable frame-work independent of events—is equally abolished. But the special theory is restricted to uniform motions, i.e. motions which proceed with constant speed in a straight line. Clearly, we must demand that all kinds of motion, including accelerated motion, must come under the sway of relativity. This demand to proceed from kinematic to dynamical relativity was made already by Leibniz who emphasised the *aequipollentia hypothesium* : all descriptions of motion, including dynamical ones, are equally acceptable. When we then investigate accelerated motion, we reach the final stage in the analysis of the concept of space. For the general theory of relativity requires us to say that space is of non-Euclidean character, and it is this statement that, when first made, aroused so much interest, and even antagonism. In order to prepare the ground for a discussion of space and time, let me give first some of the ideas and results of the general theory of relativity.

Newtonian mechanics states explicitly that absolute acceleration can be measured. In the phenomena of rotation, i.e. accelerated motion, new forces occur, the centripetal and the Coriolis force (which are absent in uniform motion). Thus it looks as if for accelerated motion the theory requires the use of 'absolute space', once more. For these forces appear, at first sight, to be independent of the relative position of all bodies, since they are found everywhere in the universe as far as our telescopes can penetrate. For this reason—on the basis of what appears to be an observed fact—Newton concluded that these forces depend upon absolute acceleration. But the existence of absolute space is here introduced ad hoc. We know of no other experiment to support this hypothesis than the occurrence of centrifugal forces ; and we seem to take absolute space as a cause of physical phenomena, which is equally unacceptable.

Newton based his argument in favour of absolute space on the famous *bucket experiment* ; and the facts seem to be simple enough. It is, again, an example which shows that facts do not suffice to construct a scientific theory : facts and hypothesis are interdependent, and any experience may suggest an infinity of possible interpretations.

Newton believed himself to have proved the absolute character of accelerated motion by the following experiment. A bucket of water is suspended by a rope from the ceiling, and the rope is twisted ; when the rope is released, what are the phenomena we observe ? In the beginning, the bucket rotates, but the water remains at rest relative to the container, and its surface is flat. After a while, the water is gradually set in motion due to friction, and finally it moves with the bucket. If we stop the bucket, the liquid goes on rotating, and the surface of the water is parabolic. According to Newton, at the beginning and at the end of the experiment the same kinematic conditions hold : while, at first, the water is at rest and the container moves, at the end, the water moves and the container is at rest. Therefore, it would appear that we have the same relative motion in both instances ; however, the observable phenomena are different. To account for this difference Newton said that the parabolic shape of the surface at the end of the experiment is due to the rotation of the water with respect to absolute space.

This argument was accepted for nearly two hundred years, although it is true that physicists felt uneasy about it, and centrifugal forces were often called 'fictitious forces'. At the end of the last century Mach pointed out that the argument was faulty. The last phase of the experiment is not the exact kinematic reverse of the initial phase : the influence of the fixed stars, and of the whole surrounding universe, has to be taken into account.

We must interpret the experiment according to a different hypothesis. At the beginning, what is at rest, is the liquid and the whole universe as well, while the bucket rotates ; at the end, the bucket and, again, the universe are at rest, while the water rotates. Thus, if the final phase were to represent the strict reversal of the first phase, it would be necessary that the universe turns around together with the liquid. We recognise that Newton's argument cannot prove the existence of absolute space. And if we extend the relativity principle to hold for accelerated motion as well, the difficulty is resolved : whether the water rotates relative to the universe, or the universe relative to the water, becomes a question that cannot be decided by experiment, and only one and the same phenomenon can be expected to occur.

That we accept Einstein's rather than Newton's hypothesis is not merely because it is more attractive from the logical viewpoint ; but it permits us also to explain other observations—that is, to interpret them by the same theory—and to predict new physical effects. The assumption of an absolute space becomes superfluous, for we can now interpret centrifugal forces as dynamical action of gravitating bodies. These forces are not the effect of absolute space but due to the *interaction* of bodies, and there is only one kind of interaction between all material bodies, i.e. gravitation.

In Newtonian mechanics it appears to be accidental that the heavy or gravitational mass of a body obtained by weighing, and the inertial mass found from acceleration experiments, always turn out to be numerically equal, at least within the accuracy of the experiments. This is the more strange since acceleration depends upon mass, according to Newton's second law, while gravitational motion is independent of mass : all bodies fall at the same rate in vacuo. Newton's theory accepts these observations but does not offer an explanation, in the sense that they are not given an interpretation within the theory of gravitation. In Einstein's theory this *equivalence* of the two kinds of mass is taken as a fundamental property of gravitation.

Consider the famous example of Einstein's elevator, or lift : a closed box in which we place an observer and some heavy objects. When the box moves downwards, the observer inside will note a decrease in weight though he cannot look outside and see the motion. If the box falls very rapidly, with an acceleration greater than that of gravitation, the objects will acquire a 'negative' weight, and fly upwards. We may describe the situation in the following way. Either the original gravitational field continues to exist but the box is accelerated in the direction of the field ; or, the masses previously exerting their attraction below the box have disappeared and have re-appeared above, so that the direction of gravitation is reversed. The effect of gravitation and of acceleration cannot be distinguished by any experiment, and this is stated as the principle of equivalence.

In classical mechanics we find two kinds of motion. If a body is left to itself, free of all forces, it moves in an inertial motion, which is rectilinear and uniform. We call a coördinate system an 'inertial system' if bodies not subject to forces show this behaviour when described in such a system. The second kind of motion is accelerated, and it proceeds in curvilinear paths and is not uniform. By merely changing our description of a given motion from an inertial to an accelerated system of reference, we transform rectilinear into curvilinear motion. If we accept the principle of equivalence, then all systems of reference are equally suitable for the formulation of the laws of physics. So it depends upon the system chosen what kind of motion we have ; the equations remain valid although their form is changed according to certain rules of transformation. This *principle of covariance* is the mathematical representation of the principle of equivalence.

It is clear that far-reaching consequences are introduced in this way. If we can make a uniform motion into an accelerated one, with a stroke of the pen so to speak, it means that the concept of force becomes relativised. Force is no longer the simple, absolute quantity as known from Newtonian mechanics. The concepts of thing and of mass are replaced by the concept of field, and with it disappear the forces between things. Since force and causality are closely connected in classical physics, the concept of causality is equally affected by this analysis.

Moreover, the principles of relativity and of equivalence allow us to describe physical events with the help of any coördinate system ; for instance, by a system whose acceleration is so chosen that it is equal and opposite to the gravitational acceleration at a particular point in space. That is, we can transform away gravitation, provided the field is constant and homogeneous at this point. Of course, we cannot make gravitation disappear in the whole universe, for its field varies over large distances. The field of the earth, for instance, cannot be fully eliminated ; but by choosing a rotating reference system we can introduce an inertial field pointing away from the centre of the earth—a centrifugal field. This field can compensate the earth's field only at a single distance : e.g. the radius of the moon's orbit, for the given time of revolution.

Thus, we can always smooth out a sufficiently small part of any field by choosing an appropriate reference system ; that is, we can have local inertial systems in which force-free motion proceeds along a straight path, and we can introduce Cartesian coördinates. But we cannot transform away the forces for the whole region by means of the same reference system ; and so we cannot have 'flat' coördinates everywhere, that is, Euclidean geometry. Our experience of space must be described by *non-Euclidean* geometry, and the character of the geometry depends upon gravitation—that is, the distribution of masses in the universe. Since all reference systems, including accelerated ones, are equally acceptable, the conceptions of straight line and curved line become relativised as well ; and Euclidean concepts can no longer be applied. Euclidean space has lost its preferential status, except as Riemann's 'flatness in smallest parts'. For the kind of non-Euclidean geometry needed to describe the actual universe passes into Euclidean geometry for infinitesimal regions of space. Gravitation and geometry are linked, and the geometry of physical space is determined by the gravitational field.

The general theory of relativity is expressed in non-Euclidean terms depending upon whichever fields exist, and in particular on gravitation. In this manner field and space are fused. Or, the idea of a space—like the space of a room—as an independent system of reference in which events are placed, becomes untenable. Space is the expression for certain physical relations between events ; and when we describe larger areas of the universe, it may show a structure quite different from the one we are used to in familiar experience. Thus, space is neither absolute nor even—in general—Euclidean.

The same holds for the concept of time. 'Time' refers to the temporal relations between events, i.e. the happenings, and they are no longer absolute. This is already demonstrated by the formulae of special relativity, while the idea of gravitation and general relativity is needed to complete the analysis of the concept of space.

Finally, the equations of motion for a material particle as given by the general theory reduce to the equations of motion of

Newton, when we consider the simplest case of a Euclidean, limited, region of space. The whole general theory, in fact, passes into the special theory of relativity, for the case in which we consider force-free motion. And so the principle of correspondence is, once again, used to safeguard the relation to simple experience and to provide the logical continuity of scientific theory. Although each of these theories is based upon completely different conceptions, they follow one another as a series of successive approximations.

The concepts of space and time, force and mass, and causality, have undergone a radical revision through relativity. The model we make of the physical universe has changed ; in other words, the language system that specifies the meaning of these terms is given by different rules. This must be shown now by a more detailed analysis of the concepts of space and time.

6. *Space*

The conceptions of space and time as given by relativity theory are, even to-day, accepted as final—that is, no essential change has been brought about so far by the further development of physical theory. The logical analysis of these concepts was worked out more than twenty years ago, and except for some change in terminology there is nothing to add to the exposition as found, for instance, in Reichenbach's book on the Philosophy of Space and Time. What, then, do we mean by 'space' in the relativistic formulation of classical physics?

The introduction of non-Euclidean geometry raises two, general, questions. What is geometry, and how does it apply to the physical world? The answer to the first question was given when the methods of mathematical logic were applied to the problem of the foundation of mathematics. This approach was most successful in showing up the character of an axiom system, and Hilbert's famous system of Euclidean geometry may be taken as example (see section 2.2). The answer to the second question demonstrates the impossibility of any *a priori* theory in physics, and in particular of the *a priori* theory of space that is the epistemological equivalent of the theory of absolute space. The importance of these answers can hardly be underestimated.

It was in his essay on 'Geometry and Experience' that

Einstein first made the clear-cut distinction between physical and mathematical geometry. For geometry as a mathematical theory is a formal calculus consisting of axioms and definitions from which, by purely syntactic rules, the theorems of geometry are derived ; and the system says nothing about the physical world. Any kind of axiom system may be invented : if consistent—that is, if no contradictory statements can be derived from it—it is acceptable as an example of pure mathematics. But geometry as a physical theory is a mathematical calculus which is interpreted in terms of experience ; the concepts contained in the axioms are, in some way, coördinated to physical things and situations, that is, semantic rules are given for their usage. For instance, 'mathematical line' is interpreted to represent an edge of a physical rod, 'mathematical point' is interpreted as the intersection of two straight-edges, and so on. We assume a meta-language that is known to us and in which phrases such as 'solid body', 'edge of a rod', and so on, occur as constituents of meaningful statements. Ordinary English, or the language of classical mechanics, can, and does serve for this purpose. In this manner geometry becomes a physical theory that describes actual or possible experience. While statements of mathematical geometry are certain and logically true, physical geometry is a description of the world that, even when supported by experiment, is never certain since a mistake in verification can never be excluded.

Or, as Einstein expressed it : 'As far as the laws of mathematics refer to reality, they are not certain ; and as far as they are certain, they do not refer to reality. It seems to me that complete clarity as to this state of affairs first became common property through that new departure in mathematics which is known by the name of mathematical logic or "axiomatics". The progress achieved by axiomatics consists in its having neatly separated the logical-formal from its objective-intuitive content . . .'. A physical geometry is obtained, for instance, by 'the coördination of real objects of experience with the empty conceptual framework of axiomatic geometry. To accomplish this, we need only add the proposition : Solid bodies are related, with respect to their possible dispositions, as are bodies in Euclidean geometry of three dimensions. Then the propositions of Euclid contain affirmations as to the relations of practically-rigid bodies . . .'. This is a clear formulation of the semantic character of physical theory. The interpretation in terms of experience is furnished by a set of semantic rules. Some of them are rules of designation, e.g. we may say that 'mathematical line' designates the edge of a physical rod. We know what we mean by 'edge of a physical rod' since it is a phrase of every-day English ; and in case of doubt we may coördinate to it an experience, by pointing, in order to establish reference (what has been called, wrongly, giving an ostensive definition). And other rules govern the relation between these terms ; they may be taken as rules of formation, and as rules of range, since they determine which kind of sentences are to be accepted into our system and what the possible situations are that may represent an actual state of the physical world. Since rules of this type are often difficult to state explicitly, they are given here by reference to a physical situation which serves as semantic model. The phrase 'relations of practically-rigid bodies' describes this model ; for we know, from experience, how such bodies, e.g. metre sticks, rods, etc., do behave when they are moved around. It is by this sort of interpretation that we obtain a physical geometry ; but whether actual space is Euclidean or not is of course a question which can only be answered by experience.

Geometry was always regarded, historically, as an ideal science. The definitions and axioms of the Euclidean system appear to be self-evident and even necessary ; and the theorems derived from them cannot possibly be doubted. But it was not recognised until recently that geometry, in the ordinary sense of the word, represents two different kinds of theory : as a physical theory describing the world which may have arisen from the practical needs of the ancient Egyptians, and as a mathematical theory given as a formal axiom system. This double rôle has given rise to the idea that all description of nature, that physical science as well, must be based upon axioms of this kind, and that the system must lead to logically true, or absolutely certain, statements. It is from this confusion that rationalism, and the quest for certainty in natural science, arose ; and with it we find the belief that some concepts—such as that of Euclidean space—are logically indispensable for the description of nature. For Euclid's axioms about space seem to be dictated by our faculty of reason, and one feels that no other axioms can be imagined for this purpose. But since experience can never provide this absolute certainty which we seem forced to ascribe to the axioms, it was argued that the concepts must be prior to all experience, i.e. that they provided *synthetic a priori* knowledge.

The axiom system of Euclid was therefore considered to be the only possible system of geometry. It was only in the beginning of the 19th century that Bolyai, Lobatchevsky, and (later) Riemann demonstrated that other axiom systems could be constructed representing various kinds of non-Euclidean geometry. The new geometries aroused violent antagonism among the 'Boeotians', as Gauss called them : he, too, had worked out a non-Euclidean system but did not publish it, for fear of public disapproval. The fact that such systems can be constructed at once abolishes the view that the Euclidean axioms are the only possible ones, or that the axioms of geometry must be self-evident. Self-evidence is a matter of psychology : what we experience in the restricted domain of every-day life appears to us as self-evident. But the axioms of geometry, or of any other theory, need not be part of our common sense knowledge ; rather, the axioms are so chosen that we can build up with their help the system of theorems we have vaguely in mind. These primitive sentences, or the concepts contained in them, must naturally be known to us in some sense, though we need not be able to visualise them. Modern theories, both in natural and in mathematical science, are based on conceptions which, at first sight, are not very clear ; they become clearer only when their theoretical consequences are fully worked out. But if such a new system of mathematical geometry is constructed, it still depends upon experience whether or not the system, when suitably interpreted, can be applied to describe physical space.

What are these various systems of non-Euclidean geometry ? A brief discussion will suffice. It is a historical accident that the construction of such systems started with the critique of Euclid's axiom of parallels. This axiom states that there exists one, and only one, straight line through any point parallel to any given straight line. This appears to be self-evident, since we find many examples in familiar experience. By denying this axiom while keeping all the others we find the required generalisation of geometry. If we say instead that more than one parallel may be drawn, we obtain a space of negative curvature ; and if we say that no parallels are possible, a space of positive curvature is

H

obtained. In general, the curvature may vary from point to point, but we need only consider spaces of constant curvature. Constant negative curvature characterizes pseudo-spherical space, constant zero curvature is the Euclidean space, and constant positive curvature spherical space which is the three-dimensional analogue of the spherical surface. Riemann gave a better representation for the multiplicity of geometries by taking space to be a three-dimensional manifold, and it is the metric given by a mathematical expression referring to distance that decides the type of geometry.

Another way of revealing the difference between the geometries is to consider the angles of a triangle. In Euclidean geometry their sum is equal to two right angles; in non-Euclidean geometry the sum deviates from this value, and the deviation is proportional to the area of the triangle. Thus, if we take the ratio of this deviation to the area, we have the so-called space-constant indicating the type of space : negative for the pseudo-spherical, positive for the spherical space ; and the greater its absolute value, the more curved is the space.

There is no difficulty in visualising non-Euclidean geometry in two dimensions. Ordinary spherical surfaces are an example. There are no parallels on a sphere if we take great circles to represent them, since these always cut each other (at the poles). The difficulty arises only in three dimensions : we would need a fourth dimension to imagine the curvature, for we normally think of curvature as the deviation from the plane surface—as a 'bump'—and we do not see *internal* curvature. This 'curved space' has led to many misunderstandings. If actual space is in some way analogous to a sphere, then the universe must be finite and closed, though boundless. The question is asked, What is outside this universe ? The universe is taken as a sort of big balloon ; and the recent discoveries about the expanding universe are used, wrongly, to support such a picture. But there is no space apart from physical happenings, and the recession of the nebulae is the outermost happening we know of. It makes no sense to speak of this 'outer space', and we cannot say that the receding nebulae, for instance, expand *into* an external space. There are, moreover, logical difficulties whenever we use the term 'universe' in this sense. Since we define 'universe' as 'everything there is', we cannot speak of things outside the universe, even if this outside is meant to refer to a void. Perhaps it is for neglect of logic that cosmological theory is so disreputable from a scientific point of view, and that arguments used there seem to be a lapse to the level of discussion popular among mediaeval schoolmen. The difficulty we have in imagining a non-Euclidean universe is due more to the 'universe' than to its non-Euclidean character. The test can only be whether or not we can visualise non-Euclidean space relations on a moderate scale.

The question is, then, Can non-Euclidean geometry be applied? Kant's theory of knowledge which represents, for the end of the 18th century, a fairly adequate reconstruction of Newtonian physics, is taken by some to prove that it cannot. But the argument is hopeless. If Euclid's axioms are assumed to be *a priori* and presupposed before any experience, they constitute the nature we observe. Thus any possibility of testing whether or not these concepts apply to nature is automatically excluded.

It is only when we show that non-Euclidean geometry *can* be applied that the *a priori* theory of knowledge is finally defeated. We cannot account for the experiences we do have if we are to keep to the *a priori*; we should have to reject a large part of modern physics. Clearly we cannot wish to do so. This is of course not a matter of proof, for 'to prove something' means to derive a theorem from its premisses *within* a theory; but we can *show* that the *a priori* theory is useless.

That non-Euclidean geometry can be applied in some, perhaps rather special manner, is no longer denied by anyone to-day. But it might still be argued that we could never have the faintest idea what such a world would look like; that we can never visualise it; and so a case for the logical preference of Euclidean concepts might still be defended. But what do we mean by 'visualisation'?

Helmholtz, when he investigated the facts in perception, said that to visualise is to imagine the possible sense-perceptions we can have under the circumstances. It is by no means impossible to imagine what would happen in a non-Euclidean world, i.e. if space, in the limited region we can directly observe, were of this kind. Many such spaces have been described by Helmholtz, and others. For instance, imagine the experiences we would have if we were two-dimensional beings living on a spherical surface. Two straightest lines, suitably prolonged, would cut each other in two points, so that there would be no parallels; the sum of angles in a triangle would be greater than 180 degrees ; similarity between larger and smaller geometric figures would not be possible ; and so on. The 'spherical men' would thus have to develop a system of axioms quite different from that of the inhabitants of a Euclidean plane.

But it will be said that this is a mere analogy. Can we imagine a non-Euclidean world in three dimensions? This can be illustrated by an example given by Poincaré. Imagine a universe in the shape of a big sphere (when seen by us from the outside) ; and let us have a source of heat at the centre of this sphere, so that the temperature decreases towards the periphery where its value is assumed to be absolute zero. This decrease is accompanied by a contraction in size of all material bodies ; they shrink instantaneously whenever they are moved away from the centre, and become infinitesimal at the periphery. An inhabitant of such a world would think it to be infinite in size, since his measuring instruments, as well as his own body, would shrink when moving towards the boundary ; he would have to take an infinite number of steps if he wanted to reach the end of his world. But he would never find out this deception, since all relative dimensions are preserved. His straightest line, again, would be an arc of a circle ; and we can even assume that light travels on such a path, if we fill the sphere with a gas of suitably varying refractive index ; there could be no parallel to any line through a given point, and so on. Certainly, such experiences can be imagined. What is of particular interest is that we must introduce, in the three-dimensional world, *universal* forces—forces which attack all materials in the same way everywhere—in order to describe the situation. Since forces of this kind may occur in any world, even in ours, this shows that there is an arbitrary element whenever we ascribe a definite geometrical structure to our universe.

Now we do say that the actual world is non-Euclidean, at least for larger portions of space (although this statement rests upon a number of assumptions to be discussed later); and we cannot deny that we can have such adventures in imagination. But we may still ask, Whence does it come that Euclidean geometry appears to us to be so preferable, and even necessary, as a description?

Indeed, it is in practice very difficult to visualise non-Euclidean relations : the psychological space we experience is immediately *interpreted* in terms of Euclidean measures, and it is naturally impossible to see non-Euclidean space with the help of what may be called Euclidean spectacles. Such Euclidean concepts—what we mean, intuitively so to speak, by 'straight line', 'plane', and so on—are immediate and natural to us, since metre sticks and other bodies in every-day life satisfy, in approximation, the axioms of Euclidean geometry. And when we try to visualise other conditions, we *see into them* at once the Euclidean measure : for it is by seeing rigid rods and bodies that we carry out this visualisation. The peculiar necessity which attaches to Euclid's axioms is a *logical* necessity. We see the equality of lengths and the similarity of figures into the space we perceive, and we can see only this Euclidean congruence since, implicitly, we have put it in before. After all, we do see parallels cutting one another at a far distance ; but we assume that solid bodies such as iron tracks do not cross when they are parallel close to our eyes. We impose upon this experience the Euclidean conception which, in this instance, is verified by a more detailed experience. Similarly we learn to interpret a situation represented by moving objects as a change in perspective rather than as change in size or form of the objects. The psychological experiments about the constancy of body-size in spite of the varying retinal size illustrate how all adaptation is a product of habits fixed in early life. Even perception is not the simple act that philosophers often take it to be : experience and hypothesis are inseparable. It is the mistake of *apriorism* to believe that there is only one hypothesis, that is, to forget that there is a hypothesis at all. 'Pure intuition' is not needed to explain the possibility of knowledge ; and the so-called agreement of reason and nature does not rest upon the *a priori* character of the Euclidean axioms but, conversely, our preference for them is based upon practical agreement in the limited domain of ordinary experience. There is no argument that can uphold any *a priori* theory of knowledge.

Non-Euclidean geometry can be visualised though it may be more difficult to do so than with Euclidean geometry. But we must understand what has been called the 'normative function' in our habits of perception ; the norm has been tacitly introduced by us into the picture to be visualised. Once more, the semantic terminology is better fitted to describe the situation. We interpret our perceptions, psychologically, in terms of previous, familiar experience; and this is then taken as a semantic model that determines the kind of language in which to describe the phenomena.

But in order to measure out space we must know what 'length' is ; what do we mean when we say that a given body has a certain length?

Before we can start our measurement we have to provide at least four definitions ; we can never measure anything unless we specify, before-hand, what we want to measure and how we propose to do so. We cannot describe experience unless we stipulate the terms in which we wish to express ourselves, if measurement is to result in a meaningful statement. Newtonian physics tacitly assumed that the length of a physical stick is something immediately given, and that it is merely the numerical value that has to be determined. But relativity theory requires an analysis of the concept of length ; for measurement is relative to certain assumptions previously made, that is, to a model.

First of all we are concerned with the body we wish to take as standard. Any kind of body can be chosen to measure length ; it is a matter of convenience. Thus we choose a rigid body ; and we must define what we mean by this term since its meaning in every-day language is not sufficiently precise.

Following Reichenbach we may give the first definition as follows : 'A rigid body is a solid whose internal forces of cohesion are very much stronger than any external forces acting on it, so that it keeps its shape. If the rigid body is subject to differential forces, it must be possible to eliminate them by computing corrections ; and universal forces are disregarded'.

It is clear that any actual body will satisfy this definition only approximately. The measuring body is considered as a closed system, that is, removed from external forces or, at least, from all uncontrollable influence. *Universal* forces may be neglected. We understand by this term forces that attack all materials to the same extent everywhere ; and there is no possible physical procedure by which we could detect their presence. (If everything in the world expands or shrinks to the same extent, say, over night, it would not make the slightest perceptible difference.) *Differential* forces, however, are such that they affect various materials in a different way ; heat, for instance, produces an expansion of a copper bar which is different from that of an iron bar, and so we can measure it. And by *internal* forces we mean to refer to molecular cohesion, whose influence must outweigh that of external forces if the body is to be called 'rigid'. We could take a rubber band as standard ; but it would make measurement rather tedious since the result would depend on its life history, and we prefer a more convenient body for this purpose.

The second definition concerns the unit of length. We must state to which arbitrarily chosen interval marked off on the rigid body we wish to ascribe unit measure.

The third definition provides for the uniformity of the length measure. We want to be able to add our units, so that we can put two or more units end to end to obtain the total length. This is by no means an immediate datum of experience ; we have to show how the scale is to be formed. It is conceivable that whenever two units are put together they suffer a contraction ; for the length measure, however, we define a linear scale.

The fourth definition is required to determine the equality of two lengths at different places, that is, to specify 'congruence'. Again, this is not a matter of immediate experience as assumed by Newton. True that, in one and the same place, we can compare the length of two rods by laying them side by side and so see whether or not their ends coincide. But if we carry one rod to another place, we cannot know whether the rod has not changed its length during transport; or, whether at the distant place there does not exist a different state of motion, so that its length is contracted compared to the first rod considered at rest. It would be impossible to find this out by experiment: for carrying the first rod to the same place to make the comparison would not help, since it would suffer the same change. Thus, it is not a matter of experience but of decision. We define under which conditions two distinct rods are to be of equal length. The definition states the physical identity of the units of measure: a unit at one place is to remain a unit at any other place.

Finally, we can also define a *specific* unit; we can take a given length—the Platinum bar at Paris—to define the metre.

It is of import to note that the concepts of force and of a closed system are involved in these definitions. Thus, length measurement becomes relative in several ways. Forces themselves are relative, for they depend upon the reference system in which we measure them; and what we may accept as universal forces will depend upon the definition of 'closed system'. But the shape of a body, and the geometry of space, will differ according to the forces we assume to be present; the geometrical form of a body is not an absolute datum but it depends upon previously given definitions. This is somewhat surprising since we feel in ordinary experience the shape of a thing to be immediately given; it shows how much the concept of a thing is changed in relativity theory.

What geometry we choose to describe physical space then depends upon the forces we admit. It is the *relativity of geometry* which finds an expression in these definitions. What we actually measure is not the geometry of space alone, but the resultant effect of geometry and forces: $(G+F)$. If experiment shows there are several geometries G^1 depending upon the material we take for our rigid body, then the forces are differential in character; and G^1 being equal to $(G+F)$ we say that space is actually described by a geometry G, and F are differential forces that distort the result of our measurements. But if we find only one geometry for all materials used, then we abolish the distinction between G^1 and G by assuming the forces F to be universal; we take them to be zero since we cannot measure them. This decision is prompted by the need for allowing only observables in our description.

It is however only the sum $(G+F)$ that is empirically found. We could save the *a priori* character of Euclidean geometry G_0 by assuming universal forces which deform all bodies in such a way that we always find Euclidean relations where we need them, just as we can 'flatten out' the earth; but universal forces cannot be measured. It is, then, not merely a question which geometry is to be preferred: the set of definitions upon which our measurements rest is simpler for non-Euclidean geometry, and it is more in agreement with the established methods of science. The attitude of *conventionalism* is too extreme, since it suggests that, for the sake of convenience, we accept sentences as factual that cannot be verified. In science we keep to a verifiability criterion of meaning.

The relativity of geometry also involves our conception of causality; for 'force' is (almost) synonymous with 'cause', both in ordinary language and in classical physics; we say that a force causes a change. Even if we reject universal forces, when we pass from one reference system to another, forces will appear and disappear if the motion is accelerated; similarly, for uniform motion, there is the length contraction and the clock retardation. But these forces cause nothing, and these physical changes are not effects. Otherwise we would violate our customary conception of causality, since it would introduce instantaneous action, or action-at-a-distance. This would not agree with the model given by field physics according to which central forces and action-by-contact (as exemplified by the inverse square law) are prescribed. In our assertion that actual space is non-Euclidean over large areas there is involved not only a definition of 'force' but also a decision to keep a reasonable kind of causality, in accordance with established science.

7. Time

The transformation formulae of special relativity theory involve both space and time. Time can no longer be regarded as something absolute, independent of events; just as 'space' describes certain characteristics of events, so 'time' refers to certain other characteristics of the same events. There is no meaning in speaking either of space, or of time, apart from events happening.

Before we can measure time, we require again several definitions. We have first to specify the physical mechanism by the help of which we carry out the measurement. In principle, any physical process can be used for this purpose; but a *periodic* process is what we consider, normally, as representing a natural clock. There are, in the main, three independent ways of measuring time. First, by a spring watch, or by the frequency of light emitted by an atom—that is, by periodic processes which are fairly independent of the environment; second, by processes that are based directly upon the laws of mechanics, and this includes the rotation of the earth, inertial motion, and the pendulum; third, by the motion of light—the so-called light clock first introduced by relativity theory.

It is a matter of experience that we obtain the same time sequence, with high approximation, by means of these three kinds of process. In a space free of all fields, or for a stationary field, the time sequence is strictly the same: this is the reason why we consider the clock as a natural measure of time.

Again, we assume a clock to be a closed system; or, at least, external forces are to be kept to a minimum: the atomic clock is more accurate than a spring watch since it is less affected by such forces. And universal forces are excluded, as before.

Then, we require three definitions to specify the unit, uniformity, and simultaneity of time intervals. That the unit has to be stated by definition is a matter of course; there are no 'natural' units. But the uniformity of time has also to be defined, that is, the uniform succession of time intervals which is taken as self-evident in Newton's system. We may take the successive periods of the earth's rotation—around its own axis and with respect to the fixed stars—to be equal; or we take the successive rotations relative to the sun to be uniform: thus we have sidereal or solar time, respectively. If we assume solar time sequences to be uniform, then sidereal time becomes non-uniform as a matter of fact. In other words, the lack of uniformity can be found only on the basis of a definition. In this instance, we measure the equality of successive intervals by the angle of rotation, with the help of space measurement. But we have equally at our disposal genuine periodic processes, such as the pendulum. There we need no space measurement at all; we recognise immediately that the system is in the same state. We count the number of periods, and this may be done by the click at the end of each interval, as in a spring watch.

It is not necessary to restrict ourselves to periodic processes for time measurement; we may use the successive equal space intervals of a falling body to define equal time intervals. In this instance, the accelerated motion of free fall becomes uniform by definition; and the earth then possess a steadily retarded motion. Which definition we prefer is a matter of simplicity; and, in general, we choose a definition that makes the laws of mechanics as simple as possible. This is a mere simplicity of description; we do not introduce 'mechanical time' in this way, as has sometimes been alleged. We can measure equal time periods only if we have a standard process whose uniformity we assume.

The third definition is the most important one; it concerns the equality of time intervals for clocks that are at different places. We must define what we mean when we say that two clocks separated by a distance beat at the same rate, i.e. by their *simultaneity*. In classical physics it was tacitly assumed that all mechanisms do so once they have been adjusted at the same place; the formulae of relativity theory show that this need not hold. If we have two clocks beating at the same rate at one place, and we carry one of them to another place, we can never be certain whether or not transportation has affected it; and there may exist a different state of motion at the new location. This change can never be measured; bringing the first clock into the proximity of the second would not settle the question. They may again show equality since they are both affected to the same degree by their change in position.

It was a logical discovery when Einstein pointed out that simultaneity can never be established by experimentation. An important advance was thereby made in the understanding of the concept of time.

We can judge at once whether two clocks show the same time when they are at the same place; but how can we determine this for two clocks separated by a distance? In order to compare time intervals of two distant clocks it is, in principle, necessary to send a signal. If we direct a beam of light towards the other clock in order to read it, then we need to know the speed of the signal. It means that we have to determine the distance as well as the time the signal takes to reach the second clock; and it is just this time we set out to find: we have a 'vicious circle' argument. No experiment can be devised to measure simultaneity of two distant clocks: it has therefore to be defined. We could measure simultaneity only if we had at our disposal a signal whose speed is known independently of space and time measurement, e.g. of infinite speed. Even light, though the fastest signal we know of, is of finite speed; and, according to relativity, it represents the limit for the speed at which any natural process may happen. Newtonian physics, with the absolute concept of time, implies that there are infinitely fast signals.

It is clear that through relativity time and causality become connected; for a signal is a causal chain, a physical action spreading through space from point to point. The principle of action-by-contact that is basic to the field model, together with the limiting character of the speed of light, prevents us ever from determining an 'absolute' simultaneity. Einstein's definition is then based upon the constancy of light velocity. We may take the velocity of light to be the same in both directions, so that the time of the distant clock is exactly half way between the times of departure and return of the signal indicated on the first clock.

Light is the fastest signal, but still of finite speed. Therefore events separated by a distance can act on each other only after a definite time has elapsed: the time it takes the signal to traverse the distance. Any changes in the first event that are subsequent to the emission of the signal and which occur while it is travelling cannot influence the second event; no causal connexion can be established for them. A causal chain starting from the second event towards a third during this time (while the original light signal is still travelling from the first to the second event) is essentially independent of the first event. There is an interval of time during which the time order is indeterminate, while the signal is in transit. This is clearly shown for simultaneous events: they cannot influence each other, for this would require infinite speed. Simultaneity indicates that all causal connexion is excluded.

The formulae of special relativity show that two distant events which are simultaneous relatively to a given system are no longer so when referred to another system. That is to say, two causally unrelated events may appear to us, on occasion, as happening one after the other: *post hoc* is not *propter hoc*. But two events occurring at two different times relatively to one system can never become simultaneous when referred to any other system. In other words, a causal connexion which *may* exist between two subsequent events within one system can never be made to disappear. Temporal relations vary with the reference system, but causality is an invariant with respect to the Lorentz transformation.

For this reason causality can be used to define an order for the time sequence. Usually, we construct an order such that an event considered as a cause is taken as earlier than the event representing the effect. The causal relation is asymmetric, and this ensures that the time order can be established unambiguously. The causal relation is invariant and can be given independently of any characteristics of time; therefore we can use it to construct the time order. But order only means arrangement: it permits two distinct directions which are equally admitted. Thus no *unique* direction of time can be assigned by means of causality.

It is for this lack of absolute direction that the concept of time as used in physics has come under so much criticism. It appears to be contrary to our psychological experience. Of course it may be that there is more than one concept of time, and that physical and psychological time differ essentially; but also that we transfer from psychological experience characteristics which are not essentially connected with physical time.

But what, exactly, is our direct experience of time? We can usually determine for two events which is earlier and which is later, that is, provided we can recognise that they are causally connected. If we find that a variation in the first event affects the second event, and not *vice versa*, we say that the first event is before the second one. A bullet hits the target after it has been fired, for changes in the position of the rifle, in the powder charge, etc., determine whether and what we hit; but we can change the target without affecting any process in the rifle.

Clearly the concept of physical time suffices to explain this. We know here the law connecting two events, and we have means for recognising the asymmetry of the causal relation. The trouble arises only when we want to order *all* events that ever happened in one temporal series and so we try to specify, explicitly or implicitly, the beginning of time. For we must know a zero-point as well as the whole universe if we want to say that there is *one* time and a *unique* direction for everything that ever happened or will happen.

This present-day physics does not allow us to say; but it is doubtful whether, even psychologically, we really need to say it. (The concept of entropy is relevant to this problem; this is discussed in section 4.3.)

The relativity of time, and of simultaneity, is also illustrated by the so-called twin paradox. We have two atomic clocks, that is, two atoms at rest in the same system and emitting light of the same frequency, and one of them is sent off for a certain distance and then allowed to return: we find the frequency of the travelling atom has shifted towards the red region of the spectrum. The uniform and accelerated motion together have made the clock go slow. This retardation is revealed when the clock is again at rest in the original system and compared to the clock which has remained there. In other words, if we are permitted to regard human beings, or at least the ageing process of an organism, as a physiological process described completely by the laws that hold for the atoms making up the body, then we may say this. Two people are twins on earth; but if one of them goes travelling, he will age more slowly so that, on his return, he will be younger.

This is, however, merely an odd consequence of the relativity conception of time; and the red-shift is confirmed by astronomical observation.

The paradox arises only through an incorrect application of special relativity which is suggested by the fact that the formula for the clock retardation can be derived from the Lorentz transformation alone. It so happens that the retardation due to uniform motion (within special relativity theory) and due to uniform and accelerated motion together (within general relativity theory) have the same numerical value, in this simple instance. But for uniform motion there exists complete symmetry: whether twin A is moving and twin B at rest, or *vice versa*, represents the same physical situation. So it seems that we can formulate two contradictory sentences, e.g. 'Twin A is younger than twin B' and 'Twin B is younger than twin A'. This is the paradox.

The paradox is resolved when we see that the special theory does not apply here and that there exists an asymmetry between the life histories of the twins. The travelling twin suffers three accelerations, i.e. when, at the beginning, he changes his velocity from zero (rest position) to some positive value; when he turns back at the end of his outward journey; and when he returns to rest. (The accelerations at the beginning and at the end of the journey cancel, of course, since they must have the same value but opposite sign. The acceleration at the turning point remains and cannot be neglected.) The special theory of relativity (and, with it, the Lorentz transformation) treats only of uniform motion and so is inapplicable; the general theory must be used here. But, even so, there remains the symmetry since all frames of reference (including the accelerated ones) are equivalent to one another according to general relativity. In other words, whether twin A travels and twin B stays, or *vice versa*, still represents the same situation.

However, this symmetry obtains only in a completely empty universe. The actual universe is far from being empty: in fact, there exists everywhere a gravitational field due to the stars. In other words, the travelling twin suffers an acceleration not only with respect to his brother but also to the universe at large, while the brother who stays at home remains at rest with respect to the universe.

It is only by forgetting the rôle the actual universe plays that the paradox can be maintained. There is no symmetry between the twins; only the traveller keeps young; and the paradox is resolved.

This example is, I think, very instructive. Our present-day theories are not formalised: they allow us to derive sentences which are syntactically valid but semantically meaningless. We can correctly derive the retardation formula from the Lorentz transformation, but this does not decide what (factual) meaning, if any, the formula possesses. In a formalised language, given a true interpretation, the syntactic and the semantic rules coincide. In ordinary language, or even in the more formal (or partially formalised) language of science, the two sets of rules must be distinguished from each other. However well constructed a (mathematical) calculus may be, it is the interpretation we may give to it that matters in physics.

Another point of importance is to see the relation between time and causality brought out by relativity theory; and that the finite speed of physical signals also limits the causal connexion which may exist between two events. Causality is nothing absolute in the sense that it may be established for all time, or that all events in nature are somehow connected, as has sometimes been said. Causality describes physical events: the propagation of a cause is a physical process, and the model in physics is the spreading of energy from one place to another. The field model, with energy as the key concept, has brought about a more concrete representation of causality. Action-by-contact, and the inverse-square law describing this action, has become the pattern of causality in classical physics.

But it is a picture which can easily be viewed in the wrong way. That two causally related events cannot be made simultaneous by changing to another reference system, or that two events simultaneous in one system may appear separated by a time interval in another system, illustrates two important features of causality. First, that causality is an invariant relation since it cannot be transformed away. Second, that causal chains are delimited: we can only have finite intervals for which causal relations can be established. It is not true that to-day we experience the effects of 'what the first dawn of creation wrote'. The whole universe is not to be described as the unfolding of a first cause. The rigid determinism *à la Laplace* is weakened as result of relativity, even within the domain of classical physics; and a first step towards the statistical interpretation of causality is made (which, incidentally, may also create a new conception of time).

IV

THE CONCEPTS
OF THERMODYNAMICS

1. *Historical survey*

Although thermodynamics unquestionably belongs to classical physics, it is a theory which shows some strikingly novel features.

The same phenomena are described by two different theories. In one interpretation, the thermal behaviour of bodies is described in terms of macroscopic quantities, and the processes are cycles of operations performed by heat engines. This is the so-called phenomenological theory because it is assumed that the terms used directly represent the phenomena. In the other interpretation, as statistical theory, the same phenomena are described in terms of microscopic quantities, as the motion of molecules governed both by the laws of mechanics and of probability. In both formulations the laws are of the widest possible generality.

The laws of phenomenological thermodynamics are expressed, mathematically, as simple functional relations between a few variables. Though of course they are based upon the outcome of certain experiments, the laws are normally used not as empirical but as analytic statements. They have therefore been called 'principles'—which name usually indicates that we take such sentences as a guide in constructing theories rather than as expressing experience.

The laws of thermodynamics, moreover, are often given in a negative form; and they state an impossibility rather than the possibility of carrying out certain experiments. This is done, partly, because physicists feel that in this way the laws retain their empirical character which, in a positive and universal formulation, they tend to lose. To take the first law as example: it refers to the experiment that a given quantity of heat is equivalent to a certain amount of mechanical work. This may also be expressed in a universal sentence as the conservation of energy: The total energy in all processes is conserved. In other words, we cannot gain energy from nothing, and all physical processes represent a transformation of energy into different forms. Thus we can also say: It is impossible to construct a perpetual motion machine of the *first kind*, that is, a machine working without fuel, or without input of any sort of energy. The negative formulation brings out more clearly the experimental basis of the law; it suggests a possible interpretation, or a model, which we need to apply the equation. But from the strictly logical viewpoint a positive universal and a negative existential statement are equivalent. To assert that for all phenomena such and such holds, is the same as to assert that there is no phenomenon for which such and such does not hold.

The negative formulation is more attractive since it restricts the possible interpretations and specifies a definite model. No one has ever succeeded in constructing a perpetual motion machine of the first kind. We may think it unsatisfactory to make a failure the basis of a law; we may also say that, one day, some lucky inventor will construct such a machine. But apart from the fact that many have tried and all have failed, the negative statement serves to show up the restrictions we must impose upon our description of the possible states of the universe. We visualise the events as representing a physical system undergoing a machine-like cycle of processes, and of all the imaginable processes only the one in which energy is conserved is the actual process. A single experiment—a crucial experiment—would decide whether or not to accept the law (taken as empirical statement) while, when the law is formulated as universal sentence, only an infinite number would exhaust all the possibilities for an experimental test. Of course, even so, if regarded as empirical, the law is tested in the same way in both formulations, i.e. by instantiation. The negative formulation shows more clearly under which conditions this test may be carried out.

We must not be misled therefore by the form of a denial which the law assumes into believing that the laws of thermodynamics are 'postulates of impotence'. They are no more so than any other law of physics: all laws, by asserting something, equally deny something else, within the given universe of discourse. To speak of 'impossibility' here is purely accidental. Since the laws are so general and comprehensive, they may easily be misinterpreted as being tautologies; by the negative form we emphasize the prohibition which they—like all laws—impose. This makes it easier to determine their meaning; by restricting the universe of discourse, we try to make the semantic system more explicit, so that we can specify better the logical range of the sentences; and the narrower the range, the larger the content of the sentence.

The three laws of thermodynamics deal with the conservation of energy, the dispersal or degradation of energy, and the zero-point of temperature and of energy. (Only the third law, referring to the experimental fact that we can never cool down any body to the zero-point of the absolute temperature scale, might be taken to indicate a genuine limitation of experience; but caution is required when we speak in this manner, as will be discussed in section 4.6.) The ideas expressed by the laws are applicable to all phenomena. The laws speak about physical systems—that is, aggregates of physical objects. The system is characterized by the state in which it may be, and the laws give the dependence of this state upon certain variables referring to observable properties. We must analyse what we mean by 'energy', 'system', and 'state' as well as define terms such as 'temperature', and 'heat', within this context.

Finally, the second law of thermodynamics—the entropy law—is in contrast to any other law of physics since it refers explicitly to time in a unique manner. According to the laws of both Newton and Maxwell any possible course of events may be reversed. According to the second law it appears that we cannot exchange the positive for the negative sign in front of 't'—the symbol referring to time—without making the equation invalid. This characteristic has made the second law one of the most widely discussed laws of physics. But let us point out that Fourier's equation of heat flow is of the same type and no one has ever found this equation very mysterious. In other words, it may be rash to jump to conclusions from the mathematical form of an equation alone; its interpretation is what matters, in this instance, the meaning of 'entropy'.

But here again, as will be discussed later in more detail, the generality of the thermodynamical laws has led to misunderstanding. The laws are extrapolated over and above all reasonable limits, e.g. they are sometimes applied to the universe at large. Moreover, the difference between thermodynamics and all other parts of classical physics is well grounded. There is really no justification for believing that entropy should possess an analogue

in the laws of mechanics, for instance. The customary division
into various, phenomenologically described, disciplines that is
introduced by elementary text-books has helped to create this
confusion. It suggests that heat phenomena are, so to speak, on
the same level as those of mechanics or of electricity; thus we feel
surprised that there is such decisive difference, or that thermodynamics is not really assimilated to field physics.

But thermodynamics is more general in scope; it uses the wider
concept of energy to describe the behaviour of all sorts of systems.
Heat phenomena are not of the same kind as mechanical or
electric phenomena—they deal with systems rather than with
individual masses or charges. It is a strange idea indeed that heat
is regarded as being a separate phenomenon: as if only special
systems exhibited the property of temperature. But the state of
all systems must be described, among other variables, by the
variable referring to temperature; not only mechanical, but
electric, magnetic, and even quantum-mechanical systems possess
this property, while 'mass', 'charge', and so on, are terms applicable only to certain systems. However, when we do an experiment at a moderate temperature, the thermal effect on any system
is negligible; mainly for very low or very high temperatures do we
find, experimentally, that temperature plays a decisive rôle in the
physical process. Such extremes of temperature are practically
difficult to produce so that we tend to forget them.

Thermodynamics describes the general behaviour of systems,
and it applies both to microscopic and macroscopic phenomena,
to field physics as well as to quantum physics. The concept of
system is applicable everywhere, and it suggests immediately
large-scale phenomena and the statistical distribution of events.
It is of course the concept of probability, and the statistical
interpretation, that ultimately reveal the peculiar character of
thermodynamics.

2. *The conservation of energy*

Poincaré once remarked that the scientist who first introduced
the noun 'heat' to describe temperature phenomena has done a
great disservice to science. For it suggests that heat is a substance,
so that the 'flow of heat' is a phrase referring to a process similar
to that of the flow of water. The *caloric* theory of heat was the

outcome of this interpretation; unfortunately, we have retained some of the principal terms of the theory up to the present day, and this does not help in making clearer our ideas about heat. But, in some sense, this view is inevitable; it is in accord with the common sense interpretation underlying the thing-language of daily life. It suggests the simplest kind of semantic system, or model, and so provides implicitly some rules for the use of certain terms within a limited context. The concepts of specific heat or latent heat, etc., belong to this interpretation, and they have been used with great success. This 'fluid' model must be recognised as a tacit assumption for some statements of thermodynamics.

The next step in the development, say Rumford's experiments, show that heat may be interpreted as a motion of the particles which make up a body. This molecular conception of heat as a kind of motion is said to go back to the ancients; it relates heat to the particle model of mechanics. Again, it was perhaps unfortunate that temperature phenomena were described, mainly, in terms of mechanics so that, even to-day, we find it difficult to interpret thermodynamics except in these terms; but temperature is a universal characteristic and it applies to every kind of physical process.

That a certain amount of heat contained within a body can be identified with the mechanical work done by outside forces on the body is the experimental basis of the first law of thermodynamics. The experiments of R. Mayer and Joule established the so-called mechanical equivalent of heat. But if heat is the internal motion of invisible molecules that makes itself felt as a rise in temperature, macroscopic—or directly observable—variables must be specified to describe the thermal behaviour of a body. And, again, the actual experiment suggests how to do this. We take a fluid (that is, a liquid or a gas) as working substance in a container which itself does not participate in the process; mechanical work may be done by means of a churning wheel; and temperature and heat may be related to volume, pressure, and work. We have a *physical system* which is in a certain *state*; and the state is characterized by observable variables.

Finally, again guided by experience, our interpretation becomes more schematic: we have the model of the *heat engine* as a standard for all thermal processes. A cylindrical container encloses the working substance; it is closed on one end, with a movable piston on the other; and the walls may be permeable (diathermous) or impermeable (adiabatic) to heat. The mechanical work done on the piston can then be converted in a definite manner into heat, and vice versa; the system is *closed* to any uncontrollable outside interference; moreover, we can recognise the *same state* by the position of the piston. The whole process is interpreted in terms of 'energy' and 'system', and described by directly measured variables such as pressure, volume, temperature, and so on.

It is sometimes said that to choose the heat engine as a model process is due to the industrialisation which started in the early nineteenth century when thermodynamics was formulated; or that to make schematic diagrams of such an engine is merely a psychological help in visualising the thermal processes in nature. This does not explain the fact that it is taken as a standard in terms of which we interpret nearly all heat phenomena, even those that at first sight do not seem to fit this interpretation; and that it shows how terms such as 'system' and 'state' can be used in a statement amenable to an empirical test.

The transformation of energy from one form into another can be understood in terms of this interpretation. Mechanical, electric, magnetic, chemical, and radiant energy produce heat and make the engine run; and all these various kinds of energy can be precisely measured through the mechanical equivalent of heat. The concept of energy becomes more comprehensive but the model shows how to use it, since it can be interpreted ultimately in terms of mechanics.

In Mayer's words: 'I therefore hope that I may reckon on the reader's assent when I lay down, as axiomatic truth, that just as in the case of matter, so also in the case of force, only a transformation, but never a creation, takes place'. Helmholtz, in 1847, extended this idea to all forms of energy and stated the principle of conservation of energy which we take as the first law of thermodynamics: In any closed physical system the sum total of all the energies involved remains constant. His paper was first refused publication since it was deemed to be too radical; to-day, one hundred years later, we tend to take the first law as self-evident and as a guide to further experiments. We assume that every process satisfies it; and we may invent new kinds of energy, and new particles (such as the neutrino) as carriers of this energy rather than give up the principle of conservation. For this reason it has been said that the first law—like many other laws in physics —functions as a convention or as a definition. Both views, I think, are wrong.

The first law is certainly not a convention in the sense in which this term is normally used; it is not arbitrary or imposed from without, and we cannot change it at will. We do not stick to the first law no matter what happens. If we find deviations from the law and invent new forms of energy to satisfy it, we do so because we can give good reasons for it: different, and independent evidence must always be available for supporting the hypothesis that new kinds of energy have appeared. To say then that laws of this sort are conventions is to simplify, and even to misdescribe, the situation.

It is equally impossible to take laws, like the first law of thermodynamics, as definitions. A definition states that two expressions have the same meaning, e.g. ' . . .' is equal by definition to ' . . .' The first law cannot reasonably be cast into a logical form of this sort. What we can say, I think, is that such a law is used to give a partial specification of meaning of the terms occurring in it. The first law, then, explains what we mean by 'process' and by 'energy', that is, we indicate a semantic rule. 'Process' designates any change in which energy is conserved. The second law provides an additional specification of meaning by stating that in a process some of the energy may become unusable (but not lost altogether). And the third law completes the specification by asserting that in a process some energy always remains unused. This interpretation of the laws of thermodynamics seems to be closer to our intent in formulating them. For we want to say, after all, that energy is not created out of nothing and that it does not disappear without a trace; we want to account for all that happens by drawing up a balance, without an unexplained or inexplicable gain or deficit. The three thermodynamical laws, therefore, state what we mean by 'natural process'.

Finally, this interpretation is exemplified by the model. It is the model of the heat engine that is the basis for the strictest formulation of the first law. Planck gives it in the following way: 'It is impossible to construct an engine which will work in a cycle (such that the initial and final states are the same) and produce continuous work, or kinetic energy, from nothing'.

That is, the work done on or by the system equals the change in internal energy and in heat; the sum of all the energies is a constant.

But what is the scope of the law? The statement is often extended to apply to the universe as a whole, and it is said that the total energy of the universe is constant. We must try to give the logical range of the statement in order to make the meaning more precise. This requires a more detailed discussion to illustrate how the heat engine works. It is interesting that thermodynamics is beset by difficulties arising from the use of the term 'universe', since it is so comprehensive a theory. Can we say that the universe is a closed system, or that it is in a definite state? It is by the help of the engine model that the use of the concepts in question may be made clearer.

If we now want to establish the energy balance of any process carried out by such an engine, it is obvious that any experiment can only determine differences in energy. The system may at the given temperature possess a certain *internal* energy that depends, to a large extent, on the previous history of the system. This is consistent, however, with mechanics. The kinetic energy of particles is shown by their motion; the potential energy is invisible since it depends upon their configuration, or on the particular position in the field, and it can be numerically determined only in special instances. Thus, the idea of internal energy leaves us a good deal of freedom in the description of physical processes; energy cannot be determined absolutely since we can always add an arbitrary constant to its value.

It is further found that only certain variables—namely pressure, volume, temperature, and so on—uniquely determine the state of the system, that is, we can ascribe the same value to them for the same state. This is not possible for other variables such as heat or work: their value depends on the manner in which we reached the same state (and it may be remembered that the engine model specifies the use of 'same state' by reference to the position of the piston). Thus the model enables us to define '*state-variable*' as an important term in our description.

Then the changes which occur—the stages of the process—must be slow, or *reversible*. For in thermodynamics, as well as everywhere in physics, we deal only with *equilibrium states*. The state-variables have a unique value only if the state reached during the process is an equilibrium, that is, a state which, when left alone, will never change. Any rapid change, or violent upheaval of the system, will not easily produce an equilibrium state; thus the kind of process we can describe is rather restricted. But it is only for equilibria that an *equation of state* can be set up and that the state-variables suffice to describe it. We must therefore analyse any process into such a series of equilibria; and, of course, the initial and final states must be of this kind. Otherwise we cannot compute the changes occurring during the process.

The restriction to reversible processes which, at any stage, produce equilibrium states is needed to introduce the idea of temperature. The concept of temperature is based upon the experimental fact that two bodies which are in thermal equilibrium with a third one are also in thermal equilibrium with one another. When two systems, or bodies, are in thermal contact, they are separated by diathermous walls and can exchange heat freely. The state of the total system made up of the two can then be described by a definite relation between four variables, two for each component system, and from this we obtain the condition for equilibrium. The transitivity of the equilibrium relation shows then that, for three systems, thermal contact is possible only if each component system is exclusively determined by its own set of two variables (pressure and volume). Thus two bodies in equilibrium are described by two functions, each depending upon two variables only; and we take one body as a *thermometer* indicating the *empirical temperature*, which is given by the universal function describing the state of that body. Since the function is to some extent arbitrary, a refinement in the concept of temperature is introduced later, by the help of the second law. But the arbitrary character is useful in practice; we assign a linear scale to temperature, and the zero and end points are suitably chosen, as exemplified by the mercury thermometer. We see, however, that equilibrium states are the only states whose temperature we can establish; it is only then that the thermometer reads the temperature correctly. And both the model of heat flow and of the heat engine are used to show what we mean by 'temperature'.

The conservation of energy supersedes the conservation of mass which, as result of relativity, we may take as a special case of the energy principle. Energy is a more universal property of physical events: it permits us to unify the description of all sorts of processes that, otherwise, cannot be easily given. In all processes we must have 'something' permanent so that we can show up the change by comparison. The process-language we need is thus not unrelated to the thing-language, but we must be careful not to confuse them. There is another model underlying the use of this language; and we can show the rules for the usage of 'system', 'state', 'energy', and so on, by pointing to the model. The model serves as a rudimentary semantic system, since it restricts the kind of processes or, rather, the sentences describing them which belong to the theory.

3. *Entropy*

But to describe the processes occurring in nature we need a second criterion, apart from the conservation of energy. The class of allowed processes selected by the first law is too wide; or, rather, the logical range of the sentences describing the processes possible in our universe must be more restricted. Actual physical systems are wasteful, and energy is dissipated as a result of the changes they undergo; so the state of any system can never be completely regained. A certain tendency seems to prevail in natural processes: the direction they follow cannot be reversed.

It is a matter of fact that heat flows from the hot to the cold body but that the reverse process never occurs. The temperature difference is levelled out, and the process stops when an equilibrium is reached. This behaviour is not covered by the first law. It would be compatible with it, if the hot body were to get hotter and the cold body colder, as long as the total amount of heat energy remained constant. In order to abstract heat from a system another system at lower temperature has to be brought in contact with it, so that a temperature difference is established. But this process of heat transfer cannot be carried to completion; the amount of heat given off is smaller than the amount absorbed, and some of the energy is irretrievably lost. Again, while mechanical work, or electric energy, may under certain circumstances be changed completely into heat, a given amount of heat cannot be changed in its entirety into one of the other forms of energy. It is this fact that suggests that we deal with one-sided changes in nature, and that all actual processes are *irreversible*.

Heat has the tendency to disperse: why is heat energy so

different from any other kind of energy? Heat may be taken as
the motion of molecules; but purely mechanical motion is reversible. Why can mechanical work be transformed without residue
into heat, while the reverse cannot be done?

To construct a theory we need an interpretation, and this is
given by a model: the heat engine again, whose action must now
be described in more detail. In Maxwell's words 'an engine of a
species entirely imaginary—one which it is impossible to construct, but very easy to understand'. The *efficiency* of an actual
engine, that is its ability to transform heat energy into work, is
never perfect; some heat is lost, not from the system as such, but
for the purpose of useful work. For instance, the inside of the
cylinder and the piston heats up, and friction occurs; this amount
of energy is wasted since it will not contribute to make the
piston rise.

The engine is in contact with two heat reservoirs (the boiler
and condenser, or the source and sink of energy) at different
temperatures, and heat is absorbed by it; as a result the engine
will run. We then have as efficiency the ratio of the work done to
the heat taken in from the source. The ideal engine works in a
prescribed manner; it is a cyclic operation in four stages and
proceeds through a series of equilibrium states, so that the process
is reversible. The model of the heat engine is re-designed to give
a more detailed interpretation which, in fact, can be visualised in
a diagram, i.e. the *Carnot cycle*. The picture of the whole process
is a closed curve, from which we read off how to use the concepts
of thermodynamics.

But all actual processes are irreversible, and we can never come
back to the initial state of the system. The model of the reversible
Carnot cycle is too idealised; yet it must be made to serve, since
only reversible changes can be uniquely described by the state-
variables. In fact, it allows us to introduce a new state-variable
related to the efficiency of the process. There is perfect efficiency
for the ideal cycle while, by comparison, the irreversible process
is less efficient through loss in energy. Thus we explain '*entropy*'.
In a reversible cycle there is no change in entropy, since we
return to the same state; in an irreversible process entropy is
increased, in proportion to the loss in *free* or available energy.
The deficiency is found only by comparison with the Carnot
cycle; in general we do not know how it comes about, and there is

no equation but only an inequality we can set up to compute it.

The transformation of heat into work requires a temperature difference. Heat is more useful for this purpose the larger the difference; the *bound*, or unavailable, portion of the heat energy increases with decreasing temperature, and the efficiency of the engine drops. It is by this sort of model that the second law of thermodynamics is formulated. We say that the entropy of a closed system increases, or at best remains the same, during any process. Or, referring directly to the experience standardised in the model we say: It is impossible to construct a perpetual motion machine of the second kind. We cannot convert heat into work in a continuous, cyclic process without losing some of the heat by transfer from the hot to the cold reservoir. And many other versions have been given for the second law which are all to be understood in terms of the same model. While the first law states that we cannot gain energy without corresponding work, the second law states that, in the process, we always lose some of the energy.

The same model allows us to make the concept of temperature more exact. The main difficulty is that the property of systems which we call 'temperature' is not additive. Moreover, the empirical temperature determined on the basis of the first law is quite arbitrary, and it depends upon the properties of the body chosen as thermometer, e.g. the expansion of mercury and glass in the ordinary thermometer. Lord Kelvin showed the efficiency of a reversible Carnot engine, working between two reservoirs of given temperatures, to be a function of these two temperatures alone. This allows us to define an *absolute* temperature scale; any two temperatures on it are related to each other as the quantities of heat taken in or ejected by a reversible engine working between these temperatures. Equal temperature differences anywhere on the scale have then the same value in terms of mechanical work, and so temperature becomes a universal, and simply measurable, property. This is what is meant when we call the temperature 'absolute'. The fact that, by this definition, temperature becomes a property which is independent of the particular system or body chosen, is of minor import. For we could have taken any physical body as standard; and, indeed, we often use in thermodynamics the *ideal gas* as the working substance undergoing the thermal cycle. (An ideal gas is an assembly of individual particles between which there is no interaction; this results in the simplest possible *equation of state*; and many actual gases can be described by this equation under suitable conditions.) The usefulness of 'absolute temperature' lies in the fact that it is defined in terms of mechanical work; this enables us to overcome the difficulty that temperatures do not add, for amounts of work can of course be added to each other. There is also a zero-point of temperature on the absolute scale, when all the heat taken in by the engine is converted into work. Obviously, the zero-point represents a 'natural' limit dictated by the conservation of energy; the limit is *asymptotic*, that is, it can never be reached experimentally, and so it restricts the range of thermal processes which are possible.

It is by this sort of discussion that we find the interpretation underlying the equations of thermodynamics. By showing what the possible processes are which may occur in nature, we prescribe the logical range of the sentences describing them: we indicate the rules for the usage of the concepts. And we are bound in practice to the model of the reversible Carnot cycle, if our sentences are to be meaningful. Other models than the heat engine and the Carnot cycle are of course logically conceivable, e.g. the model of Carathéodory (described in the next section). But, so far, physicists have been unable to invent a model process that is not *inherently* reversible.

When we wish to describe an actual, irreversible process, we have at our disposal only the model of the reversible process which we superimpose, as it were, upon the actual process. The violent explosion, for instance, is described by means of an idealised process that proceeds infinitely slowly, through a series of equilibrium states. The state of the system, its temperature, energy, and entropy cannot be determined in any other manner. All we can show is that the increase in entropy is larger in an irreversible change from one equilibrium state to another than for the corresponding reversible change taken as standard of comparison. We have an inequality rather than an equation, as usual in physical theory, to symbolize this statement. We know of no mechanism for the entropy production in an irreversible process, so that we can compute the exact amount of entropy in a given process and formulate the entropy law as an equation (although, recently, attempts in this direction have been made). We speak of the 'creation of entropy' and of the 'tendency of entropy to increase'. Since entropy is not a visible parameter such as temperature, we have great difficulty in finding out to what this term refers. It is for reasons of this sort that entropy has been said to be a 'ghostly' quantity. Indeed, 'entropy' is an unfamiliar and technical concept; but we can apply it since the model prescribes the rules for its usage.

But if we forget the restrictions the model, or interpretation, imposes, we may misapply the concept. Thus, it is open to doubt, whether Clausius's formulation of the second law is acceptable: 'The entropy of the universe tends towards a maximum'. It is equally doubtful whether this tendency may be taken to indicate a direction of time in natural processes, so that we have an entropy clock, as has sometimes been asserted. The meaning of such sentences depends upon the model tacitly implied, or on the accepted interpretation of the thermodynamical equations which prescribe the rules for the usage of 'entropy'. Can we say that the universe is a closed system, that it is in an equilibrium state, or that it is in any way undergoing a process similar to the Carnot cycle?

4. *Carathéodory's axiomatization*

It has to be admitted, so Professor Born said a long time ago, that thermodynamics in its traditional form has not yet realised the logical ideal of separating the physical content from the mathematical representation. This ideal is to a large extent, though not completely, achieved in what is known as the axiomatization of thermodynamics. We have here, then, an example of the sort of formulation which scientists, or at least physicists, consider to be most suitable for a scientific theory. It is therefore an important example, a test case, for demonstrating whether or not, and how well, semantics can provide a logical methodology for science.

Apart from the engine model, and the Carnot cycle, there is still another way of describing the experiences that underlie the first and second laws. This is given by a more abstract, 'mathematical', model. Its syntactic structure is based on the Pfaffian equation (in three variables), and its interpretation is formulated in Carathéodory's principle.

Our experiments show that we can never make good any changes in a closed, heat-insulated (adiabatic), system. When we heat some water in a vessel, however slightly, we cannot cool it down to its original temperature by taking away the same amount of heat (or by applying an equivalent amount of work). This can be expressed in a system-state language in the following way. 'In the neighbourhood of any state, however close, there exist other states that cannot be reached from the first state by adiabatic processes'.

From this principle we can derive the second law in its more usual form, i.e. that the entropy increases in any actual process. It is not possible here to go into technical details; but let me illustrate how, with the help of the principle, we can construct a function like entropy which exhibits the required behaviour.

First, we have a container representing the closed system. Its walls may, or may not, permit heat to pass through them, i.e. the walls are either diathermous or adiabatic. These terms are then defined in mechanical terms, without employing the objectionable concept of heat. For example, 'an adiabatic wall' is 'a wall such that the equilibrium of a body enclosed by it is not disturbed by any external process so long as no part of the wall is moved'. Such adiabatic vessels are in practice obtainable, e.g. the Dewar flask.

Then we specify what we mean by 'thermal contact between two bodies' and by 'thermal equilibrium'. This allows us to introduce the concept of empirical temperature. We take as axiom the statement that the thermal equilibrium is a transitive relation, i.e. if two bodies in thermal equilibrium are in equilibrium with a third body, all three bodies have a common property, that is, the same temperature. From this the theorem is derived that one body in contact with another may be used as a thermometer, or that one body 'reads' the temperature of the other. This theorem is sometimes referred to, somewhat jokingly, as the zeroth law of thermodynamics. All this is expressed by simple functional equations involving only pressure and volume as variables.

Finally, this interpretation is applied to a certain equation (i.e. the Pfaffian). If the equation is to describe the thermal contact between two bodies it must contain at least three variables. An equation of this type possesses a solution (an integrating denominator) only under very special circumstances. This solution is a function which is then interpreted as 'universal temperature', for it does not depend on the arbitrarily chosen bodies and the system composed of them. Rather, this temperature is the characteristic of any equilibrium state, and our usual temperature scale can be obtained from it by a suitable calibration. Having then the concepts of temperature and of adiabatic process we can construct a state function like entropy, i.e. a function whose values can never decrease and, at best, remain unchanged.

The special circumstances that must hold if this solution is to be possible are interpreted, then, in this manner. 'A solution of the equation exists' means that there exist impossible processes, or that not every transition from one state (of the physical system) to any other is allowed in nature. In other words, we always find adiabatically inaccessible states in the vicinity of any given state. The number of accessible states will be smaller if the process of transition is quasi-static, i.e. if the states involved are equilibria and if the process is reversible. This at once suggests the view that, on this interpretation, 'entropy'—or, rather, 'entropy change' —refers to the number of states that can be reached or to the allowed transitions. We can state the rule, for example, that 'increase in entropy' designates a proportionately greater number of accessible states. So we can say that the entropy change is always smaller in a reversible than in an irreversible process (having the same initial and final states); and this is the second law in its customary form.

This sort of language is also suitable for stating the first law. We say that in order to bring adiabatically a system from an initial to a final state the same amount of work is required regardless of the kind of transition. This is, in fact, much closer to the original paddle-wheel experiment of Joule—which is the basis for the first law—than are the more usual formulations.

What can we say, then, about Carathéodory's theory? A quite definite model is provided which, though unfamiliar and mathematical, is founded on the schematization of some simple experiments. We can even visualise the interpretation, that is, represent it in geometrical figures: we picture points that can, or cannot, be connected in a continuous curve. These curves are used in the mathematical derivation to show that there exist inaccessible points.

Physicists recommend and prefer the theory for several reasons. It does away with the relics of the *caloric* conception, e.g. terms like amount and flow of heat suggesting that heat is a substance. Fluids and ideal gases are no longer needed to exemplify what we mean by 'process'. And the main advantage is that the artificial model of the heat engine is abandoned. Moreover, the theory is presented as a deductive system, with definitions and axioms; and a large part of the formal calculus, i.e. the Pfaffian equation, is clearly separated from the interpretation, i.e. Carathéodory's principle. But not all the syntactic rules, for example the purely logical ones, are explicitly specified; and not all the semantic rules, for instance those giving the meaning of 'entropy', are written down. Perhaps this is only a blemish, a certain lack of logical elegance, which can be remedied. But for this reason it is still necessary to appeal to the model in order to derive the theorems, that is, to make use of the interpretation formulated in ordinary words but not formalised in terms of rules. It is abundantly clear, however, that thermodynamics as an axiomatized theory is represented, very closely, as a semantic language system.

It has been said that the irreversible process itself is outside the scope of thermodynamics. The phenomenological theory as we have it to-day suffers from many troubles, both for reasons of logic and of physics. That a process-language, in contrast to a thing-language, offers perhaps insurmountable difficulties has often been noted in the history of philosophy. From Heraclitus to Whitehead we find obscure sentences involving the term 'process' which appear to be incapable of empirical verification. In Newtonian mechanics the particle picture allows us to analyse 'process' in a simple manner: the process consists in the particle moving from one space-time location to another, and the laws of motion are known. In Maxwell's theory the field model permits us, e.g. to take 'process' as designating a wave propagation through the continuum, and we know the laws describing how the wave travels. In both instances, a detailed description of the mechanism can be given: there is always something permanent, or thing-like, whose progress in space-time represents the process. In thermodynamics the model of the heat engine allows us to picture a reversible process; in this instance, too, there are some constant elements, such as energy and entropy, so that a simple visualisation is still possible. But all the models seem to break down for irreversible processes; we can only compare them to reversible processes and in this way arrive at a description. This even holds for the Carathéodory model: though 'process' means here 'transition between states', the irreversible process is explained only with respect to the reversible process by saying that more states

K

are accessible. In other words, we cannot speak of 'process' or 'change', except relative to something that does not change—a standard of comparison of some sort—, and in an irreversible process there is a conspicuous lack of constancy. Another interpretation has to be sought. It is the statistical theory which, though essentially restricted by the same conditions as the ordinary theory, still allows us to describe thermal processes in more detail and so to obtain a better understanding of 'irreversibility'.

5. *Kinetic theory (statistical interpretation)*

The theory of statistical mechanics (including the simpler kinetic theory of gases) provides a more detailed, and comprehensive, interpretation of thermal phenomena. The problem of entropy and irreversibility is better understood when we have recourse to the model these theories offer. Instead of the rather general, functional relationships of classical thermodynamics we obtain a description in terms of mechanics and of statistics.

Heat is considered as motion of small particles, and this motion is analysed in more detail. We have the particle model of mechanics, suitably enlarged to allow the introduction of the concept of probability. The particles are spheres of finite size and supposed to be completely elastic, so that their mutual collisions proceed without loss in kinetic energy. The body under consideration is, again, taken as a closed system, say, a gas containing a great number of these molecules enclosed in a vessel. The Newtonian equations are assumed to hold for the complicated zig-zag motions. From this assumption, together with statistical hypotheses regarding the individual molecules, we establish laws of the average behaviour of all the molecules; this average is then taken as representing a macroscopic, observable quantity. The observables are not any intrinsic properties of the microscopic, invisible, particles, but they are given by the statistical distribution of the energy (or velocity) over the molecules. Pressure is then nothing but the force of impacts that the molecules suffer with the walls enclosing the volume; and the absolute temperature is proportional to their average kinetic energy.

Clearly Newtonian mechanics alone cannot suffice to compute statistical behaviour. Additional hypotheses have to be introduced: for probabilities can be computed only on the basis of other probabilities initially given. In fact, there are two kinds of assumption which have to be made—about the probability of a certain state of the system, and about the probability of the whole course of the process the system undergoes.

The mechanism of thermal behaviour of a gas, say, is then described in the following way. The individual particles move independently from one another; there is no interaction between them: in the simplest example we assume an ideal gas. This, not very essential, assumption makes computation easier; we can take account of molecular forces if we know a law of interaction for a specific case. The paths and the collisions of the molecules are strictly computable according to the laws of mechanics, if we know the initial values for the position and momentum of every molecule. But the number of particles participating in an observable process is immense, and we cannot in fact determine the initial conditions for each molecule; so we make some general assumptions about the average behaviour.

This is the usual argument by which statistical hypotheses, and the concept of probability, are introduced in classical physics. It is said that, in practice, we are ignorant of the initial conditions, and we would not live long enough to be able to determine their values for each molecule. In principle, there is no reason why we should not be able to do so; no theoretical limitation holds us back, it is merely a task which it is technically impossible to perform. This is of course a rather clumsy argument. We try to deny the essential need for the introduction of probability, and so it is said that an omniscient being, such as Laplace's *superman*, could do without it. The reasoning becomes clear only when we look at quantum mechanics: there it is a matter of principle that we require probability to describe the events, since quantum-mechanical laws prevent us from specifying exactly the initial conditions. Within classical physics there is no such law, and we must take our incapacity as excuse for introducing statistics.

The laws of mechanics are strictly independent of the sign, plus or minus, of time: there is no preferred direction of time, and all mechanical motions are completely reversible. However, a thermal process appears to develop only in one direction. Thus, still more hypotheses are needed so that we can reconstruct, in our model, this actual behaviour. The introduction of probability as such cannot give this direction. Very special sorts of statistical assumptions have to be made so that we can construct a mechanical-statistical model of entropy: the probability attached to the initial and final states of the system must be chosen in a special manner.

The microscopic properties of the gas, that is the energy and velocity of the individual molecules, must then be correlated to macroscopic properties, i.e. to the state of the system characterized by pressure, volume, temperature, and so on. Of course the molecules will possess all sorts of energy, from zero to infinity (exclusive), or velocities within this range. The distribution of these values is such that, for a state of given temperature, there is a most probable value, while all other values are less probable, and the extreme values are improbable. Thus a definite value of energy, or velocity, can be correlated to the observable parameters characterizing the state. But how does this distribution come about?

There are *at least three assumptions* prescribing the mechanism of collisions which maintains this distribution. First, there is *molecular chaos*: the molecules may occupy all positions and possess all directions of velocity. In other words, it is only how large the speed is that counts, and all other characteristics of the molecules are unimportant. Second, in the equilibrium state there is *detailed balancing*, or microscopic reversibility, as it is sometimes called. Every collision is exactly balanced by another one of equal strength and direction, so that no over-all change occurs, and the equilibrium is maintained. Since the laws of mechanics are indifferent to the direction in space or time, each microscopic event can be exactly matched by its reverse while the equilibrium lasts. Finally, the third, and most important assumption about the total course of a process within a closed system: each molecule will assume eventually every value of energy, or of velocity, compatible with the total energy of the system. This *ergodic hypothesis* is more clearly expressed when we represent the system of molecules, not in ordinary space, but in a 2-N dimensional *phase space* whose axes are given by the positions q and momenta p of the N molecules. Then we can say that the system will run through all the possible phases p, q of its molecules that lie on a given energy surface. In other words, the system when left to itself will occupy all sorts of states, and the ratio of the time it spends in each state to the total time approaches a limit: this limit is the relative frequency of occurrence of a given state, or its probability. We must assume that within the system all states occur with a certain relative frequency, and so we introduce the concept of probability.

Unfortunately, the ergodic hypothesis can be shown to be incompatible with the ideas of mechanics; but a weaker formulation the *quasi-ergodic* hypothesis suffices to save the foundations of statistical thermodynamics. It was proved by v. Neumann that there exists a large class of mechanical systems which at least *approach* in the long run every possible state. And if we accept probability as an essential element in this interpretation, a still weaker formulation will do: the *pseudo-ergodic* hypothesis of v. Mises stating that there is an overwhelming probability that the system will eventually pass through all states compatible with its total energy.

The ergodic hypothesis, or one of its variants, is necessary for introducing the concept of probability. But it says a good deal more, and some of what it says is rather objectionable. However we initiate a process in the system, its ultimate behaviour will not depend upon the initial conditions: the final state is always an equilibrium state, and moreover the same state (for any given system) whatever process we have. Thus we achieve the result that the final state is the most probable state, and all processes go always in one direction. Once this final state is reached, however, the system must repeat its behaviour: we have an eternal return. Although, on the basis of these assumptions we can construct a function—Boltzmann's *H-function*—which refers to the collisions among the molecules and which always decreases, eventually it must increase again, and so on for all eternity. This H-function may be taken as the statistical-mechanical analogue of entropy, since it exhibits a one-sided change in time; however, this holds only for a limited, though very long, time interval, so that entropy which increases in all natural processes must eventually decrease again. Entropy does not specify a unique direction of time; it allows us merely to order events, or states of the system, within a limited time interval. Even the statistical interpretation of thermodynamics cannot escape the idea of reversibility inherent in our basic conceptions.

How can we assign a definite probability to a state of the system? The statistical model is made more clear by considering the possible arrangements in space in which the individual molecules may be ordered. To represent this geometrical model a two-dimensional phase space may be used as example, with co-ördinates p and q; the whole of this space is divided up into small cells of unit size, each of which will then correspond to a small range of momentum, or velocity, or energy, out of the total amount available. The system is visualised as a *honeycomb*, and into each cell a number of molecules may be placed such that there is a definite distribution of molecules over the cells characteristic for a macroscopic state of given temperature. Now it is clear that a great number of these microscopic arrangements, or *complexions*, will all correspond to the same state: for the molecules are indistinguishable, and the same distribution may be realised in a great number of ways. The number of possible complexions belonging to the same macroscopic state we take as a measure of the probability of this state; and there are, in fact, three ways of counting which result in three different distribution functions. This thermodynamic probability may then take on all values from zero to infinity, in contrast to the ordinary probability which is defined for values within the range of zero and unity; it is, however, only a superficial difference. According to the fundamental, ergodic, hypothesis the fraction of time each molecule spends in a particular cell specifies a relative frequency, or ordinary probability, and so the thermodynamic probability equally determines the relative frequency of a certain state. In this manner we obtain a geometric representation of the situation, and the entropy can be shown to be proportional to the logarithm of the thermodynamical probability.

The geometrical model then illustrates another property, i.e. the *order* or *disorder* of the arrangements of molecules which correspond to a given macroscopic state. The more disorderly, or random, the distribution of molecules over the cells, or the larger the number of possible complexions, the higher is the probability of the observable, macroscopic state. If all the molecules are in the same phase cell, there will be only one possible complexion since nothing new results from the permutation of the particles among each other within one cell. If the molecules are spread over more cells, a larger number of permutations, and therefore, of possible complexions will be obtained. Thus, we call 'order' a configuration of molecules in which all of them have nearly the same values of parameters p and q, that is, if they are keeping together in the same cell. This usage of the word 'order' is suggested by a simple experiment: the spreading of a stream of gas into an evacuated vessel. At first, the molecules will stay together in one part of the vessel, near the aperture through which they have entered; after a while they will occupy all the available space in a random manner. Thus, order is identified here with spatial asymmetry, though in every-day life we are more inclined to regard any symmetrical arrangement as orderly. The situation in which all the molecules cluster together in one corner of the vessel shows a high degree of asymmetry relative to the available space, while the random distribution is more symmetrical.

Arguments of this sort allow us to specify more clearly the statistical model of thermodynamics; and there are many more details which may be filled in to complete the picture. It suffices, however, to show how we visualise the course of a process within a closed system. The process will always tend towards a state of highest disorder, or dispersal of molecules; this state is characterized, by our definitions, as the state of highest probability. Entropy is identified with the random element, or disorder of the system. And the second law of thermodynamics is sometimes stated in the following way: In all natural processes the disorder of the system increases.

In the simple experiment describing the spreading of gas into a vessel we never observe that the molecules suddenly cluster together again and evacuate the larger part of the vessel. Similarly, we say here that the random mixture of molecules remains and represents the final, equilibrium state of the system. Thus the one-way tendency of natural, or irreversible, processes is *reproduced* in the statistical model. If the process starts with a rare state of high order, or low probability, it will develop in such a way that it ends up with the more frequent state of greater disorder; if the process starts with a state of relatively great disorder, or high probability, it will end up in more or less the same state.

But just as in phenomenological thermodynamics the irreversibility is an illusion. In order to initiate a process within a closed system, we have to open it, and this represents a rare state; thus we can expect that the future development of the process will bring a more frequent state. But if we wait long enough, the original state must re-appear again: this is a consequence of the ergodic hypothesis. It is only because the time of observation is always short that we do not witness the reversal of the sequence. In other words, once entropy has increased, it must decrease again, in a closed system. The irreversibility, or the increase in randomness, occurs only within a limited, though very long, time interval.

This difficulty was recognised long ago when the statistical theory was first formulated; it was stated as the 'objection of the reversal' by Loschmidt, and as the 'objection of the return' by Poincaré and Zermelo. Every mechanical system is at least quasi-periodic, and the initial and final states must eventually approach one another. Thus, entropy cannot give a direction of time; at best, it may be taken to specify an order of time within a limited time interval.

It is a most objectionable feature of present-day theories that we must use conceptions such as 'closed system' and 'equilibrium state' to interpret our equations and that, therefore, we have a kind of eternal return for all processes so described; but, so far, no other theory has been developed. Moreover, there are some experiments supporting, to some extent, this interpretation. Looking at the Brownian motion of small particles under the microscope, or observing the critical opalescence of a gas near its condensation point, we find that there are fluctuations of the system around its equilibrium state: the particles sometimes, although very rarely, do cluster together, that is, the entropy does decrease under favourable circumstances. The existence of such fluctuations cannot be denied; it shows that, in spite of its limitation, the statistical theory of thermodynamics is quite adequate for describing our experiments.

However, fluctuations cannot be used to evade the restrictions imposed by the second law: it is still theoretically impossible to build a machine that could derive useful work from these fluctuations. Although the occurrence of a fluctuation indicates that, temporarily, some energy becomes free which before was bound, this occurrence is completely haphazard. Any machine designed to take advantage of molecular fluctuations could only do so by energy transfer to the molecules of which it is itself constructed; but these molecules in turn carry out random fluctuations, and the two series of fluctuations are independent of one another. Thus, no mechanism can, in principle, be designed to effect a regular and controlled transfer of energy. It would require a *Maxwell demon*—an omniscient being of molecular dimensions who, nevertheless, is not himself swayed by the fluctuations—to select the rapidly moving molecules according to their velocity and concentrate them in one corner of the vessel; then the temperature would be raised and the entropy decreased in a gainful manner. Although in present theory we must describe all processes as if they were only quasi-irreversible, it still requires the services of a supernatural being to violate the second law.

If the universe is considered as a closed system, the second law is often taken as predicting its *heat death*—that is, the eventual cessation of any change since all temperature differences will be finally levelled out. If the entropy has increased to its maximum, all available energy has become used up, and the universe is *run down*. But we must say, on the basis of present thermodynamics, that irreversibility is only temporary; so the prediction of eternal gloom need not be taken seriously—quite apart from the fact that it is most doubtful if we can apply thermodynamics to the universe as a whole.

To explain that, at this present epoch, all natural processes seem to be irreversible, Boltzmann proposed the fluctuation hypothesis. Our corner of the universe is assumed to be in the process of carrying out an immense fluctuation which is just such as to make all processes appear irreversible, i.e. accompanied by an increase in entropy; if this fluctuation is eventually reversed, we shall observe an entropy decrease everywhere. In this way Boltzmann tried to reconcile the essential reversibility assumed by our theories with the irreversibility observed in our experiments. But to extend the application of thermodynamics to the universe at large is hardly justified, and there is no need to overcome the restrictions of our theory in such a speculative manner.

The existence of fluctuations is of import for another reason: fluctuations set a limit to the observability even of macroscopic events. The more accurate we make our measuring instruments, for instance a galvanometer, the lighter must be the indicating needle and the thinner the fibre by which it is suspended. This will result, however, in an increased small-scale motion of these parts due to the fluctuations of their molecules; the greater the sensitivity of the instrument, the more noticeable will be these irregular motions. The noise level, say of a loudspeaker, becomes higher when we increase the amplification. Thus, there is a natural limit to the sensitivity of the instruments of observation. This is an idea that re-appears again, in a somewhat different formulation in quantum mechanics which specifies a numerical limit to the observability of microscopic events, through the quantum of action.

Whatever the restrictions of the statistical interpretation of thermodynamics, we can give a model to guide us in the correct usage of the concepts. In fact, the restrictions show up the range of our sentences (within the language system used) and help to indicate the semantic rules implicit in the theory.

6. *The third law* (*limits in nature*)

In the statistical interpretation heat is regarded as the motion of particles, and 'temperature' designates their (average) kinetic energy. On this model we would expect the motion to stop completely only when an infinitely low temperature is reached. The third law of thermodynamics states, surprisingly, that the lowest possible temperature is finite: this zero-point is at about minus 273 degrees centigrade.

The third law, then, not only states an interdiction—as all laws do—but it seems to set a definite, numerical, limit to our efforts; we cannot cool down any body below a certain temperature. The number assigned to it is, however, arbitrary; we could equally give to the lowest possible temperature the value of minus infinity, since it represents an *asymptotic* limit which can never be reached experimentally. The situation is unlike that in relativity theory where we say that of all signals by which a message can be transmitted, light is the fastest; though material particles can never reach this speed since it would attribute an infinitely large energy to them, light can travel as fast as this (at least, *in vacuo*). The velocity of light cannot be 'made infinite' arbitrarily: this would be incompatible with experimental evidence. In other words, while the speed of light seems to represent a genuine *constant* of nature, the zero-point of temperature does not.

The experiments show that, with decreasing temperature, certain properties of physical bodies disappear and all processes stop; or, certain thermodynamical functions approach the zero value. For example, the ability of a body to store heat—its specific heat—diminishes with temperature; and the change in entropy occurring when the system passes from one state to another tends to disappear for temperatures near the absolute zero (i.e. the zero-point on the Kelvin scale which is the same as about minus 273 degrees centigrade).

As with all the laws of thermodynamics we can give the third law a number of different, though equivalent, formulations, e.g. It is impossible to reach the absolute zero of temperature. Or, reverting to the engine model which we used before we may say that it is impossible to construct a perpetual motion machine of *the third kind*. This means that no machine can be built by which a body can be completely deprived of its heat content, that is, cooled down to absolute zero. In a positive, and universal, statement the third law can be formulated in this way: For all processes involving pure substances the change in entropy tends to vanish as the temperature approaches absolute zero.

How can we interpret this law by the mechanical-statistical model of thermodynamics? Like the first and second laws the third law is concerned with the terms 'energy' and 'system'. The first law states that, for a closed system, only such processes occur in which energy is conserved. If during a process the visible, kinetic energy of the particles disappears, we must say that it is changed, without residue, into non-visible, or internal, or potential energy of the system; and we may have to construct the closed system in a special way, i.e. take the actual bodies involved in a process together with their (somewhat indefinite) environment, in order to keep the conservation law. We then assume energy to exist in various forms, and all processes are described as the transformation of one kind of energy into another. This indicates a rule for the usage of 'energy' with respect to the model assumed.

The second law states that, for a closed system, during a process a certain amount of energy becomes unavailable for further use. Some energy is lost for useful work but remains as part of the total (constant) energy of the system; it can, however, never be re-converted into work. This, once more, sets a range for the use of 'energy'. While in the particle interpretation of mechanics 'energy' is defined as 'the ability to do work', in thermodynamics it is only 'free energy' which can be so defined.

The third law, finally, states that, for a closed system, there exists a limit below which energy cannot be extracted from the system. There is a *zero-point energy* which is characteristic of the system and can never be changed. The later theories of quantum mechanics account for this constant amount of irreducible energy in terms of the quantum of action.

In their customary formulations the three laws of thermo-dynamics are, it seems, empty of factual meaning; they function as analytic sentences (within the theory), or as rules (within the corresponding meta-theory), which tells us how to use the con-cepts of energy and of system. Naturally, we would not choose to speak in this way if it were not, in practice, useful: and the energy-system language has been applied with great success. This does not alter the logical form of the sentences in which the laws are expressed. Originally, the laws were invented by physicists on the basis of certain, very simple, experiments. For this historical reason physicists are inclined to regard such sentences as factual, even when the laws are 'generalised' over and above the experi-mental findings and when the sentences are of unrestricted uni-versality (within the language of thermodynamics). In their usual formulation, the three laws form the logical or, better, semantic skeleton of thermodynamical theory. The same happens in other theories as well: not all statements which are called 'laws' in physics are factual, and this will have an important bearing on our account of scientific method.

We must also note that the particle model of mechanics which underlies the statistical theory of thermodynamics is somewhat changed. Instead of a thing-language another way of speaking in terms of 'energy' and 'system' is developed which opens up a wide domain of possible applications and which comes nearer to a genuine process-language. Ordinarily, in every-day language, we use the word 'energy' differently: energy may completely disappear—we say 'there is no energy left' when the motion of a body ceases. But we always need concepts stressing an aspect of experience that could possibly be interpreted as thing-like, or permanent; we seem unable to do without the idea of substance in order to have something identifiable as the carrier of a process. We feel inclined to interpret 'zero-point energy' in this manner: it is an expression referring to something constant and permanent, and this brings the energy-system language closer to the more usual type of thing-language.

There is another interpretation of the third law with the help of the geometrical model, in terms of the concept of order. A state of the system may be described by the order in which the molecules are arranged; and 'order' means here the number of possible geometrical configurations of the molecules. The state of greatest disorder which is realised by the largest number of such complexions is the most probable state, or the state of equilibrium towards which the system as a whole tends to develop. This tendency is identified with the tendency of entropy to increase.

The order is a function of temperature: the higher the temperature, the more haphazard are the motions of the molecules. That is, the order will increase when the temperature is lowered; there will be fewer complexions, or microscopic configurations, representing an equilibrium state at a lower temperature. Finally, there is a limit. The thermal motion of the molecules becomes so small that only one configuration, or pattern, is possible, and we have obtained the greatest order of which the molecules of the system are capable. This is the state at the absolute zero of temperature. According to the mechanical model the particles are arranged in the most orderly fashion if they are as close together as the peculiar properties of the particles under consideration allow. Thus the regular pattern of atoms in which a crystal is arranged is the model of a physical system at absolute zero. This suggests, as before, that order can be pictured as a geometrical configuration of a certain symmetry. Low entropy, order, and (spatial) asymmetry are associated: this is known as Curie's principle. But we see that these properties do not belong to the individual thing, that is, the crystal which usually possesses a high degree of symmetry. Rather, these properties must be ascribed to the system as a whole, that is, to all the various things which, in some way, interact with one another. For at low temperatures the crystal occupies only a small part of the available space and so can be said to be in an asymmetrical position with respect to it. The inability to reach absolute zero is then sometimes explained as the tendency towards disorder or greater symmetry; and cooling down a body requires working against this tendency. The main point is that, in the energy-system language, the concept of individual particle, or thing, is used not quite in the same way as in the particle-language of mechanics.

These are some of the explanations found in the textbooks telling us how to use the equations of thermodynamics. The engine model, the Carnot cycle, Carathéodory's inaccessible states, and the mechanical-statistical model suggest the interpretations that are permissible. Thus all these models function as semantic language systems indicating rules of designation and of range for the sentences which the theory allows us to formulate. No doubt these, established, models are somewhat deficient, in the sense that they do not permit us to say all we want to say and in the way we want to say it, e.g. about irreversibility. It may be of course that the rather vague ideas which we try to make precise by the help of our theories are mistaken. But it may also be that the orthodox interpretations are too idealised since they do not seem to describe completely our experiments. All the same it must be admitted that the various models offered by thermodynamics as we know it to-day meet with a large measure of success. The concept of probability helps us in explaining what is meant by 'irreversible process', at least within certain limits; this allows us to forego the use of 'tendency'—a word found objectionable by most physicists since it is surrounded by an aura of Aristotelian teleology. Further development may succeed in dispensing with the mechanistic feature of present theory and in emphasizing the rôle of statistics; for it appears that the use of mechanical concepts makes us regard thermal processes as being essentially reversible. As Professor Born remarked in his recent book, 'the idea of a completely closed system is also almost fantastic'; but he concludes that 'the statistical foundation of thermodynamics is quite satisfactory even on the grounds of classical mechanics'. So long as we realise that all description makes idealisation inevitable, and that all our theories are temporary however well they may work, the way to new discoveries is not barred.

V

QUANTUM PHYSICS

1. *Historical survey*

The discovery of the *quantum of action* in 1900 heralded a radically new departure in physics; it led in 1926 to the theory of
quantum mechanics which was widely acclaimed as a revolution.
Quantum theory has created a fundamental change in our ideas
as relativity theory had done before. But while relativity theory
is essentially classical in its conceptions—it is in fact the culmination of classical physics—quantum mechanics is founded on some
new principles. The quantum laws are very different in character
from the laws we find in classical theory. In particular, quantum
mechanics is a strictly statistical type of theory: from this arises
the different conception of causality that marks the new outlook
of modern physics.

The novel feature of this theory is that energy is regarded as existing in discrete amounts, i.e. quanta. Any given amount of energy
may be thought of as an integral multiple of an isolated unit while, in
classical physics, energy is something which varies in a continuous
manner. And, from the logical viewpoint, the strange and 'abstract',
not to say abstruse, nature of the new concepts made it necessary
to be more critical about the construction of our theories; it
resulted, ultimately, in a better understanding of all physics.

Planck introduced the idea of a discrete quantum of energy in
order to overcome the failure of the classical laws of radiation.
Einstein, in 1905, extended this idea to the description of the
phenomena of light; and he formulated his famous *photon* theory
which, in a different form, re-created the corpuscular theory of
light as held by Newton. Finally, basing his work upon the experimental research of Rutherford into the structure of the atom,
Bohr in 1913 applied the conception of energy quanta to the
emission and absorption of light by atoms. He invented a theory
about the constitution of atoms which, immediately, led to great
success. In this way a radically new type of theory was constructed
in order to describe atomic processes on the microscopic scale.

As a result of Einstein's hypothesis which ascribes a kind of corpuscular character to light—the photon particle—the so-called dual nature of light was established. That is to say, it was shown that light phenomena may be described either in terms of particles or in terms of waves. This latter concept alone was employed in classical physics. However, the photons do not obey the classical laws of motion; their behaviour is described by a wave equation which has to be interpreted in a special way.

This dual conception was applied, in 1924, by de Broglie to describe the motion of all particles, that is, even of those which, unlike the photon, we believe to be solid and permanent: he postulated that electrons and atoms which we normally take to be material particles may also be 'associated with', or describable by, a wave. It was a bold proposal although, no doubt unknown to de Broglie, it had been made before. A pupil of Gassendi had invented a theory according to which atoms of the various elements differ by the waves, or internal vibrations, supposed to exist inside of them. This seventeenth century idea is very close to de Broglie's: for he proposed that the electron revolving in an orbit inside the atom according to Bohr's theory, may be regarded as a standing wave running into itself. The context of de Broglie's idea is, naturally, quite different; and he was able to give a mathematical formulation for it. Moreover, the hypothesis so obtained lends itself to an experimental confirmation that would have been impossible to carry out in the seventeenth century. The wave conception was substantiated by Davisson and Germer when they showed that a stream of electrons—usually considered to be particles—produced diffraction phenomena which we always take to be characteristic of waves.

These new ideas led, finally, to Schrödinger's wave mechanics and to the matrix mechanics of Heisenberg and Born. While Schrödinger based the theory of atomic processes upon the wave picture, Heisenberg chose a more mathematical and logical approach. He emphasized the need for the empirical verifiability of our sentences; and he demanded that in the description of physical processes only such symbols should be employed as refer, in the most direct manner possible, to observable quantities. This demand for observability leads to a calculus which is best interpreted in terms of particles. It resulted in the new principle of *uncertainty* or *indeterminacy* which we regard to-day as fundamental in the description of microscopic processes.

Finally, by introducing the concepts of special relativity into quantum mechanics Dirac constructed a refined theory which was quite successful. (The relativistic correction of the older quantum theory of Bohr was carried out by Sommerfeld who, in this way, explained the fine structure of the hydrogen spectrum.) Dirac's theory can account for the *spin* of the electron which before had to be assumed specially in order to explain the structure of atoms. The second result of Dirac's theory consisted in predicting the existence of a new particle, the positive electron; and it was promptly found in cosmic ray experiments by Anderson and by Blackett and Occhialini.

Dirac's theory is a new formulation of quantum ideas with which some concepts of special relativity are mixed; it does not present the complete fusion of these two conceptions which many physicists still hope will one day be achieved. Since Dirac's theory there has been an increased application of quantum mechanics: but no new, fundamental, theory has been put forward. The *meson* theory originated by Yukawa is, so far, merely an attempt to extend quantum concepts to high-energy processes. Other theories as well, such as the zone theory of solids, the neutrino theory of β-ray disintegration, quantum electrodynamics, or the various *drop* and *shell* models of the nucleus, must all be regarded as attempts—not always successful—to increase the application of quantum concepts. At this moment the brilliant succession of theories which has occurred in physics since the times of Faraday and Maxwell seems to have come to a temporary halt. Most physicists feel that the time is ripe, again, for a radical change in our ideas, and for a new theory; but, so far, there is no sign of it.

2. *The correspondence principle*

Classical theory describes the so-called *macroscopic* phenomena, that is, things and events which are more or less of the same size and kind as we find them in ordinary life; and so a description can be given in terms of concepts close to the ones we use in ordinary language. This is largely true even of relativity theory though it is concerned mainly with describing events in the *megaloscopic* domain, that is, events involving high speeds and large distances. It is no longer so with quantum theory describing *microscopic* events which are far beyond the possibility of being observed even

L

with the help of ordinary instruments, like telescope and micro-scope. Classical physics can be explained, in general, by means of simple models and the events described are easily visualised. Quantum mechanics, however, is a theory employing unfamiliar concepts for which this is possible only with great difficulty, if at all. Moreover, the uncertainty principle—with its restriction of the possible space-time location of particles—introduces a differ-ent conception of causality. Indeed, it abolished the classical view and, instead, quantum theory has made it necessary that we describe the events in terms of probability and statistics.

It is this change that has been deemed to be so revolutionary. Some Marxist physicists have even claimed that it indicates the decay of 'bourgeois' physics since it does away with the rigid determinism required by their political faith. However, this view of causality has always been mistaken, even in classical physics. Although the ideas of quantum mechanics are indeed very radical, there is no essential break with classical physics: the change is part of the natural development of science. This is clearly ex-pressed by the first of the three main principles that underlie all quantum theories: the correspondence principle first enunciated by Bohr. This principle is of great practical import and is equally indispensable for understanding how, in fact, we build up the language of physics.

Modern physics has become more and more technical and specialised as the formulation of our theories has passed beyond ordinary language into a symbolism incomprehensible to the lay-man; even the physicist may fail to understand a particular theory in a realm in which he is not an expert. It is a current joke to say that physics has become too difficult even for the physicists. Relativity, though a classical theory, is often reputed to be of this sort since it introduces concepts which are not quite like those customary in previous theories. These concepts are needed in relativity theory as it is both more detailed and comprehensive in its description of events than preceding theories. This increasingly abstract, or non-representational, character of our conceptions has become more obvious in quantum mechanics which describes processes which are not, and cannot be, directly observable.

How does it happen that we can push our description beyond the 'natural' limit of direct observability and so make use of concepts so different from our ordinary ones? After all, in the last resort, we must be able to interpret our theories by simple sentences that directly relate to the happenings in the laboratory.

It is exactly the fact that modern physics is so difficult to visualise which allows us to see more clearly its logical structure. The very familiarity of classical concepts prevents us from being critical about them; and since these concepts are somewhat vague and so deeply embedded in ordinary language it is all the more difficult to criticize them. While, as practical physicists, we may complain about this fact, as logicians we have some reason to welcome it. For it has forced us not only to discover new laws but also to formulate statements about these laws, that is, to give explicitly general principles regarding theory construction. And it is the correspondence principle which is the most important guide for this task.

The principle shows that we may regard a physical theory as a descriptive semantic system. That is, not only can the theory be split into a formal calculus and an interpretation, but there is also a meta-theory, or meta-language, in terms of which we can speak about the theory. This admittedly very incomplete formalisation suffices, however, for explaining a new theory by enabling us to state the meaning and truth of its statements. The tendency of modern physics, towards formal, and more formalised, theories has therefore a good reason.

The physical theories we have to-day are, of course, not completely formalised. The mathematical treatment, however, gives us at least a partial formalisation; for it helps to separate the syntactic and semantic rules involved in the use of a formula, even though we still rely—to a large extent—on pictures, diagrams, and the general description of the context in order to show what the formula means. The complete formalisation of the language of physics may be perhaps an unattainable ideal, yet it is undeniable that it has guided the development of physics. Physicists, with pragmatic dexterity, have learned to make do with this incomplete formalisation.

It is for this reason, as was argued before, that we construct *models* for interpreting our theories. In this way, we obtain a *partial* interpretation of the new theory in terms of simpler concepts directly related to our experiments. The theory of light exemplifies this semantic function of models. The concept of wave originally stems from observations on elastic waves, the waves we can produce in water, or on a string. It is a mechanical model, and the waves require a medium to carry them. When wave theory was applied to light, an aether was postulated for this purpose. But this mechanical interpretation is too limited for explaining optical phenomena, though the elastic theory of light can be made to work to some extent. Our increasing knowledge of optics thus made it necessary to re-interpret the concept of wave. In mechanics, 'wave' is interpreted by the picture of a medium in motion; the geometrical shape of the medium, and the displacement of its particles, is taken as the main property designating the term 'wave'. In Maxwell's theory the particle picture is suppressed, and instead of the displacement of particles from some equilibrium position we have the concept of energy to characterize the processes. The field interpretation of electromagnetic theory still allowed us, however, to make use of a continuous medium, though we had to strip the medium of all its mechanical properties. Thus the aether became a very tenuous thing: it had no weight, it could penetrate all bodies—in short, it acquired a ghost-like character. Relativity taught us to give up the concept of aether altogether, and we became accustomed to regard electro-magnetic waves as energy held together in a wave-pattern which could travel even in empty space. Finally, the so-called matter-waves in quantum mechanics turn out to be still more 'abstract'; and all that remains of the original wave model is a statistical distribution.

Physical theory developed by gradually overcoming the limitations of the original model; but this does not mean that we no longer use models in physics, nor even that the original model is completely abandoned. Some connexion with the original model is retained; the model is re-designed and, thus, refined in order to agree better with our latest experiments. What remains is the wave equation, together with a minimum interpretation in terms of experience upon which the application of the equation rests. It is like the grin and the Cheshire cat; the picture of the cat has receded into the background, but knowing that there was once a cat we understand that the residual phenomenon may be interpreted as a grin.

The development of physics shows that successive theories usually become more general and less easy to visualise; we see also that each theory is based upon a previous, accepted, theory.

The theories follow each other in a series of successive approximations; and the new theory is a better approximation, a more detailed and a more accurate description of the phenomena. It would be wrong to say, however, that the better approximation, or the more advanced theory, is simply obtained by leaving out some superfluous features of the previous theory. Very often this kind of 'abstraction' does, in fact, happen; but sometimes we may also add new features: for instance, when we pass from the Newtonian particle to the elementary particle. It is true that we seem to drop certain mechanical properties; but we add charge, spin, and unit size. A new theory is created when we change the model in a definite manner so that a closer description becomes possible. Moreover, the new theory is related to direct experience whence it arose; and it is by virtue of this relation that we are enabled to apply the more abstract, or unfamiliar, theory and to understand the new concepts.

The development of quantum theory brought to light this fundamental requirement of theory construction. Even the older theory (in the formulation of Bohr) is so removed from ordinary experience that it cannot be understood except in terms of a simple model. No computations can be made otherwise—and, indeed, it is the value of the model that it permits us to set up equations. The atom is interpreted, for example, 'as a small mechanical system which resembles in certain main features our own solar system'. Certainly, as physicists, we are aware that this is too simple an interpretation for atomic processes. We have to be cautious when making use of this model; for the quantum conditions which must be added show that the correct interpretation of the equations is more complicated though we cannot express it in a simple thing-language. All the same, this mechanical model is more than a simple analogy (though, as with all analogies, we must be aware of its possible limitations). For this so-called planetary model establishes the link with mechanics, and hence it leads us to sentences that can be tested by experiment.

It is the correspondence principle that shows us how to construct a better and more comprehensive theory, on the basis of a simpler and narrow theory, or of a model. The principle formulates the condition which the new theory must satisfy: there must be an *asymptotic* agreement between the main formulae of the old and of the new theory.

The new theory reduces to the old one for the special case in which the refinement introduced by the new theory may be disregarded. In other words, the new semantic system contains the calculus of the previous system as a special sub-calculus. For example, the formulae describing the orbits of the electron within the atom must become identical with those of the mechanical model for the limiting case in which the quantum of action—the concept introduced by the new theory—may be neglected. In a similar manner, the formulae for the probability distribution of a quantum-mechanical particle reduce to the equations of motion for a mechanical particle. Or, to take an example from another part of physics: the Lorentz transformation describing relative motion according to the special relativity reduces to the Galilei transformation of Newtonian mechanics, provided we deal with speeds which are small compared with that of light. This is accomplished by the procedure that certain mathematical formulae of the new theory pass, in the limiting case, into known formulae of the old theory. In this manner, the equations of quantum mechanics are given a *partial* interpretation in terms of mechanics; and the new theory, although 'abstract', can be made to link up with experiment. We have reached a higher approximation, and we have achieved a closer description of nature. True that the visual model is used merely as an intermediary for the interpretation of the more advanced semantic system; however, it would be wrong to say that it is completely abandoned. We have recognised the limitations of the mechanical model; but some of the original semantic and syntactic rules are kept though others are modified or dropped altogether. Since we are not always able to formulate these rules explicitly it remains to some extent a matter of practice and skill to derive and prove theorems within the new theory. To see the restrictions imposed by the simple model, however, helps us to isolate the logical structure of the new semantic system. But it is a necessary part of theory construction that the new theory reduces to the old theory for the limiting case in which the old theory alone has proved to be sufficient. It is in this way that we have overcome the limitations of the previous theory.

The new system does not contain directly and explicitly the simpler semantic system; it reduces to it only under special conditions. Let C—S represent any semantic system indicating its two parts, the calculus C and the set of semantic rules S; and let us distinguish the two systems by subscripts. The more advanced system C_2—S_2 reduces to the simpler system C_1—S_1 if C_1 equals C_2 for a special case. The main formulae of the one calculus (involving a 'key concept', that is, a principal descriptive constant) pass into the formulae of the other calculus; in this way the two sets of rules become related. This is necessary since S_2 is abstract, in the sense that it does not refer directly to experiment. By this partial re-interpretation in terms of the system S_1 we have found a meaning for the sentences of S_2 and, thus, we are able to apply the new theory. The first, inadequate, theory is replaced by a new theory which, although its concepts are removed from ordinary experience, has now obtained a meaning that can be put to the test by experiment.

But how does it happen that the agreement of some mathematical equations under special circumstances allows us to transfer meaning, that is, to obtain an interpretation in terms of experience? If we were to regard our equations as purely formal mathematics, would this not force us to accept some strange, Platonic, view of the world? But it is not true to say that equations if they belong to a physical theory, are uninterpreted. Nor can we say that the formal, syntactic, rules of mathematics—that is, of our language—represent some sort of 'real' structure of the world: many different mathematical calculi (involving various rules) can be given the same interpretation. The situation is in some way similar in ordinary language. The syntactic rules (assuming we can isolate them clearly in standard grammar) are in a sense arbitrary; but they are chosen in such a way that the sentences we may form describe simple experience in the simplest manner. Thus they are often inadequate to describe more complex experience; for underlying this choice of rules is the common sense interpretation of the thing-language, and the syntactic rules are chosen to agree with the semantic rules of the interpretation assumed.

Following the terminology for semantic systems which has been proposed by Carnap we may say that an interpretation is true if the semantic rules of S are in accordance with the syntactic rules of C; that is, every theorem which is logically true in C (or provable) becomes semantically true in S. One of the functions the correspondence principle fulfils, therefore, is to ensure that the new theory is a true interpretation, from the semantic point of view. And it is because the theories involved are true interpretations of their respective calculi that the asymptotic agreement of the two calculi connects the two interpretations.

The correspondence principle, then, is a rule we must follow in the construction of physical theories. When we invent a calculus for physics, we must restrict its possible interpretations ; for a calculus can be interpreted, in general, in an indefinite number of ways. Since the principle states that the new theory must contain the old theory as a special case, it prescribes the conditions the new calculus must satisfy ; and the possibilities for constructing new theories are curtailed in this manner. Thus, the correspondence principle safeguards the relation to experiment. For the modern theories do not lead directly to observation sentences : the intervention of the simpler theories of classical physics is required. Bohr describes the procedure by saying that 'it lies in the nature of physical observation . . . that all experience must ultimately be in terms of classical physics'. For all human experience is in the medium-sized domain, and measurements are carried out by means of instruments whose functioning is described by classical physics. Classical physics is already somewhat more technical and specialised than the common sense theory about the world which underlies ordinary language. But, as physicists, we have trained our imagination and learned to think in terms of classical physics. The correspondence principle expresses the condition that, in the last resort, we must interpret our theories in terms of a language which is directly known to us.

In science the *semantic type* of a language is given by the principal descriptive sign : the key concept in terms of which the model is represented. The particle model in classical mechanics, for instance, ascribes a definite position q and momentum p to the particle, and its path is determined by any set of simultaneous values p, q. In quantum mechanics a particle occupies a certain state of given energy, and we cannot speak of the path of the particle since there are no statements in which simultaneous and exact values of p, q occur. This indicates a change in the rules of formation for the sentences to be admitted to the system. Moreover, the particle in quantum mechanics is not quite the same thing as the classical particle. Their difference in behaviour is illustrated, for instance, by the so-called tunnel effect. The elementary particle described by quantum mechanics may penetrate an energy barrier though possessing less energy than the barrier. This is the reason why we can explain the phenomenon of natural radio-activity (i.e. that certain nuclei spontaneously disintegrate by emitting a particle) and still regard the nucleus as a stable arrangement of particles. The 'classical' particle can never jump over a barrier if it does not have sufficient energy. Such difference in behaviour may be taken as indicating a change in the rule of designation for 'particle'. Finally, the universe of discourse for which quantum theory holds differs from that of classical theory : it shows that the rules of range are changed. Different semantic rules are involved in each theory though the same word occurs. We may not be able to give the rules in an explicit form, but we can show them by giving a model.

The correspondence principle not only allows us to construct a more advanced theory ; it also reveals the limitations of the simple, original theory and so makes clearer the semantic rules used. By the change in these rules we are made aware of what the conditions are under which the simpler theory may be applied. The two theories mutually correct one another : this self-correction is the most important feature of scientific method.

The 'abstract' interpretation of quantum mechanics, however, is obtained only because it can be made to coincide partially with the classical model which is directly related to experiment. By the asymptotic agreement of the two calculi the abstract, or technical, concept of stationary state, for instance, is shown to correspond partially to the classical concept of orbit ; and the change in model, the difference in semantic rules, is demonstrated by the fact that the re-interpretation is only partial. But this partial interpretation in terms of simple experience makes it possible to work with, and apply, the more 'abstract' theory.

Science, or at least physics, has been developed by inventing new and unusual concepts or, rather, by finding unusual ways of using old concepts. But we can propose a new way of speaking only by basing it on established theories : we want new ideas that are radical but not rootless. In the history of physics, there are examples of theories which did not satisfy the correspondence principle though, otherwise, they might have been of some interest : the vortex theory of the atom was somewhat of this type, and a recent example is Eddington's *Fundamental Theory*. We have no guide for interpreting the formalism given ; and however correct the mathematics may be, the theory is useless.

Thus, for an advanced theory, we have *multiple* interpretations which, through many steps, lead back to the observation sentences. These *intermediate* interpretations may overlap to some extent but they are, nevertheless, *partial* interpretations. Only a few, important, sentences, i.e. those in which key concepts occur, need be related in this manner. By partially interpreting the 'abstract' theory in terms of known expressions we ensure that we do not limit the advance in knowledge the theory may provide ; but we have succeeded, all the same, in anchoring the advanced theory in experience.

3. *The complementarity principle*

A physical theory consists of a formal calculus and of an interpretation. But the relation between calculus and interpretation is in fact not unique. A single calculus may be interpreted in terms of various concepts. Moreover, we often have at our disposal several calculi that may be interpreted by the same set of concepts. That is to say, we may have various ways of speaking about our experiments ; we can construct several theories covering the same field of experience. Nature allows us a wider latitude for its description than is usually believed.

Quantum mechanics provides an illustration : there are at least two systems of description that are permissible. The wave mechanics of Schrödinger employs a calculus of partial differential equations and is usually interpreted by means of the wave concept. The matrix mechanics of Heisenberg and Born uses a certain kind of algebra for its mathematical formulation, and its interpretation is normally given in terms of the particle concept. But both calculi are susceptible of either interpretation ; moreover, the two calculi are shown to be formally equivalent. This feature indicates that both interpretations, the 'wave-language' and the 'particle-language', are true from the semantic viewpoint. These two systems represent *equivalent* descriptions : they are equivalent in the sense that the same *observable* events are described. No possible test by experiment is satisfied by the one system which is not also satisfied by the other ; thus both are equally acceptable in physical theory. This far-reaching freedom in the choice of the concepts by means of which we describe nature is characteristic of modern science.

The particle-language allows us to make use, at least to some extent, of Newtonian mechanics ; and the wave-language permits us a somewhat limited visualisation according to classical optics. But the use of the language of classical physics must be *restricted* in quantum physics. We can no longer ascribe a definite and exact position to the particle or imagine it to move along a definite path, as we may do in classical theory ; and the propagation of the wave must be described as taking place, in most instances, in a multi-dimensional hyper-space, and not in ordinary space. These are some of the reasons why we say to-day that quantum mechanics must be given an interpretation in terms of proba-ability ; the equations allow us to compute only the probable values of the space-time location of the events. This statistical interpretation which was originally proposed by Born might be considered as a third variant of the language of quantum mech-anics. However, it is an 'abstract' interpretation ; we can speak about it in ordinary language only if we express it either in terms of 'wave' or in terms of 'particle'. We can even visualise it to some extent by taking the intensity distribution of a wave-pattern to indicate the values of the probabilities. The language of quantum mechanics is restricted in its application when we compare it to the language of classical physics ; this restriction shows that we must use the concepts according to different rules —rules which include sentences about probability. The concepts of wave and of particle are re-defined implicitly by giving new rules of usage for them ; but the classical concepts from which they arose allow us to use ordinary language, at least with caution. In this sense, we have only a dual interpretation, if the statistical character is included in the two basic concepts.

Because modern physics has become less pictorial and more technical it has often been said that we have given up the use of models. This is largely a question as to how we wish to use the term 'model'. There is not much justification for limiting its use to the domain of classical physics where the visual representation is given in terms of familiar experience. It appears to be reason-able to consider a model as a rudimentary semantic system which shows the rules but does not state them explicitly. The classical models are no longer acceptable simply because we wish to describe non-classical phenomena, that is, microphysical events which lie outside the realm of classical theory. But the probability interpretation is equally a model, though an unfamiliar one ; it is not completely formalised as a semantic system, and in order to relate our equations to experiment we must still rely on the diagrams of probability distributions. Thus, the manipulation of our models is more difficult since mathematical rules have to be added. It is true that modern physics has renounced visual representation as a condition for accepting a theory. We no longer believe that the world must be as simple as the physicists of a previous generation had imagined ; and we reject such visual models as the 'ultimate' picture of reality. But this changed attitude is also due to other motives since the epistemology upon which this belief was based has to be rejected. We still make use of models in the sense of a non-formalised and not completely formulated interpretation, that is, as a simple kind of descriptive semantic system. The kind of model used in modern physics is different from that of classical physics.

Let us add that the mathematical part of the theory may be given also by still other kinds of formalism ; and, in general, for a limited part of quantum mechanics almost any kind of mathematics has been used, at one time or another. True that, on occasion, this has been done only for heuristic reasons to facilitate computation. Since the mathematical equations of a theory are certainly a part of the formal calculus, we must agree that there is a good deal of choice as far as some syntactic rules are concerned. Of course, the rules of mathematics are not the only syntactic rules we have in the system ; there must also be rules governing the use of the word symbols. Finally, we must add that the relativistic formulation of quantum theory as given by Dirac represents still another semantic system, since it involves a different sort of mathematics—transformation theory—as well as a somewhat modified interpretation. However, it suffices here to restrict ourselves to the discussion of the original wave and particle interpretations in order to see the logical construction of modern theory.

In quantum mechanics, then, we have two possible interpretations, and each of these equivalent descriptions alone can account for all the observable results. In practice, however, we need both of them : it would be most inconvenient if we were to retain only one of these interpretations. For we are accustomed from classical physics to describe certain phenomena by the wave concept, and others by the particle concept.

Every experiment consists of several, causally connected, happenings. If a beam of electrons is sent against a diffracting slit, we describe the happenings at the slit in terms of waves. Indeed, in classical optics, the diffraction phenomenon has been taken as the crucial experiment demonstrating that light consists of waves. But the electrons are shot from an 'electron gun'; they are emitted from a heated filament, and this process, as well as the focussing of the beam by electric and magnetic fields is more naturally described by the particle concept. After the electrons have passed the slit, we may again describe the happenings on the screen in these two ways. The flashes of light we see when an electron impinges upon the screen—particularly at low intensity—obviously call for a particle interpretation. The over-all distribution of maxima and minima—of illumination and shadow—is more naturally described by a wave pattern.

But in quantum mechanics there is a definite rule prescribing the correct usage of the two interpretations. As Bohr has formulated it, we are forced 'to adopt a new mode of description designated as *complementary* in the sense that any given application of classical concepts precludes the simultaneous use of other classical concepts which in a different connection are equally necessary for the elucidation of the phenomena'. Once we have decided to describe a certain event in terms of the wave concept, we cannot *at the same time* make use of the particle concept for the same purpose. If we mix these two interpretations, we get into difficulties. These difficulties are of an intriguing kind ; they are due, in the last resort, to the rules inherent in the language we are accustomed to use. The principle of complementarity, then, states that we have two interpretations on the basis of two different *key-concepts*. Each is capable of providing a complete description of the phenomena ; and both are of equal value and are in fact used, provided they are not used simultaneously.

Of course, in practice physicists are not too cautious in obeying this injunction. But this laxity in linguistic usage merely shows that the trained physicist knows how to avoid the difficulties.

To illustrate the situation, let us take once more the simple diffraction experiment. If we describe the electrons as a wave, then the events at the slit are explained in the normal manner ; for we are accustomed to account for diffraction in terms of the wave model. But, then, we must keep to this interpretation when we speak about the events on the screen : we must speak about the maxima and minima of the diffraction pattern. However, we are inclined here to change over to the particle interpretation, for we see the pattern as scintillations ; and these flashes of light are more normally interpreted as electrons impinging upon the screen. If we mix our languages in this manner, we arrive at a difficulty. We are forced to say that the extended wave front coming from the slit has suddenly contracted into a point here, or a point there, and these points are seen as flashes. In other words, we violate the principle of causality, according to which trans-mission of action—the contraction of the wave into a point—must take a finite time. Classical physics, and particularly rela-tivity theory, has always required that cause and effect are linked by an action-by-contact. Similar difficulties would occur if we were to use the particle interpretation, originally, and then change over to the wave language ; this becomes more obvious when we describe a double-slit experiment. The various happen-ings of one and the same experiment must be described in terms of one concept alone. Although one description may be more convenient or natural to use for a particular part of the experi-ment, we cannot use both interpretations at the same time. This prohibition is formulated by the complementarity principle.

If we disobey this principle, we find what has been called by Reichenbach a *causal anomaly* : our usual conception of causality is violated. We must never say in quantum mechanics that waves cause particles, or vice versa. We can formulate the causal relation between two events only if these events are described within the same language-system ; for a law is a theorem *within* a theory.

It must be noted that these anomalies are not due to the revi-sion of the concept of causality which is required by the uncer-tainty principle ; though we have to change from the determinism of classical theory to a statistical causality this is separate diffi-culty. Since the discussion of the uncertainty principle is important for our understanding of causality, this problem will be taken up later.

The difficulty regarding complementarity is mainly linguistic.

The concepts of wave and particle, however modified they are in quantum mechanics, are still endowed with some characteristics of classical theory, and we have therefore to take care when we interpret micro-physical phenomena with their help. There are certain semantic rules of usage for 'wave' and 'particle' which we cannot give up completely without playing havoc with our language. These rules work well enough when we describe macro-physical phenomena ; but their insufficiency is revealed in micro-physics.

As a matter of fact, the complementarity of a pair of concepts occurs also in classical physics. It is only because there we are hardly ever tempted to misuse them—the phenomena are familiar and directly observable—that the complementarity does not show up so clearly as in quantum mechanics. It is always preferable not to use these two concepts simultaneously. This is borne out by the historical development of the theory of light, with the rival claims of Newton and Huygens. When we say that a stone thrown into a pool of water produces waves, we may think that this illustrates how events described by these two different concepts can be causally related. But classical physics is more cautious in formulating causal statements than ordinary language. We say that the stone—a particle—sets the particles of water, or the water molecules, into motion ; and this motion as a whole is then described as a wave pattern spreading over the (continuous) surface of the water. Another example, the experiment on the pressure of light, might be thought to illustrate the reverse : we say, on occasion, that waves set particles in motion. But, again, classical theory prefers a different formulation. We introduce the concept of the energy of the wave ; and we express the energy in terms of elasticity, as stress and strain of a medium, so that we can keep within a continuum picture or field theory. Many such examples could be found. Admittedly, their explanation is somewhat vague. But we see that even in classical physics causal relations are not so simple as they appear and that we must choose carefully the language in which to describe them.

The language of quantum mechanics is based upon a duality principle ; and most of our ordinary language is equally dualistic. The use of two-valued logic *tends* to create a syntactic usage of pairs of expressions so that they become contradictories. There is evidence from the study of linguistics for saying that this happens often in actual, historically given, languages. This duality is shown by the many pairs of expressions we find everywhere in ordinary speech : the *twin words*, and they have more than once given rise to philosophic problems. It is suggestive to consider, from this viewpoint, the problem of mind and matter, or of heredity and environment, to see how much they are due to the syntax of our language. In the wave-particle pair, for instance, one concept seems to belong to a thing-language, the other to a process-language. All descriptions of physical events can be analysed in terms of one or the other concept. Every event is either a wave phenomenon or a particle phenomenon, and it cannot be both at the same time. Thus the two concepts are *mutually exhaustive* within our usual language, and they become *contradictories*.

The complementarity of the two interpretations of quantum mechanics is created by the key-concepts that are used. Since the terms are normally taken to be mutually exclusive and to exhaust the universe of discourse, they become syntactically contradictories. According to semantics, in a true interpretation the syntactic rules agree with the semantic rules. Thus, terms which are syntactically contradictory become *semantically complementary*. Complementarity of interpretations mirrors the syntactic rules of the dualistic language we are accustomed to use.

Every description of nature is also an interpretation. Whenever we use language to describe our experience, whenever we take words or symbols to refer to some event or other, it is for us to decide what we want our symbols to mean. For the events do not speak for themselves ; and language is the instrument we have invented in order to describe them. The way we speak reflects our attitude towards the events described, and the language we adopt thus expresses a certain interpretation.

But when we use a natural (or historically given) language, we are not completely free to put words together to form a sentence in any way we like. However flexible our ordinary language may be, there are limits beyond which we cannot stray if we want people to understand us. This normal manner of speaking is explained and reproduced by the rules of grammar. These rules have developed through the course of history ; accident, mistake, and prejudice have played a rôle in their development ; and past usage and convention have fixed them. So when we use natural language, our usage is given by the rules of grammar and based upon some unspoken assumptions. There is always some sort of interpretation, however vague, an interpretation of experience that is implicit in our use of language and limits it.

This—so to speak, psychological—interpretation of past experience guides our semantic interpretation, and it is embodied in the accepted rules of ordinary language. Thus, in conversational language we can find the separation of nouns into thing-words and process-words. The rules for their usage largely pre-suppose an interpretation of experience in terms of simple things, and this is the attitude represented by common sense. We interpret 'process' as a thing changing its location in space-time or, at least, as one thing changing into another thing.

There are always some main concepts providing the interpretation in a given context, and they determine the type of language we use, from the semantic point of view. We isolate a certain vocabulary from ordinary language, for a certain purpose ; we set up a rudimentary language system so that we can make our rules a little more clear. It is the special interpretation we choose that characterizes the language and specifies, to some extent, the semantic rules ; and, naturally, both reflect the assumptions current in ordinary language. From the theory of logic we have learned to make use of symbols according to their *logical type* and to distinguish logical levels of language. In the same manner, we might speak of the *semantic type* of interpretation. Just as the syntactic rules assumed for a language furnish the various logical types of words, so the semantic rules implicit in an interpreted language specify its semantic type. The concepts used in the description furnish the key to the interpretation : they give a model, or suggest the possible experience to be expected in this context. Simple kinds of experience encountered in every-day life provide the standard on which we base a model ; and so we try to isolate the semantic rules. The correct use of natural language requires not only that we follow the syntactic rules but also the semantic rules : grammatical rules are in fact a mixture of both.

Thus, we apply ordinary language—as we do in science—in a context widely different from that of ordinary life, but we are still bound to the original semantic rules. This is due not only to the inertia of human minds, or to the 'petrification' of natural

M

language : we should have no language at all if we did not keep to the rules. In physics, though we continue to make our language more specialised and technical, we still keep to some of the rules originally established, however implicit they may be. The ordinary word-language, then, becomes more artificial when the rules are altered to some extent ; but we cannot change them completely. This is after all the reason why a language system of arbitrarily chosen symbols, and the introduction of mathematics, has been so successful in the development of physics : it allows us to overcome the restrictions of established rules and to set up new rules better fitted to describe the world. But this is no longer the natural language of everyday use but an 'artificial' language, that is, a special way of speaking. The semantic type of the two languages used in quantum mechanics is, then, due to the usage of the two key-concepts in ordinary, actual, language.

The dualistic language of quantum mechanics uses this pair of concepts in accord with certain rules which prevent us from formulating causal relations between the events described by them. It is for this reason that we split the dualistic language and use a monistic language system by taking either the one or the other concept ; but the two ways of speaking cannot be used at the same time. The difficulties are not due to the nature of the phenomena ; they arise from the choice of concepts, a choice dictated by psychological requirements, by the need for simple models, and by the desire for visualisation. We simply cannot imagine a physical process to be other than a particle in motion or a wave propagation. The attempt made in the beginning of quantum theory to interpret the phenomena in terms of a 'wavicle' did not lead to success. We are unable to make a model of such a wavicle since we cannot then make use of our customary rules. The dualism inherent in ordinary language makes it impossible to apply this concept. A particle, or a wave, however, presents a reasonably clear picture so that we have a logically and psychologically sufficient basis for constructing a language system. And we need the model since we are unable to formalise the language completely, that is, to state the semantic rules explicitly. Our imagination, guided by simple experience, thus influences the development of the language of science.

The principle of complementarity shows that not every sentence of the form 'A causes B' describes a causal relation. This is so not for any strange, metaphysical, reasons as when it is said that cause and effect must be of the same kind ; but because the language used for formulating such sentences must be semantically consistent, i.e. of one semantic type. The uncertainty principle shows that the customary conception of causality must be revised in quantum theory. Two micro-physical events are connected in a different way from two macro-physical events : the laws differ in the two instances. That the deterministic causality between two events does not hold is a feature peculiar to quantum phenomena. That no causal relation can hold between two events described in two different language systems, interpreted in terms of complementary concepts, is a matter of language.

4. *The uncertainty principle*

It is now generally agreed among physicists that the uncertainty principle represents the fundamental law of quantum physics. What does the principle state?

In classical mechanics the motion of a particle is completely determined if we know the exact values of its position q and momentum p at an instant of time t. Similarly, knowing the amplitude and the phase of a wave, that is, its energy E at a time t, we can predict its future behaviour. In quantum mechanics this no longer holds since we cannot measure both parameters at the same time with *unlimited* accuracy.

The two parameters suffice to provide a complete description of the phenomena by means of a differential equation. But these *canonically conjugated* parameters are independent of one another only in classical theory ; in quantum mechanics they are connected through the uncertainty principle. We can measure simultaneous values of both parameters only in such a way that the numerical product of their inaccuracies is, at best, equal to the quantum of action h. The more accurately we determine the value of one parameter, the less accurate becomes the measurement of the other ; and if we were able to find the exact value, say, of q, then the value of p escapes us completely. (In mathematical notation : $\Delta q \cdot \Delta p \geq h$ and $\Delta E \cdot \Delta t \geq h$.) The mathematical formulae of quantum mechanics permit us to predict future events only within a certain margin of error.

Why should it be of such import to say that measurement in the micro-physical realm is subject to error? After all, we would never claim that even the simplest measurement of a macroscopic quantity is absolutely correct ; we always state the degree of accuracy for our observations. This is true : but according to classical theory there is no limit to the accuracy save our skill and the precision of our instruments ; in quantum mechanics there is a law which limits it.

This restriction of measurement is a fundamental feature of micro-phenomena ; and it has been said to represent a limitation of possible knowledge, at least by comparison with classical physics. But such a statement is easily misunderstood. It is not right to say, for instance, that this limitation is due to the insufficiency of the concepts we use. The concepts of wave and particle, of position and momentum, of energy and time, have arisen from classical physics ; and although they are refined and re-defined in accord with the correspondence principle so that they can be used in quantum theory, these concepts are bound to some extent to the simpler interpretations of classical theory. But they are limited only in the sense that we can no longer visualise the events completely with their help, since we do not deal here with the familiar experience the concepts were originally invented to describe. That, strictly speaking, we cannot visualise the microphysical phenomena, and that the classical concepts, however refined they may have become, are limited in this sense, does not constitute an essential failure of the new theory. Moreover, the concepts are adequate in the sense that even in quantum mechanics the position or the momentum, and the energy or the time, can be measured separately with unlimited accuracy ; thus each of the concepts 'fits', and is applicable, within the interpretation chosen.

The limitation in obtaining our data is not due to the language in which we describe them ; the complementarity of our descriptions is not an explanation for it. That the values of conjugated parameters when measured simultaneously, are *indeterminate* is a law of micro-physics. We must say, with Heisenberg, that 'this indeterminateness is to be considered as an essential characteristic of the electron, and not as evidence of the inapplicability of the wave picture'.

Since the initial data upon which we must base our description are necessarily inexact, we can predict the future behaviour of the events only within a certain limit, that is, with probability. Although the equations of quantum mechanics may have the same mathematical form as the classical equations, the deterministic conception of causality has to be abandoned. We say for this reason that the micro-physical events are essentially indeterminate : the determinism of classical theory is replaced by the statistical type of causality.

Heisenberg was led to discover this indeterminacy—e.g. of the values of position and momentum of an electron—when he decided to look at theory construction from a critical viewpoint. He wished to avoid the kind of idealisation often occurring in classical theory by which the description of a physical situation is more simplified than observation would warrant. In order to keep to the empirical verifiability of all statements he made use only of such symbols as could be made to refer directly to observable quantities. The array of numbers given by spectroscopists as the result of observations on the emission and absorption of atoms suggested to him the use of matrix algebra as a mathematical calculus for the new theory. The algebra turned out to be of the *non-commutative* type, that is, the value of the product of two quantities depends upon the order in which they are multiplied. This proves to be another way of formulating the uncertainty principle.

Thus it becomes necessary to consider the procedures of measurement which we carry out to obtain our data. But any physical process by which the value of any parameter is measured essentially changes this value. For measurement must be a physical process of interaction between the electron or the wave to be measured and some instrument. Examples of actual or imagined 'Gedanken' experiments show that the microscopic size of the processes must make this interaction considerable even for the smallest instrument of measurement. The γ-ray microscope demonstrates that the Compton effect of the rays we use to find the exact position of an electron will change its momentum. Or, we may use a slit to make a diffraction experiment on a wave. Then, the narrower the slit, the more exact will be the value of the position ; but the diffraction is the stronger so that we do not know the momentum of the particle except within a certain margin.

The use of the word 'position' and 'momentum' in quantum theory must be restricted. They have a sense only within the limits permitted by the uncertainty principle if we enquire after their simultaneous values. Sentences containing the phrase 'the exact and simultaneous values of p and q' are excluded as meaningless within quantum mechanics. That they do occur in classical theory is due to the idealised character of measurement which is admissible there. It is true that when we measure a property of a macroscopic event there must equally be an interaction between the event and the instrument of observation ; but this interaction is negligible relative to the magnitude of the measured quantities. We may neglect the resulting error since there is, in theory, no limit : it is merely our failure in practice. In quantum mechanics, however, we have a definite law which specifies this limit. So we are permitted to treat classical measurement as an idealised act which does not disturb the events measured, and we take the actual interaction as negligible. When we measure, say, the temperature of some water contained in a vessel, a part of the heat energy of the water will be needed to drive up the mercury column of the thermometer ; this energy loss is so minute in comparison with the total amount involved that the reading of the thermometer may be regarded as giving the exact value of the temperature *before* the thermometer was inserted.

But this disturbance of the event by measurement is not the reason for the uncertainty in our data. The interaction of the instrument with the event is necessary for measurement to be a physical, and not a ghost-like, process. It was said, incorrectly, (at the beginning of quantum theory) that the observer, i.e. human agency, plays an important part in the theory. But the rôle of observers in quantum mechanics is no different from what it is in other theories of physics. For that matter, we need no human observers at all as far as the actual, micro-physical, events are concerned : mechanical, or electronic registration devices would do and, in fact, are used. And the readings of these macroscopic instruments are taken by human beings in exactly the same manner as in classical physics. The uncertainty of our data in the quantum domain is not due to human fallibility, or to the influence of the mind of the observer, or whatever else has been said : it is an actual property of physical events.

It must be painfully obvious from the preceding discussion how difficult it is to speak adequately about uncertainty. We employ words like 'margin of error', 'inexact data', 'indeterminate position', etc. for describing it and so, immediately and insidiously, we introduce a 'classical' bias into our language. For, normally, we say that a measurement is inexact because of the failure of instrument or of observer ; it is a defect that should, and could, be remedied. This is not so in quantum theory ; but it is most difficult to explain clearly. We may say that quantum-mechanical particles are *not* like classical particles ; such a negative way of speaking is obviously not very successful since it is compatible with almost any interpretation. The most positive way of speaking seems to be in terms of 'probability'. There is the analogy with ordinary statistics, say, of motor accidents : we cannot predict where and when *exactly* an accident will occur, only within a certain margin, e.g. in London on a Sunday afternoon.

The concept of closed system also changes somewhat as compared to classical physics. While, there, we can always construct a system which is closed relative to the measuring instrument so that it remains undisturbed, in quantum theory we must include the instrument in the system. But this, again, is no catastrophe : it implies a slightly changed definition of 'closed system' to show that measurement is a physical process and cannot be simplified, or idealised, in the classical manner.

The use of the term 'simultaneous' must be discussed in this connexion. In relativity theory, as in classical physics, this term refers to the measurement *of* the same time of two spatially separated events ; here we refer to two different properties of one event *at* the same time. Obviously, we can never do two things at the same time ; we cannot make two simultaneous measurements. But when the process of measurement is so idealised that the effect of the interaction becomes negligible, subsequent measurement of two different parameters can always be taken to refer to the same time-point. We can *extrapolate* all our data so that they refer to the same time, a time t_0 *before* any measurement was made. The values of position and momentum of a particle are measured one after the other ; but we refer them to the same time to in classical mechanics and so have exact and simultaneous values of the initial data. In quantum mechanics the measurement affects the events in an *unpredictable* way, though within certain limits given by the constant h, and we can no longer extrapolate our data. Measuring, say, the q, and then the p, of an electron, we cannot compute the value of the second quantity p for the time at which the first quantity q was measured, except with a certain indeterminacy. The two conjugated parameters which are independent in classical mechanics, are no longer so in quantum mechanics. They are connected through the uncertainty principle ; and this is a new law of nature in which quantum theory differs from classical theory.

The laws of classical physics are such that, from given initial and boundary conditions, we can compute the behaviour of the particle, or of the wave, at a later time and at a different point in space. We have normally what have been called *laws of development* which enable us to predict future events on the basis of our present knowledge. This is equally true in quantum mechanics when we compute, say, the behaviour of an elementary particle. But the inexact values of the initial data allow us to predict the future events only within the margin set by the uncertainty principle. This *indeterminacy* shows that the laws of quantum mechanics are essentially *statistical*. Although quantum mechanical formulae, just as the formulae of classical mechanics, may be represented by differential equations, there is this difference : we must give up the determinism by which we customarily interpret the laws of physics. This break-down of the classical interpretation has been widely discussed, and it has sometimes been alleged that quantum theory has given up causality. It is not quite clear what this sort of assertion may mean : it has too often served to support strange statements about the freedom of will which human beings are now said to enjoy after determinism has been eliminated. But the indeterminacy of quantum mechanics as little supports any hypothesis about the freedom of human actions as the determinism of classical physics denied this freedom. The fact that there are different types of law has nothing to do with the feelings men have regarding their actions ; and whether or not a person is responsible for his actions must be decided on other grounds.

The view that quantum physics has 'abolished' causality arises from a misunderstanding of what we mean when we say : 'This statement is a law of nature'. And it seems to get support from an idea to which most physicists would subscribe nowadays : it is said that, at bottom, all laws are statistical. For we can show, for instance, that the classical law of motion may be derived from the quantum mechanical formulae when we neglect the specific character of the micro-physical events and take the average of their properties. By levelling out the differences due to the quantum of action we obtain a description that agrees with the formulae of macroscopic physics. This is of course required by the correspondence principle. But it is not true to say that we 'reduce' the macroscopic events to microscopic events and that, because of it, all laws are statistical. If we say that the deterministic laws are derivable (in some sense) from the quantum laws by the mathematical procedure of averaging, we mean exactly what is said : it is a formal relation between formulae which we can establish. And this is the reason why some may feel inclined to say that all laws of physics are statistical. But, in fact, this is much too sweeping a statement.

Quantum mechanics has not abandoned causality, nor is it true to say that all phenomena are chaotic : we still have laws and hypotheses which permit us to predict the future, but they are statistical laws. Only if we mean by 'causality' the laws of classical physics, is it true to say that they no longer hold in quantum physics. This is hardly a reasonable objection. For we can speak of 'causality' only within a definite context and must refer to a specific law. In the sense that quantum mechanics contains statements which can be used for predicting the future, there is no failure of causality in present-day physics.

Quantum mechanics is a statistical theory. Its interpretation is in terms of probability ; and so it is often asserted that the theory is purely mathematical. I presume this is to mean that there is no interpretation in terms of experience. Of course such a view cannot be correct ; apart from the need of using the wave or the particle model to interpret the equations, the term 'probability' itself is not uninterpreted. In this instance, as everywhere in physics when statistics are used to describe the phenomena, we employ the frequency interpretation of the formal calculus of mathematical probability. That is, we cannot speak of the probability of a single datum ; we must have an extended series (finite or infinite) of similar data before this type of probability can be used for interpretation. Thus, in quantum mechanics we must either repeat the observations a great number of times, or we imagine a virtual assemblage of similar particles one of which we take as the given particle, and so on. The interpretation in terms of probability, then, also requires a model ; at least, it needs an extension of the previous model in this, the probability, sense. There is no longer a picture in the classical manner, but we still have an interpretation.

This statistical interpretation might be considered as a third system, separate from the interpretations in terms of 'wave' or 'particle'. The solution of Schrödinger's equation is a wave function, the so-called ψ-function ; this seemed at first to support a simple wave interpretation of quantum mechanics. But it was soon seen by Born that the ψ-function could not be interpreted in this manner. Rather, a mathematical expression formed according to a certain rule specifies the probability of finding, say, an elementary particle having values of its parameters within a certain margin of error. That is, given an initial probability distribution of these parameters, the Schrödinger equation lets us compute this distribution for a later time. In this way we can describe the behaviour of the particle under investigation. This interpretation makes it more difficult to give a simple picture of the phenomena, and it is perhaps impossible to do so in a satisfactory manner. But when we try to visualise the events, or when we express them in ordinary language, we always make use of the wave or the particle model as well. These models, then, become somewhat more schematic. Physicists have sometimes spoken of the 'probability wave'; but this phrase must not be taken literally. Probability is not a thing which is propagated in space-time like a wave ; but the probability distributions for a given instance, say of an electron in an atom, may be represented by a simple diagram which is derived from the wave pattern.

This *principle of the ψ-function*—that all information about a micro-physical event is contained in the solution of the Schrödinger equation—provides an explanation for the uncertainty relations or, rather, their peculiar mathematical formulation. For we derive the values of the two parameters p,q (in the particle interpretation) from one single source : the ψ-function. And no wonder these parameters are linked to one another by the uncertainty relations : they represent one datum only which is then split up into two data in order to make use of the particle or the wave model. It is in this sense that Bohr has said that the uncertainty principle is a logical consequence of the complementarity of the two interpretations with the help of classical concepts. But we must be cautious here in our formulation. The uncertainty of our data as measured is a property of the physical events and arises from the statistical character of the ψ-function. This uncertainty is expressed in one or the other interpretation : it is only the peculiar, mathematical form that reflects the interpretation by making use of certain symbols, i.e. p and q, or E and t, to represent the equation (or inequality). It is the same as to say that the ψ-function which is the complete solution of our equation is a statistical function. Thus, once more, we see that the uncertainty is not to be blamed on any insufficiency of our concepts, but that it is a property of the events.

The *inverse* correlation of two conjugated parameters as given by the uncertainty relations is contained in the ψ-function since it is the solution of certain mathematical type of equation, i.e. a wave equation. Such functions can always be represented mathematically as a superposition of an infinite number of sine and cosine functions which we usually interpret as simple harmonic waves. The function thus obtained depends upon the properties of the individual waves composing it : its shape is the steeper (i.e. it has a sharper maximum) the narrower the range of frequency of the simple waves ; and its shape is more flat, the wider this range. That is, we have the same *inverse* correlation as we find in the uncertainty relations which, therefore, are contained in the ψ-function.

It is a relation which is often illustrated by a simple example. If we wish to have a radio receiver which separates perfectly the various transmitters (i.e. their frequencies) it should respond only to one frequency at a time. Then we cannot expect it to give a good reproduction of the music ; for this would require the receiver to respond to a wide range of frequencies—and this second requirement is incompatible with the first.

Thus we cannot expect the probability distributions for the p's and q's as derived from the ψ-function to possess a sharp maximum at the same time : we cannot know the exact and simultaneous values of these two quantities. The situation is similar with the other pair of parameters, the energy E and the time t. Consider an electron in an atom ; the electron is in a stationary state to which we ascribe a definite energy. The more exactly we wish to measure this energy, the longer we will have to observe the electron ; and if we observe the electron for a very short time only, we cannot be certain of the exact value of its energy. Many such examples can be found which enable us to visualise, to some extent, the unfamiliar behaviour of micro-physical phenomena ; and there is little doubt that they serve as models and so help us to establish semantic rules for the correct usage of our language.

The radical change in ideas which quantum mechanics has brought about has given rise to many misinterpretations. Some physicists felt, and perhaps still do, that quantum mechanics must somehow attain the ideal set up by classical theory ; it is understandable that one should dislike the 'abstract' character of the theory, a reaction which was equally provoked when relativity theory first made its appearance. We must not deny that there are reasons why quantum mechanics—even to-day, twenty years after its inception—still gives rise to discussion ; and though much agreement has been reached, the final word may not have been spoken. This will occur, if ever, only when the next step, i.e. a new theory superseding quantum mechanics, has been reached. After all, is any interpretation of physics, however well established, ever final in the sense that increased knowledge may not reveal flaws that need correction ? To give up opinions which once commanded strong support, to renounce dogma of any kind, to be willing to learn from experience—that is, from our mistakes—is the most valuable lesson science has to teach us. Admittedly, it is easier said than done. We are too often inclined to be 'stiff in opinions, always in the wrong'. But it is surely mistaken to say that quantum mechanics is a temporary stop-gap, or that its concepts are essentially inadequate, or that the description is incomplete.

We say that we cannot measure exactly the position and momentum at the same time, although the knowledge of both is required to predict the future behaviour of the particle ; this statement does not mean that nature is as it were hidden from us. As Einstein is reported to have said in a joke, God has made nature very complicated but he is not malicious. Of course we admit that the classical concepts of wave and particle, of position and momentum, of energy and time, are not simply taken over but that they are re-interpreted, in the sense that the rules according to which they are used are somewhat changed. It is equally true that the rules provide us only with a partial interpretation ; they enable us to speak about the phenomena in a simple language approaching classical theory, but do not allow us to visualise the events in the classical manner.

Measured by the standard of classical theory the concept, say, of particle is inadequate only in so far as we have no complete picture of its motion : we cannot speak of the path of the particle. In classical mechanics we are able to *intrapolate* between observations and to say that, between the space-time points where it is observed, the particle follows a definite path. Since the initial values of p,q at t_0 are only known within certain limits set by the constant h, the particle in quantum mechanics cannot be said to possess a path. To compute the path requires the knowledge of the exact value of p,q, and the concept of classical path is no longer applicable. It is, however, replaced by 'orbit' (in the older quantum theory) and by 'state' (in quantum mechanics), at least to the limited extent required by the correspondence principle. In other words, the semantic rules for the usage of 'particle' differ in the two theories ; this is no catastrophe save that it prevents us from making a simple, i.e. classical, picture. Even in classical mechanics we do not need the knowledge of the unobserved portions of the path in order to make predictions. Whenever we wish to observe a particle at a certain time, our equations allow us to compute the values of relevant parameters at that time. The idealised character of classical mechanics lets us interpolate between these observations : this is a gratuitous addition which aids us in visualising the process but adds nothing to the predictive power of the theory. Statements containing phrases such as 'the path of the particle' *need not* be used in classical mechanics, and they *cannot* be used in quantum mechanics.

It is only when we insist that the semantic rules, say, of 'particle' must be the same in both theories that we find grounds for complaining about the inadequacy of the quantum-mechanical concepts. But this is tantamount to denying that a new theory represents an advance over the old theory, which is certainly an irrational attitude to take. Why should the laws holding for macroscopic processes also apply to microscopic processes ? If our language is so chosen that it does refer to the external world, we cannot expect the same statements to occur in both theories. It is not very convincing to argue that, by dropping the concept of path, we have left out something in quantum theory which must be brought back in order to make it complete. Of course, we can never assert the completeness of a theory so complicated as quantum mechanics ; nor can we deny the possibility that by introducing a new idea, or by changing the concepts a little, we may not reach a better description of the events. It is, however, very unlikely ; unless we think of a new theory which, by introducing a radical revision of previously accepted notions, supersedes our present theories. The proof given by von Neumann that, within present quantum mechanics and using the accepted ideas, no hidden parameters can exist, gives added support to the view that quantum mechanics is complete.

Since the laws of quantum mechanics are statistical—that is, the results of measurement are expressed in terms of probability —the objection has been made that the phenomena they describe are not 'real'. Classical physics expresses its results with unlimited accuracy, and this is taken as the standard of reality. It is reminiscent of the views held by some physicists at the turn of the last century who, disbelieving the kinetic theory, denied reality to atoms and molecules. But this is a fallacy. Microphysical phenomena are as real as those of macroscopic physics, and we need not even change the rule for the usage of 'real' (that is, if we use the word at all) : it is the same everywhere in physics. The events are recorded by the instruments and procedures of physics and they can be described by laws. This is the necessary and sufficient condition for the use of terms like 'existence' and 'real' as has been discussed before. The fact that the laws of quantum mechanics differ from those of classical mechanics cannot deprive the micro-physical events of their reality.

It is only within a given theory, that is, with respect to a language-system, that we can decide which statements are synthetic and which are analytic. In the language of quantum mechanics the statement of the inverse relation of parameters— the uncertainty principle—appears to be factual, while the complementarity of pictorial interpretations is a matter of language. And it is therefore advisable to differentiate more sharply between the use of the terms 'complementarity' and 'uncertainty' than is often done. Both the relation of wave to

particle concept as well as the relation of two conjugated parameters are sometimes designated as 'complementary'.

From the critical viewpoint we want to emphasize the differences rather than obliterate them : two different characteristics
of quantum theory are referred to here. True that it appears that
in both instances we find a peculiar reciprocity—a term originally
used by Bohr in this connexion. But we may take *either* concept
to interpret the whole mathematical formalism : we do need *both*
parameters to describe the events regardless of which interpretation we choose.

That we cannot use both interpretations at the same time, and
that we cannot measure both parameters with unlimited accuracy
at the same time, are two different statements. The language in
which we express the uncertainty is, indeed, either the particle or
the wave language since they are the only language-systems we
have. They approach the language of classical physics, and so are
convenient to use ; but the language-systems differ somewhat
from this simple language, and the difference is prescribed by
the uncertainty principle. We cannot accept the view, then, that
the two principles are logically related to one another, as when it
is said that the uncertainty principle follows logically from the
complementarity principle. The uncertainty principle corrects
complementary language by requiring that each of the two
language-systems must be restricted to some extent when compared with their application in classical physics.

In his recent book (Natural Philosophy of Cause and Chance,
Oxford, 1949) Professor Born proposed to use the term 'complementary' to designate the inverse relation of conjugate
parameters and to take the word 'dualistic' to refer to the two
interpretations. Naturally this is a possible usage ; but there are
reasons why it may be somewhat misleading.

The complementary interpretations of quantum mechanics are
more than merely dual. In many parts of physics we have dualistic interpretations, e.g. we may interpret Boyle's law by
classical thermodynamics or in terms of molecular motion as in
kinetic theory. Again, as another instance, we may interpret
Ohm's law from the viewpoint of Maxwell's field theory or by
Lorentz's electron theory. And, indeed, there are often more
than two interpretations : we may have *multiple* interpretations,
at least for some specific part of a more comprehensive theory.

The simple laws of optics about reflection and refraction may be interpreted by Newton's theory of corpuscles, by Huygens' wave theory, by Fresnel's elastic theory, by Maxwell's electromagnetic theory, and by a simple electron theory—and these are, strictly speaking, different interpretations though they overlap to some extent. However, this kind of dualistic, or multiple, interpretation is not complementary. Over and above duality, the complementarity of descriptions introduces the idea that the two interpretations—or, rather the concepts which determine them —are contradictory. This is a significant addition to mere duality which is due to the semantic rules giving the usage of the two concepts in ordinary language. We do make use of ordinary language and so cannot avoid respecting its rules, even though these rules are only implicit.

Moreover, the complementary interpretations of quantum mechanics have a limited applicability. This is due to the kind of phenomena described, and it is in this way that the uncertainty principle comes in. Each language-system needs correction since we must use a *restrictive* interpretation if we wish to avoid difficulties regarding our normal conception of causality.

5. *Causality in quantum mechanics*

Modern physics has provided a new point of departure for the description of nature. Two interpretations are offered in quantum mechanics which furnish equivalent descriptions of all phenomena ; these interpretations are incompatible in classical physics, and events there can be described only by one or the other concept which determines the interpretation. Since by using classical concepts we invoke (deliberately or unwittingly) the rules acceptable in the classical domain for these concepts, we have to forbid their simultaneous usage. A new semantic rule is formulated in the meta-language governing the usage in the new theory ; and this is expressed as the principle of complementarity. The two concepts may not be used simultaneously ; otherwise we cannot describe the events according to our normal conception of causality.

But these causal anomalies may also occur within each interpretation, if used in the classical manner. Neither interpretation can be made to avoid the anomalies unless it is restricted in some way. Although the deterministic conception of causality is given up as result of the uncertainty in our data, and a statistical conception is introduced, there are still assumptions implicit in the use of causal description which hamper us. The deterministic conception of causality includes at least two assumptions : first, that exact data are obtainable ; second, that cause and effect are connected through physical processes occurring as a continuous chain of actions, i.e. through action by contact. Einstein pointed out that the ideas of quantum theory as we understand them to-day are not compatible with the principle of action-by-contact. This principle has been of great value in classical physics, and it is a major constituent in the field conception of relativity theory. Since most physicists believe that relativity must apply also when micro-physical events are described—and, indeed, in the limited manner in which it has already been used there it has proved of great value—we seem to be confronted with an insuperable difficulty. Einstein predicted that physicists no doubt will drop this principle, a solution he himself is reluctant to accept.

To illustrate the situation consider once more a simple experiment. Light is sent through a double slit and falls, finally, upon a fluorescent screen. In the wave interpretation we describe the experiment as follows : at the slits the extended wave front is diffracted, and at the screen the interference pattern characteristic of the double slit is observed. At low light intensity we can establish however that the pattern consists of many individual flashes. It would be more natural—i.e. more according to classical ideas—to describe these scintillations as due to individual particles, or photons. But having once decided to use the wave language, we cannot now introduce the particle language : otherwise we would have to say that the extended wave front suddenly contracts into a few isolated points. This would represent a violation of customary causality and of the principle of action-by-contact according to which all actions are transmitted with finite speed. The principle of complementarity therefore states the injunction that the two interpretations cannot be used simultaneously.

If we use the particle language to describe the same events we find, naturally, that we can account for the scintillations on the screen without difficulty ; but now the difficulties re-appear at

N

the double slit. For the interference pattern in which the scintillations are arranged on the screen is not a mere superposition of the two patterns due to each slit alone ; it is a different pattern characteristic of the double slit. This forces us to say that, although a particle can pass only one of the slits, it must 'know' the existence of the other slit so that the final pattern on the screen is modified in the correct way. That is, we must again assume action at a distance with infinite speed, and this action on the particles arises because a second slit is present. This shows that the particle interpretation *alone* cannot avoid causal anomalies if it is used to describe the experiment to the full extent customary in classical physics. The wave interpretation of this experiment can do so, provided we are content with observing only the interference pattern, and do not at the same time wish to account for the scintillations on the screen. In this instance, the anomaly occurs only when we 'mix our languages'; in the particle interpretation the anomaly shows up when we attempt to give a complete description of all the events making up the experiment as is usual in classical physics.

There are then two reasons why these anomalies occur. They may be due to the simultaneous use of two language systems (forbidden by the complementarity principle) ; and they may occur in one single language if it is used according to classical rules so as to give an *exhaustive* description. It is not difficult to find examples in which the exhaustive description of an experiment by the wave language leads to causal anomalies : the photoelectric effect, for instance. Light is sent against a photo-sensitive surface and, as a result, electrons are liberated ; if we use the wave interpretation, we must say that the wave is contracted into points where the electrons are knocked out of the surface. In this example, the particle language could be used to give an exhaustive description without leading to causal anomalies. We can always find for every experiment a suitable language in which we can avoid mentioning causal anomalies although we give a *classically* exhaustive description. Unfortunately, we do need both languages in quantum physics if we wish to describe all there is to be observed, e.g. when we wish to speak both about the scintillations *and* the interference pattern on the screen, for the diffraction experiment.

These difficulties have been analysed by Reichenbach in great

detail. In classical physics we assume that the things we observe
persist even when they are not under observation, and that the
same laws hold both for observed and unobserved phenomena.
By 'unobserved phenomena' we mean of course that the phenomena can, in principle, be observed and are observed on occasion,
but that they are not observed in the given experiment. Thus, the
events at the slit in the diffraction experiment are not observed :
we are more interested in finding the interference pattern on the
screen ; but we could observe them by placing a suitable instrument near the slit. This, however, would prevent us from seeing
what happens on the screen, since the particles or waves would be
absorbed by the instrument, and there would be nothing left to
see on the screen. That is, we have to restrict our description to
what is actually observed in a given experiment. There are no
such difficulties in classical physics ; there we may intrapolate
between observations and assume that we know what happens,
say, at the slit ; for the unobserved phenomena are supposed to
follow the same laws as the observed phenomena. The idealised
character of measurement in classical theory allows us to speak
about these *interphenomena*. Thus, we may always give an
exhaustive description of the experiment, in the sense that the
unobserved parts of it are equally described by the theory.
Moreover, this will be a *normal* system of description, in the
sense that the contact-action of classical theory also holds for the
unobserved events.

This intrapolation between observations is not, as such,
required as support for the theory ; but the introduction of interphenomena allows us to visualise more easily what happens. In
quantum mechanics we must use a *restrictive* description which
does not include the interphenomena ; otherwise, we may on
occasion find causal anomalies. This restricted use of language
may at first sight look very artificial, and we may think it suspic-
ious ; perhaps, there is something radically wrong with quantum
mechanics, after all. However, the restrictive interpretation is
quite natural here : the uncertainty principle makes it impossible
to introduce interphenomena. For instance, since we cannot
obtain simultaneous and exact values of position and momentum
of a particle, we cannot ascribe a path to it ; sentences including
the phrase 'path' in this connexion are meaningless. Thus, what
happens *between* observations can never be talked about in this

theory. Or, as Reichenbach has shown, the principle of uncertainty allows us to *eliminate* causal anomalies.

Since even in classical theory the description of these interphenomena is based upon an assumption, we might think that in quantum mechanics we can equally supplement our theory by a suitable hypothesis about these unobserved events. No change would occur in the results observed, and the theory would say as much as before so far as the experiments are concerned. This hope, however, is not justified. We cannot construct an exhaustive system for all phenomena in micro-physics which is also normal with regard to causality. Although we can describe a definite experiment in this manner—e.g. the wave interpretation for the slit experiment—we cannot banish causal anomalies from the whole domain.

The two principles, of complementarity and of uncertainty, are necessary and sufficient to avoid these causal anomalies. The principle of action-by-contact can be kept if we do not make simultaneous use of two complementary language-systems and if we remain within a restrictive description of what is actually observed.

But what does this amount to ? We have replaced deterministic causality by a statistical causality but kept the principle of action-by-contact which is part of determinism. This principle is indispensable in macroscopic physics. But can we ever expect it to be reconcilable with the description of micro-physical phenomena, and with the idea of the quantum of action ?

It is well to remember that Newton refused to speculate whether or not cause and effect are connected through space, and his system of mechanics does not require this *contiguity*. It is an idea necessary only for a field theory which involves the conception of a continuous medium and of continuous action. It does not hold good in quantum theory when a discontinuous form of action is introduced by Planck's constant.

And there are other reasons why it may become necessary to drop contiguity from our conception of causality. In modern theory the elementary particles, such as the electron, are considered to have a definite size. On the assumption of a spherical shape the radius of an electron can be computed, and the value found agrees with experiment. But it is clear that we cannot take the electron as an elementary particle unless it is absolutely rigid ; for a deformable body can always be taken as being composed of smaller parts which slide against one another, so that the body loses its character as an elementary particle. This means, as was pointed out by March, that within the dimensions of an electron action must be propagated with infinite speed, against the requirements of relativity.

Recent discussion of radiation theory (involving the concept of electron) suggests that such difficulties do appear. For it is necessary to make use of the so-called *advanced potentials* in order to describe the phenomena correctly, at least within distances of the order of magnitude of the electron radius. Outside this region the ordinary *retarded potentials* suffice as a solution of Maxwell's equations ; they describe events at a given point as a function of other events having taken place earlier, at the source of radiation, so satisfying classical causality. The advanced potentials, however, refer to a later time and, thus, depend upon future events. Their introduction represents a break-down of classical causality within a space of this small size, and this may be interpreted as a failure of the principle of action-by-contact (its relation to the concept of time is discussed in section III). These difficulties of radiation theory had been under discussion previously, when the theory was first developed, and at that time very provocative statements were made regarding causality and the concept of time. Thus Tetrode asserted that 'for each act of emission it is predestined when, where, and how the absorption is to happen. The sun would not radiate if it existed all alone in the universe and no bodies could absorb its radiation'. Such a view is surely mistaken since it is now understood that the advanced potential is needed only within a space of the size of the electron. However, we might agree with the continuation that 'if radiation is emitted from the sun and absorbed at the earth eight minutes later, it is according to classical theory at any intermediate time somewhere as field energy. Our theory knows no field, and radiative energy is temporarily lost to re-appear later on the earth. No observable difference . . . is caused by this behaviour'. Since we have to account for this peculiar behaviour only within microscopic spaces, the difficulties are perhaps much less than we may fear. After all, there is reason to believe that the laws of macroscopic physics do not hold for microscopic physics, and indeed quantum theory has provided a demonstration. The concepts of position and momentum are applicable only with restriction ; and since momentum is the product of mass into velocity, we might say that the concept of velocity is of limited value in quantum theory. Or, as it was expressed by Born recently : 'Though in our every-day experience we can ascribe to ordinary bodies definite positions and velocities, there is no reason to assume the same for dimensions below the limits of every-day experience'. If this is an acceptable restriction on our theories, then the demands of relativity theory—the finite speed of light exemplifying action by contact—are not incompatible with the need for abandoning contiguity in microscopic dimensions : the concept of velocity is simply not applicable in this domain.

Needless to say, this would not mean giving up the causal description of nature. We can still describe all events by means of laws : we have universal sentences from which instantial hypotheses are derived with the help of initial and boundary conditions, and we can still predict the future. But what is given up is the attempt to explain causality with the help of the concept of *contiguity*. We renounce a model of causal action that requires a mechanism to transmit the action, and we cannot speak of a 'causal chain' when we describe micro-physical events. Quantum mechanics has already introduced a revision of 'causality' very near to this ; for we can no longer make use of the concept of path, we have discontinuous action, and a statistical type of theory. The rules of language used in quantum mechanics are so devised that no reference to an action-by-contact need be made ; therefore causal anomalies occur only in a *specious* manner, and we can speak in a way which is conveniently close to the language of classical physics, and of every-day life. There is little doubt, however, that not *both* exact predictability and the action-by-contact are required to give a complete description of micro-physical phenomena.

Whenever we make a theory we must start with some assumptions. We take intuitive concepts—that is, concepts suggested by familiar experience—as primitive, and upon them we build the theory as a deductive system as well as we can manage. But these simple concepts do not suffice when we come to describe more complicated phenomena. Thus we start out with a concept of particle in Newtonian mechanics where the particle is taken to be without extension but endowed with mass ; it is considered as a point since we want to use it as an 'ultimate' unit so that it must be indivisible. This is a relic of Greek philosophy ; space is a void, and particles float in it. When we want to give shape, or extension, to the particle, the conception becomes somewhat more difficult. The Cartesian idea that 'the essence of matter is extension' is reconciled with it by saying that matter is constituted by many point-particles which are spatially separated ; and so we feel justified in saying that the point-particle itself has mass. Thus our intuitive conceptions are by no means very clear and embody a number of ideas which are not always compatible. No wonder that, with the progress of science, we have to re-interpret them continually. We add the idea of extension to the particle, as in kinetic theory ; and we arrive at the concept of elementary particle, when we also attribute to the particle the properties of charge and spin. In the end we say that the particle does not possess an exact and simultaneous position and momentum. As a result of this uncertainty we may describe micro-physical events in terms of both the concepts of particle and wave, while in macroscopic physics we can describe them only either by the one, or by the other, concept. Certainly, the mechanical and the quantum-mechanical particle have become very different things : the correct usage of 'particle' requires different rules in the various theories. But the concepts are still related to one another, and some of the rules remain : otherwise we would not speak of particles in all these contexts. Similarly, we describe events in classical mechanics as a simple, continuous change of particles, e.g. moving along a *path*. A special instance of a path is the *orbit* of a particle relative to another particle taken as centre ; this leads to the planetary model of the atom in which certain orbits are allowed only, each having a definite energy. Finally, we arrive at the *stationary state* of an atomic system in which the energy is exactly determined only if the state lasts for an infinite time, that is, we bring in the uncertainty of measurement.

Since our conceptions have changed so much it is natural that our laws have equally changed. What we mean by 'causality' depends upon the theories and their basic concepts : for the various parts of physics a different analysis must be offered. Any discussion of causality in general terms tends to become meaningless, and only specific laws can be discussed in their relation to the different theories to which they belong. No ontological assumptions are needed in the causal description of nature. Both Newtonian mechanics and quantum mechanics, each theory for its respective domain of application, correctly describe the events as they are. Our conception of causality has changed since Aristotle ; the idea of the four causes was followed by the epistemology characteristic of classical physics, i.e. determinism, and now we have arrived at a semantic conception in terms of 'law' and 'theory'.

Many years ago Bohr suggested that modern physics may lead, in the end, to an even more radical revision of our concepts than we have already accepted. He expressed the belief that 'the failure of classical theories may even affect the validity of the laws of conservation of energy and momentum. These laws . . . would then, in the description of atomic processes, be only statistically valid'. Moreover, we may be faced 'with an essential failure of the pictures in space and time'.

At the frontier of science there is, by necessity, a good deal of speculation which leads to a new theory only when theoretical insight is combined with experiment. We should not want to deny the practical, mainly psychological, value of 'wild ideas'; we know from history that they can be 'tamed'. It would be rash, however, to discuss the many attempts which have been made to develop new theories. Most of them seem destined to fail— partly because the basic ideas are not sufficiently cleansed of ancient, philosophic fallacies, and mainly because they do not lead to verifiable statements over and beyond those already obtained by more traditional methods. But it is instructive to see that science is not always so certain and reliable, and that its progress depends upon human imagination, provided it is checked by experiment. Scientific method itself is not absolute, and it changes with science.

6. *Summary*

When we survey the theories of physics, we cannot help being struck by certain features of their construction. It may not be so striking how few key-concepts there are ; it is more remarkable how diverse the usage is to which they are put and how many different theories can be built up in this manner. The most important feature, however, is that a theory contains many

assumptions which are expressed only in the context and, sometimes, are not even verbally formulated but merely shown by
pictures and diagrams ; and that they are indispensable for giving
the meaning of a scientific statement.

But how can we characterize, methodologically, these assumptions ? Scientists themselves make use of certain concepts when
they speak *about* their theories and want to explain them. The
central problem is always to be able to state, as explicitly as possible, the meaning of a sentence, particularly if it belongs to an
advanced, and highly technical, theory ; otherwise we are not
sure whether, and how, such sentences can be brought to the
test by experiment. In physics, the concept of *model* and the
principle of *correspondence* are used to achieve this end.

I have tried to explain physical theory in these terms, following
as closely as possible what physicists themselves say ; naturally,
there is some divergence of opinion but, I hope, I have committed
no serious error either of fact or of interpretation. I have then
tried to support, and to explain in its turn, the methodology
which is actually in use to-day by relating it to modern logic and
semantics. I feel that, in this way, a new and better understanding of physics and, possibly, of all science can be obtained.

It will be convenient here to give a brief summary.

(1) The model is taken from a simple, and simplified, situation
or experiment ; we use it as a standard of comparison for other,
more complex, situations and as a basis for building up a technical language.

(2) Its logical function is to provide an equation, i.e. some
syntactic rules for describing the new phenomena, e.g. the wave
equation. Previous usage, etc., has endowed the equation with an
interpretation, and so we obtain also some *semantic* rules for
using our symbols and expressions.

(3) The model, however, is not the same as the thing or process it models ; it is analogous to the metaphor. The interpretation by model is *partial*. But this lack is compensated by the
requirement that the model, in fact, must not be a complete
interpretation since we want to introduce, with its help, new concepts and construct a higher theory. Mechanical models cannot,
and must not, completely interpret, e.g. electromagnetism,
since we need room for new concepts, like charge.

(4) The model *specifies* the meaning of an expression, or set of

expressions, by making explicit *some* of the syntactic and semantic rules for the key-concepts used in a new theory. In kinetic
theory, for example, 'atom' designates a small billiard ball. The
possible processes that may occur, e.g. collisions, are expressed
in certain sentences (or equations) within the theory. These
state-descriptions allow us to give rules of truth, or of range, for
the theoretical expressions ; and so their meaning can be established. The model, then, represents a way of speaking, or a
universe of discourse, or a language system.

(5) 'Atom' may be interpreted according to the mechanical
model, in kinetic theory, or according to the planetary model, or
to the vector model in quantum theory ; or in terms of energy-
states, of charge-clouds, and of probability distributions, in
quantum mechanics. We have *multiple* interpretations for a given
expression. The models may overlap, in part, and they may
become more 'abstract', i.e. less visualisable.

(6) The *main* model is more comprehensive and serves as
basis for a whole theory, e.g. the particle-force model of mechanics, the heat engine of thermodynamics, the planetary model,
etc. The *auxiliary* model is more specific, e.g. the oscillator. A
modern theory is pieced together out of many, loosely inter-
related models. The more models we have, either *within* a theory
or *for* a theory, the more complete is the interpretation. But in
spite of this *freedom* of interpretation, the meaning of the
theoretical expressions is safeguarded by the *restriction* the model
imposes.

(7) The model relates to some simple experience, though
sometimes a series of such models is needed, e.g. for the atom.
There is some similarity to the *Gedanken* experiment which,
however, is mainly used for illustrating rather than for explaining, e.g. the uncertainty relations with the aid of the γ-ray micro-
scope. The model is used to put an advanced theory on an
empirical or, better, an experimental basis. An experiment is an
application of a theory, and the model is a *link* between theory
and experiment. We test a theory in terms of a model.

(8) The construction of a theory by model, and of the hierarchy of theories by the correspondence principle, are methods
supplementing each other. The correspondence principle
requires that a new theory must reduce to the old one for the
special case in which the refinement introduced by the new

theory may be disregarded ; they are related to one another as higher to lower approximation. It is a necessary (though not a sufficient) condition that the calculi of the two theories are in asymptotic agreement. This holds only for a 'true' interpretation in which syntactic and semantic rules coincide. It happens in physics, on occasion, that the meaning of an expression is, seemingly, determined by the syntactic rules alone, i.e. the mathematics ; but, in fact, this is not so, particularly since in the non-formalised language of physics the two sets of rules do not usually coincide. The mathematical character of physical theory makes us overlook this ; the lack of success with which axiomatization has met is largely due to the fact that the mathematical, rather than the semantic, features have been considered. The correspondence principle, however, makes sure that an advanced theory is based on a previous, and *established*, theory and, therefore, on experiment.

This summary shows once more, I hope, that semantics can be used with profit for explaining the theories of modern physics and the methods by which they are constructed.

VI

SCIENTIFIC METHOD
AND SEMANTICS

1. *The concept of deterministic law*

The concept of causality has a natural basis in simple experience : things are moved around either by other things or by human agency. The anthropomorphic character of the customary conception of causality has often been noted ; it suggests the view that all the things in the world are mutually connected by little strings, or the world as a puppet show. This *string* model of causality is often employed in every-day life and re-appears, in an improved version, in the simplest interpretation which is sometimes given to Newtonian mechanics. We have particles, and forces act between them : force is considered as a cause since it produces a change. The *particle-force* model of this naïve kind is often said to express the mechanistic view of the world.

The identification of force and cause has led to what is commonly called 'dynamical causality'. In spite of its obvious faults it is a step towards a better understanding of how physical events are related to one another. It is true that the obscurity of the concept of force, and its connexion with human effort, is objectionable. As Poincaré remarked : 'Quand on dit que la force est la cause d'un mouvement, on fait de la metaphysique'. But the use of the term 'force' at least allows us to speak about causal relations within the context of a definite theory and to discuss specific laws. For Newton's second law takes forces as the accelerations of mass particles, and all change is expressed in terms of the coördinates of space and time. Causality is then the relation between two events described by a differential equation of the second order which, moreover, does not contain explicit functions of the time. The precise mathematical formulation of the laws of mechanics permits us to correlate two events by an invariable relationship : if we know the law of force, the values of position and momentum of a particle at any given time are determined through the differential equation, provided we know the *initial* and the *boundary* conditions of the problem.

In this way we arrive at a well-known world picture of classical physics. Causality is given in the form of laws which are mathematically represented by differential equations, and these refer to the physical forces existing in the universe. The course of the whole universe is amenable to computation, and we have the view that has been called 'determinism'. This view finds its most striking expression in Laplace's ideal of a *world formula* : the universe is regarded as an aggregate of particles and forces, and so its future course is completely determined. All events can be predicted without residue ; there is no escape from the rule of law. But it needs an omniscient being—Laplace's superman— to know all the initial conditions of an infinite number of particles. In fact, the world is even in a sense predetermined : the idea of force introduces a feeling of compulsion. And in the usual formulation of determinism we find the causal connexion between events described as a physical necessity. The course of events is unique and proceeds with necessity ; the world rolls along like a ball in a groove, and it is only our ignorance that prevents us from knowing the future. This extreme interpretation of classical physics represents the strictest formulation of the idea of determinism.

The advent of field theory weakened this view to some extent, while at the same time it provided a more detailed description of a causal process. Whatever occurs at a given time and place in the field depends only upon the values of the field quantities that exist in the immediate past and proximity of the events. Causal relations are transmitted from point to point by an action-by-contact, and the inverse-square law becomes the prototype of causality.

In this way causality is made to refer to a physical process of a certain kind. Action spreads through space, and the series of observable happenings which ensue represents the *causal chain*. The simple idea of the central force first introduced by Newton is used to describe complicated motions as being due to causal action. Kant's statement : 'Alle Veränderungen geschehen nach dem Gesetz der Verknüpfung von Ursache und Wirkung' is given a definite interpretation. Causality is specified as the law according to which force acts through space with an intensity proportional to the inverse-square power of the distance. In Newtonian mechanics this action may be propagated with infinite speed so that there is no limit to the causal connexions which may be established, and the causal chain can bridge any two or more events. But the concept of field, and the finite speed of transmission demanded by relativity theory, limits the length of a causal chain : it is finite and broken completely at some points. There are always events between which no causal relation can be established since action cannot reach from one event to every other event. This reduces the scope of causality : though all events may be members of some causal sequence, these sequences need not, and often cannot, be related to one another. The telephone call of a friend to tell me that he cannot keep the appointment with me does not affect my actions, if he rings after I have already left my house. Whatever he does while I am on my way to the appointment does not cause me to do anything : the causal chain is broken, and my actions are truly independent of his.

In this interpretation we take action rather than force, or change, as the main characteristic of causality. Since a force is relative so that it may disappear according to the choice of reference system, this behaviour would not be in agreement with our ordinary conception of cause. Nor can 'change' be used to indicate the presence of a cause, at least not without some restrictions. For the length contraction which a moving rod shows when measured relative to a rod at rest cannot be said to be due to a cause. Thus force and cause can no longer be identified ; for we take causality to be an invariant relation while force is covariant with the coördinate system. Cause is then not efficient in the sense in which we feel that a force is ; we do not ask why, but how events are related to each other ; and this seems to be a step forward in our understanding of causality.

By taking a particular law as *the* law of causality it is clear that we commit ourselves to a definite theory, and to a special interpretation, or model. It is therefore not surprising that this conception of causal action is closely connected with the ideas of time and space as given by classical physics. For action is described as a function of the space and time coördinates, and there is an actual, observable path along which the particle travels. This allows us to define the time sequence in terms of causality within relativity theory. The causal connexion between events is a physical process ; it is described by an asymmetric, transitive, and connective relation which generates a series and thus defines an order. Some combinations of two events are observed to possess certain physical properties, namely, that a change in the first event frequently also changes the second event, while the reverse never happens : that is, the signal, or the causal action, goes from the first to the second event. This sort of variation is a criterion of causal order which does not make use of the temporal order, and so it may be used to define an order for the time sequence, although it cannot give a direction. All that can be achieved is that, within a finite interval, certain physical characteristics allow us to order events in a series, but causality does not specify an over-all direction.

The Lorentz transformation formulae support this interpretation of causality as a chain of action. When we say that two events are simultaneous it means that no causal connexion can be established between them. Although two events simultaneous in one system may no longer be so when transformed to another system of reference, yet no causal chain can be found to link them ; and two events which are causally related can never be made simultaneous by such a transformation : it would require a velocity greater than that of light, which is not admissible for any physical process. Thus, causality is invariant with respect to the Lorentz transformation ; but it is also very restricted in application to actual events.

There is equally a connexion of the inverse-square law with space, as was pointed out by Exner many years ago. If we consider a physical process going on in a linear or one-dimensional space and describe it in terms of the central force model, we may say that the force attenuates in proportion to the zeroth power of the distance, that is, it is constant : there is no propagation of action in such a space. In a two-dimensional space, or plane, we find the force to be proportional to the inverse first power of the distance : action spreads in concentric circles. If this analogy holds, we would expect in a four-dimensional space a force law expressing a proportionality to the third power of the distance, and so on. But in macroscopic physics no instance is known as yet which would require action to decrease with a power higher than the second. This illustrates the close connexion between force and space which is, of course, clearly brought out by relativity theory ; and it suggests that causal action exemplified by the inverse-square law is connected with the three-dimensionality of space.

This classical model of causality is due to the character of *contiguity* attributed to it by field theory. Hume already said in the Treatise : 'Whatever objects are considered as causes or effects, are contiguous ; and nothing can operate in a time or a place, which is ever so little removed from those of its existence. We may therefore consider the relation of contiguity as essential to that of causation'. We introduce a mechanism for causality ; this makes it a physical process but it also introduces a special interpretation tied to the classical ideas of space, time, and motion. No wonder that in quantum mechanics we encounter causal anomalies—i.e. a violation of the principle of action-by-contact. This violation can be obviated by the restriction imposed upon the classical particle or wave languages, that is, by suppressing this particular interpretation of causality. And it suggests also that the ideas of relativity, since they are based upon the field theory, may be applied to quantum mechanics only with reservation.

But is this classical interpretation of causality the only one we can admit in science ? Again, to quote Hume : 'We have no other notion of cause and effect, but that of certain objects, which have been always conjoined together . . . we cannot penetrate into the reason of the conjunction'. This statement is of course directed against the idea of necessity attributed to causal relations by some philosophers. But clearly any statement of causality which asserts more than the regular succession of events makes additions not needed in theory, although perhaps useful in the practice of application. The inverse-square law as the model of causality adds details by showing how the causal process works ; and it helps us to avoid the danger of using the principle of causality as a tautology. It also restricts us to a discussion within a given theory, in this instance, the field theory of classical physics. But there are other theories in physics, and each describes the events by means of different laws : we cannot reject those theories which are equally confirmed by experiment.

The language of cause and effect is used normally within a simple and familiar context, and even there sometimes only with difficulty. We have a certain type of causal description—the deterministic causality of classical physics—but we need a formulation that can encompass other types of causal processes as well. For what is the purpose of a causal law ? It is *prediction* which is the most essential feature of causal explanation. We want to establish universal sentences from which, by the help of initial and boundary conditions, we can derive existential sentences referring to future events. This formulation of the principle of causality is suggested by the differential equations used in physics, and it seems to be both necessary and sufficient. There is no need, it appears, to commit ourselves to any special interpretation in terms of a particular theory ; we do not need to know the 'why', and we can even dispense with the 'how' of causal action. All we require, so it is often said, is a universal law which permits prediction. For this reason we are sometimes advised to abandon the cause-effect language altogether. Or, if we do wish to keep it, we may use 'cause' according to another, and more 'abstract', rule : the initial conditions represent the cause, for they are necessary to specify the occurrence of any event. The stone falls to the ground only if there are certain initial conditions, e.g. the position of the stone is ten feet above the ground at time t_0, and the motion is then causally explained by the differential equation of free fall.

This is of course a possible use of the word 'cause'; but there are difficulties. We would not want to say that the position of the sun below the horizon at midnight is the cause of its being in the zenith at noon. Rather we take the earth's rotation about the sun as the cause, or the force of gravitation. In other words, we cannot keep the cause-effect language unless we specify the law, and with it a *special interpretation*, in this instance Newtonian mechanics. We can always invent universal sentences which, together with suitable antecedent conditions, allow us to predict future events. The astrologer supports his pleasant prediction 'You will meet with good fortune' by appeal to a universal sentence 'All people born at such and such date are fortunate if the stellar configuration is so and so' together with the condition 'this configuration occurs on your birth date'. This is not a testable statement since I do not know what 'good fortune' means. But even if something happened to me which could be so interpreted, I still would not accept the universal sentence as a law since the theory of which it is a part is not acceptable.

It is indeed correct that the sentence 'this is the cause of an

o

event' means 'the event occurs according to this law, together with certain initial and boundary conditions'. But the law must belong to a scientific theory : the purely formal, logical, requirement needs to be supplemented by another demand, that is, the law must lead to a factual, or testable, sentence. Since there are sentences in physics which are called 'laws' but function as analytic sentences within the usual formulation of their theories, we see once more how difficult it is to avoid empty talk when speaking about causality. If a causal statement is to be testable by experiment, it must be given as a specific law or hypothesis within a definite theory of physics, and so is part of a particular interpretation.

This illustrates the reason why physicists take the inverse-square law as the prototype of a causal law in classical physics, but also why in other parts of physics we may expect a different type of causality. To say that causality is the belief in the lawful-ness of nature, or that it presupposes an *a priori* assumption about the world—and whatever else has been said—is therefore quite meaningless. No such 'faith of the scientist' is needed, for we can describe any events by means of law-like sentences. It is the specific law that we must find and test under very specific experimental conditions : only in this way can we hope to speak meaningfully about causality.

Two more qualifications have to be made in order to characterize the deterministic causality of classical physics. The differential equations do not provide unambiguous solutions, unless—apart from *initial* conditions—we also specify *boundary* conditions. This is a point that is often forgotten. We must say something about the region of space which the equation is to cover : while the initial conditions state that something holds at a given time, the boundary conditions prescribe the behaviour for the whole time the process is going on. The boundary conditions therefore make the description more specific ; according to what conditions we choose, a different sequence of events will ensue. If we predict the behaviour of some particles, we must know what is to happen at the boundary of the volume in which they are enclosed. If we predict processes in a field, we must state the conditions at its boundary. In other words, we must prescribe the kind of universe in which the events occur ; we may take the universe as an infinite space but still need to know the conditions which are to hold at its boundary. Otherwise we cannot solve the equations, and we cannot use the causal law to describe the events. In most instances, both in Newtonian mechanics and elsewhere, we tacitly presuppose an infinite universe, and we specify a simple behaviour for the events at the boundary : the solution is to vanish there, and nothing is to happen at infinity. Although often this boundary condition is not explicitly stated, it is still of import from the theoretical view-point. In quantum mechanics—say, when we describe the behaviour of a particle in a box—we prescribe that the solution vanish at a finite distance. This condition produces the desired result, that the particle possesses discrete energy levels, i.e. its quantisation, which would not occur if we had made the box infinite in size. By prescribing these conditions we limit the universe for which our causal statement is to hold. The range of applicability for the law is given, and we make clear the limits of the theory or model which underlies our description. Our laws allow us to describe the physical world only if, apart from initial conditions, we also prescribe the kind of universe in which the events take place.

Over and above the representation of a causal law as a partic-ular differential equation, the determinism of classical physics demands a further assumption. It is this : the initial as well as any later values of the variables can be measured, in principle, with unlimited accuracy, and therefore the prediction is equally exact. This is a main constituent of the deterministic hypothesis —and possibly the last residue of the idea of necessity which the mechanistic, and perhaps the every-day, conception of causality seems to demand.

Now it is clear that we can never measure any quantity with unlimited accuracy : our powers of observation are fallible, and however well our instruments are constructed, their precision is limited. All mechanical and electric instruments are limited by the Brownian movement of their smallest parts, and optical instruments cannot do better than their resolving power will allow. This limitation is not only due to practical imperfection, but the classical theory of measuring instruments demands it. However, this inaccuracy does not directly affect the phenomena themselves : e.g. the position and momentum of a particle can be determined simultaneously with unlimited accuracy since their values are independent and not related through the uncertainty principle, as in quantum mechanics. The demand for complete determination of the variables used in the differential equation can be formulated only when we put it into contrast with quantum theory. The usual formulation is, then, that there exists no natural limit to the accuracy of our measurement, if we imagine that the progressive refinement in technique can be carried out without end. Only practical difficulties are said to stand in the way of achieving this aim, in the sense that the instruments are to blame and not the phenomena which are observed.

Obviously, once more we are treading on dangerous ground. An ideal is set up which no human being, working with an actual instrument, can ever hope to realise. Again, in order to characterize deterministic causality we have recourse implicitly to supernatural intervention in the manner of Laplace. Somehow we are supposed to be in the possession of absolutely exact data, and measurement is regarded as a completely idealised process. No interaction with the phenomena we want to measure is needed to make our instruments register, and how we can say that our values are exact is not a matter determinism takes into account. Of course all description involves idealisation to some extent ; and the question how far we may go in this way is difficult to answer. It suffices to say that, as far as classical physics is concerned, there is no law directly limiting the values of the parameters, if we disregard how they are measured.

But even this formulation of determinism is still fraught with many difficulties. We say that certain events *always* succeed other events according to a law, or that the future is *determined* by the past. How can we construe the verb 'to determine'?

Ever since Hume the necessitarian interpretation has been rejected, and the reasons are too well known to bear detailed repetition. There is the mistaken identification of cause with force ; there is the confusion of supposing that the logical necessity with which the prediction follows from the universal law corresponds to a physical necessity in nature ; there is the assumption that the world is like a machine ; and so on. The idea of causal necessity is in fact useless. To say that some events necessarily succeed other events, is to say no more than that there is only *one* course of events ; and this is a truism. The addition of the phrase 'necessarily' changes nothing in the actual world. Even to say that some events always, or without exception, occur in a certain sequence is not to say very much. If an exception is found, we can always maintain that the same initial and boundary conditions were not present, or that we were mistaken in our observations, or that the events belong to a different sequence : so that we can assert *a* law no matter what happens. When we use the word 'always' we merely indicate that certain events *usually* occur as members of the same, familiar sequence and that we *intend* to describe them by the same equation, provided we have no reason to do otherwise. The idea of necessity is of no import to science, though it is of great psychological interest : the feeling of compulsion whence it arises may lead, according to temperament, to a gloomy fatalism or to an incorrigible optimism regarding the future.

Yet within this somewhat purified and more restricted formulation of determinism, there are still some difficulties left.

In physics we restrict ourselves to investigating a small volume—a physical system closed off from the rest of the universe. What do we mean when we say that the processes in this system are causally determined ? We wish to assert that the same sequence of events always arises under the same conditions. Whenever we release a stone from a height, it drops to the ground : the same future states succeed the same initial states of the system. Then we must know a criterion by which we can judge the sameness of events, or of states. We need a direct and independent criterion without using the law itself for this purpose : otherwise the law turns into a tautology. For we often say that two events are the same if the same future events arise from each of them, that is, if both event sequences are described by the same differential equation. Let it be granted then that we possess such a criterion and that we know everything about the processes, e.g. that the system is closed so that the rest of the universe does not affect it, and that exactly the same conditions hold as in a previous instance, and that we know all the parameters needed to describe the state.

Even if all these qualifications are met, the words 'to determine' entail the unpleasant idea of eternal return. The same event must bring with it the return of the same sequence of other events which has occurred previously. Perhaps the difficulties regarding the ergodic hypothesis in thermodynamics are connected with the deterministic character of the laws of mechanics which we use there. If we assume a law to hold for ever—that is, if we take it to express an invariable relation between two events—it is not easy to see how the idea of eternal return can be avoided. The remedy might be to say that the rest of the universe does not stay constant but changes in an unpredictable manner, so that some conditions are changed, and the system need not always return to the same state. And it is necessary to say that the changes occurring on the outside of the system are unpredictable. If they are governed by determinism, then all we have done is to divide the universe into two closed systems, and each of them must eventually return to the same state. Here again we meet with the difficulty of the idea of closed system without which, however, it seems impossible to say clearly what determinism is to be. We might admit, in desperation, that the law itself may change, say, within a very long period of time, or within a cosmological epoch ; then we can be content with a frequent repetition of events.

These are only some of the arguments that have to be examined before the deterministic hypothesis can be said to possess a reasonably clear meaning. Certainly, at least in science, determinism does not hold the universe under its sway in the sense that is often attributed to it. The hypothesis of deterministic causality merely implies the modest statement that we have differential equations which, under special conditions, allow us to derive exact predictions of future events, *within* the interpretations customary in classical physics.

2. *The concept of statistical law*

In classical physics already we find laws which differ from the deterministic type. Thermodynamics, in its two interpretations, admits apart from determinism the concept of probability. And in quantum mechanics there are only probability laws, as a result of the uncertainty principle. What is the difference between deterministic and statistical laws?

We might state the difference simply in this way. We need statistical laws whenever we deal with a large number of events, or mass phenomena ; these are usually on the microscopic scale and therefore not directly observable. When we describe individual events, on the macroscopic scale and thus directly observable, deterministic laws suffice. In both instances, however, we have definite laws. And it is sometimes said that determinism represents the lawful *connexion* of events while statistics is a principle of lawful *distribution*. Deterministic laws allow us, under suitable conditions, to derive exact predictions of the future course of the events ; and statistical laws furnish predictions as to the probable course, that is, within a certain margin of error.

It is the vague concept of chance, current in every-day language, which makes difficulties in understanding what we mean by a statistical law. We speak of chance when we wish to say that we do not know how to explain the event, that is, when we cannot state the law according to which the event in question is described. It is on this view that it has been argued that causality and statistics are incompatible.

But the writers on probability theory have made it clear that this *absolute* concept of chance is not used in science and that, indeed, it could never find a reasonable application. A chance event, in the absolute sense, cannot be related to any event sequence ; it would be a haphazard occurrence relative to all laws. But to assert that a certain event is not a member of any sequence has a meaning only if we know all the laws. Once more we encounter the difficulty so frequent in discussions on causality : only the assumption of a higher intelligence can help us to define an absolute concept of chance. A human observer can merely say that there is an event which does not belong to the causal sequence usually found for events of this sort. 'An event is due to absolute chance' is a sentence which can never be tested by experiment.

This confusion has prompted the view that chance events are lawless ; and to describe natural phenomena by the help of probability is supposed to mean that miracles are possible. We often say in every-day life that this or that event is pure chance, and we claim not to know why and how it could have happened : but we do not mean to make the event a miracle.

The occurrence of miracles is excluded, both from ordinary life and from physics, even if we introduce a statistical description. To take a miracle as a transgression of natural law is not of much use ; we can always assume a causal sequence of which it is a member, however unique the miracle may be. We are free to invent a universal sentence, that is, a law to fit the occasion. Tacitly, the assertion of miracles entails that there exists a definite sequence of events to which the miracle belongs, and that this sequence arises from a supernatural source. This can be said of any event, and it is therefore an empty assertion.

We can speak significantly of miracles only in this way : 'This particular event usually succeeds that other event, and here is the law describing the sequence ; but, being a miracle, it did not have its usual antecedent'. Two events being ordinarily members of a well-known event sequence are suddenly no longer so related. But then it is a question, apart from mistaken observation, whether we cannot find another sequence to which the two events might belong. If we do not find it, we can always maintain that one day we will : otherwise, we should be forced to say that all the events we have not yet discovered are miraculous. And if we do find another law relating these two events, then there is equally no question of miracles. In other words, we speak of a miracle if two events normally described by a familiar law are related, in fact, by an unfamiliar law. All miracles recorded by the Church authorities seem to be of this kind : and the mistake lies in incorrectly explaining these events by a law of physics, instead of psychology. For example, we ascribe a 'miraculous' cure to psychological factors in the patient, and not to the physical intervention of a supernatural person ; and this results in a statement that can be tested by experiment.

We do not make sense when we take 'chance' as synonymous with 'no cause'. It is the *relative* concept of chance, or probability, that is used in science, and mathematics furnishes us with the formal rules we require. We can sometimes predict only the frequency with which a certain property will occur within a large number of events, and then we say that the result is due to chance or that we have found a certain probability. The chance is relative to a given law ; it is a probability law rather than a deterministic law ; but there still exists a lawful dependence of the result upon the initial conditions.

Statistical laws are equally laws ; the introduction of probability into science does not indicate the break-down of causality, unless we mean by 'causality' the dynamical laws of Newton. Indeed, statistical laws are also given, usually, as differential equations of the same type as in classical deterministic theory, and we derive predictions from them, provided we know certain conditions. They possess the same mathematical form as the deterministic laws, and it is merely the *interpretation* that is changed. Thus it is reasonable to speak of statistical as well as of deterministic causality as the two kinds we have in present-day physics.

The concept of probability can be interpreted in at least two different ways. When we apply it to a physical situation, as the probability of events, it is always taken as the *relative frequency* with which events of a specified kind occur in a long series of events. Mathematically, this probability may also be taken as the limit of the relative frequency in an infinite series, and the limit is a constant to which we can ascribe a suitable numerical value. This is of course an idealisation but, so far, it has met with so much success that there is no reason to revise the definition. (Certain technical objections against the use of the limit can be overcome as will be argued in section 6.6.) How can we further characterize this probability? The throws of a die are the prime example. And we may say that probability is a physical property of physical events which is manifested under very specific, observable, conditions : it is a collective property of a large number of events.

In classical thermodynamics we use a mechanical-statistical model. The concept of probability is said to be needed only for practical reasons : in principle, we could determine the initial position and momentum of all the molecules in the gas, although it would take too long a time for any mortal being to carry out this measurement. And this *argument from ignorance* is offered to justify the introduction of statistics.

Since Laplace this argument has often been used to explain probability, but it is now generally recognised to be faulty. It is not true that it is merely the ignorance of initial conditions that compels us to employ probability. To take a well-known example: it is not ignorance that decides us to assign equal probability to all six sides of a die. We have information based upon counting the frequencies of their occurrence, and we know that the die has a regular shape, and that the laws of mechanics apply when the die is thrown ; and so we have good grounds for the statistical hypothesis. Indeed, if the throws made with a particular die give peculiar results, we abandon the hypothesis of equiprobability ; we say that the die is loaded.

In kinetic theory, then, we cannot say that probability is introduced merely because we are ignorant in this sense. We always have to make some assumptions about the initial conditions. And, as with all mathematics, the calculus of probability allows us to compute probabilities only if other, initial, probabilities are given. Given the initial probability distribution of the properties of a large number of particles, the statistical law predicts the distribution at any later time. At best we can say that we are ignorant *how* to apply the laws of mechanics, but we do know *that* they apply. And, as Exner remarked, we do make use of this knowledge ; it is the dynamical law that we take as the basis for prescribing an initial probability distribution so that we can establish the statistical law. The assumption of molecular chaos and the ergodic hyopthesis are based, among other arguments, upon dynamics. Whenever we deal with mass phenomena, we are not interested in the parameters of the individual particles but how they are distributed, and this requires assumptions for which we must find reasons.

Statistical laws and deterministic laws, however, are strikingly different, and this difference is exemplified by the existence of fluctuations. Under favourable conditions we are able to observe the individual events of a mass phenomenon, say, in the Brownian movement of very small particles suspended in an emulsion. We find that the individual motions are quite unpredictable—they may, in fact, on occasion show a behaviour opposite to the behaviour of the whole mass phenomenon. That statistical laws are such that they allow exceptions for individual events has always been regarded as their most important feature. But these are not exceptions to the probability law : they deviate only from the average behaviour, and so fluctuations are at best exceptions from the deterministic law by which, sometimes, the average behaviour may also be described.

The situation is illustrated by Maxwell's demon—another supernatural being who is introduced to characterize statistical causality as Laplace's superman characterizes determinism. Imagine a vessel divided into two compartments by a partition with a small opening. This opening is fitted with a trap door ; and the demon chooses to let pass only certain molecules, that is, to separate the fast molecules from the slow ones. In this way the temperature in one compartment is spontaneously raised, and lowered in the other ; and the demon can thus reverse processes which, for human beings, are irreversible.

Maxwell believed that his demon required only abilities which are no greater than those of human beings. But to be able to 'see' the molecules, the demon must be of molecular size, and so must be his trap door. Thus, it is doubtful whether he could separate molecules according to their speed ; the door, or he himself, might suffer a fluctuation and close the aperture just when the right molecule came along. The fluctuations of each participant in the process are independent of one another, and they are uncontrollable : thus, there is no guarantee that the Maxwell demon would succeed in his task.

Within classical physics we have then two types of law side by side. And it is a natural desire to try so to relate one to the other that there is only one kind of causality. Electromagnetic theory may be interpreted in terms of electrons, on the particle model ; we say that their average behaviour—taken over large volumes and long time intervals—represents the field quantities, and these are then described by Maxwell's equations. Similarly, in kinetic theory, the average motions of the gas molecules can be correlated to the macroscopic state variables, and these are of course functions occurring in a deterministic law. In spite of the randomness of statistical phenomena, there are some constant properties to be found as well : it is sometimes said that the irregularity in small regions entails the regularity in larger regions.

In classical theory we have then the following situation. The individual events are supposed to be describable by the deterministic laws of mechanics, although we cannot in fact supply this description. Therefore we introduce certain statistical hypotheses so that we can formulate laws for the probability distribution of certain properties and of their change during a process. By taking suitable averages we can correlate them to macroscopic quantities which are then described by laws customarily interpreted as deterministic. From Maxwell's distribution of molecular velocities we find the average energy and correlate it to the absolute temperature.

Clearly, these statements imply special assumptions. Both the statistical hypothesis about the initial distribution and the correlation of averages to macroscopic quantities assert something about the physical world, and this is one difference between statistical and deterministic interpretations. Moreover, a probability law can never predict the course of events with certainty as does the deterministic law. Even if the probability is unity this does not amount to certainty, and the law of large numbers does not bridge the gap : but averages are statistical quantities. Thus we cannot really say that the averages obtained by the help of probability follow a deterministic law, although they may be described, when suitably interpreted, by mathematical equations belonging to deterministic theory.

Rather this is due to the special interpretation, or the choice of semantic rules, when we relate one theory to the other. It is again the correspondence principle which prompts us to say that determinism is an *approximation*, in the sense that statistical theories contain deterministic theories as a special case. For this reason it is sometimes said that, at bottom, all laws are statistical and that deterministic laws are obtained by averaging.

But we must not say that macroscopic phenomena *reduce* to microscopic phenomena, or that the world is 'really' statistical. We do not reduce the motions of large masses to the statistical distribution of small particles : the two descriptions, or theories, can be made to relate to each other under special conditions. There is a marked tendency among modern scientists to assert that all laws of nature are to be expressed in terms of probability. But we must be careful not to substitute one kind of metaphysics for another. For instance, the theory of errors is given as reason for saying that nature is 'really' statistical : after all, not even in Newtonian mechanics can we ever find a determinate result, but we have a dispersion from which, by the theory of errors, we construct it. But the theory of errors is concerned with measurement, and it has nothing to do with the theory the measurements are to confirm. We can of course reject determinism altogether. A plausible argument might go like this. Determinism disregards the physical character of measurement, while statistical theory takes it into account in one way or another ; and we can never in fact obtain exact data and neglect the influence of the measuring instruments. So there is not much use in keeping the fiction of a deterministic causality. From a practical viewpoint there is much that would recommend this attitude ; but, as theoreticians, we would be too radical if we were to adopt it. Classical mechanics assumes measurement to be idealised; this is an essential part of the interpretation, and the assumption is justified within the context of application of the theory. In classical physics, where-ever there are both deterministic and statistical interpretations, it is more reasonable to acknowledge this difference.

In all modern physics, that is, in quantum mechanics, there is only one type of law : the statistical law. The uncertainty prin-ciple prevents us from specifying the exact initial data, and so all computations are based upon an initial probability distribution of the parameters whose future values we wish to find. All micro-scopic phenomena occur *en masse :* we cannot speak of the behaviour of a single atom, or of an individual electron. Radio-active decay laws, for instance, do not tell us which particular atom will disintegrate at this moment, but they state that a certain number of them disintegrate within a given time interval ; and on this basis we ascribe an average life time to the atom.

Together with this loss in individuality we give up also the detailed description of the mechanism according to which causal action proceeds. Statistical theories are more 'abstract', and the rigid description in terms of space, time, velocity, and related notions, is somewhat loosened. We cannot speak of the path of the particle, for instance, and the action-by-contact of deter-minism must be given up since it refers to an interpolated inter-phenomenon. If we keep the classical model, then we find causal anomalies ; and the use of a language inherited from classical theory must be restricted to avoid these difficulties.

The vague idea of dynamical causality which identifies force and cause suggests that causality answers the question 'why does this event happen?'. The improved conception of deterministic causality is taken as rejecting this idea and as answering only the question 'how?'. The statistical conception of causality seems to abandon even this answer, though only in a certain sense, and to replace it by the flat statement 'that'.

Let me summarise this discussion. The formal requirement for being able to speak of causality may be formulated in a *syntactic* definition, e.g. 'A law' is 'a mathematical expression (usually a differential equation) whose solution, i.e. a function, determines new values of the variable from given values if certain conditions are satisfied'. In classical physics, this syntactic definition is supplemented by a *semantic* definition, e.g. 'A law' is 'a statement from which descriptions as well as predictions of the *exact* data of future events can be derived, given certain conditions'. This statement is exemplified, in the most general way, by the principle of contact-action ; that is, the spreading of action from point to point through space-time is taken as the most general kind of causal process. In quantum physics, the syntactic definition remains unchanged. But the semantic definition is now, e.g. 'A law' is 'a statement from which descriptions as well as predictions of the *probability distribution* of future events can be derived, given certain conditions'. This statement is exemplified by any probability law, and there is no general type of such a law ; we have no longer a simple picture illustrating how a statistical process works.

We now interpret 'causality' as meaning that there can be formulated a universal sentence which, together with initial and boundary conditions, allows us to derive a singular, descriptive, predictive or retrodictive, sentence. The epistemological conception of causality in terms of a *principle* has changed to the semantic conception : a law is merely a statement, or theorem, within a scientific theory.

3. *The hypothetical-deductive method of science*

Scientific method can be made clear only by analysing in logical terms the actual theories of science. There may never be a final answer, not only because a complete analysis can hardly be achieved for theories so complicated as we have them to-day ; but also because science changes continuously, and new theories may introduce new methods. Moreover, there are many psychological problems and questions which creep into any explanation of scientific method, and they have to be recognised as such and kept apart from the logical problems involved. Otherwise we cannot hope ever to arrive at a satisfactory understanding of science.

Traditionally, the philosophic theory of knowledge, or epistemology, is supposed to explain science. Philosophers have assumed that there is a problem of knowledge, in the sense that we have to demonstrate *why* and *how* we know in order to justify *that* and *what* we know. The whole host of *-isms* as we find them in the history of philosophy arose in this way ; and though they all differ from one another, the various epistemologies have this in common : they introduce, openly or tacitly, ontological assumptions about the Nature of the human mind or of the physical world and so they determine, *in advance*, what is supposed to be unknown.

It is therefore said that we obtain scientific knowledge by means of *induction*. Inductive reasoning so becomes a special faculty with which human beings are endowed ; and we must follow the rule of induction in order to leap successfully from what is known to the unknown, ready-made and waiting to be discovered. But, to-day, our attitude towards the problems which the peculiar grammar of the word 'to know' (and its cognates) generates has completely changed. Philosophers no longer, or at least very rarely, write treatises on Human Nature or on the System of the World ; such matters are nowadays left to the scientist, that is, the psychologist or the physicist who, more modestly, only write about human nature or the physical world. It is usually understood that words like 'knowing', 'thinking', 'reasoning', 'experience', etc. belong to the context of psychology; and that a term like 'induction', if it has any sense at all, can be used only for the very different, and *technical*, methods scientists employ in their work.

Of course, the individual scientist may be quite in the dark as to the method he actually pursues. He may give us a number of procedures as they fit his personal temperament : more often than not the scientist follows his 'instincts', and training, memory, and native ability make sure that he obtains results. The practical procedures of achieving certain results must be distinguished from the theoretical methods of confirming a statement.

For to follow a recipe telling us how to do an experiment is not the same as to confirm a statement by an experiment. An experiment may have been carried out correctly according to accepted procedures, but it does not say anything unless we make it speak : it is an experiment only if it is *designed to prove or disprove a hypothesis*. We must first formulate what we intend to do and what we mean to prove by so doing—otherwise the experiment says nothing. Experiment is controlled experience :

experience by itself is 'silent', and it requires a hypothesis in order to give it a voice. Nature is not a book, and certainly not an open one, which we have merely to read when we do science. Things, events, and facts do not speak ; but the scientist does.

How do scientists ever arrive at formulating a hypothesis? This is indeed an important question for the understanding of science. But it is a psychological question : and however we may answer it, the result is not part of the logical structure of science. No doubt past experience arouses the imagination of the scientist and suggests to him a possible hypothesis. But there are a great number of possible ways of describing any experience ; and a practically limitless choice of possible hypotheses that could account for the result of any experiment. It is true that the number of hypotheses is cut down, possibly to a set of alternatives, by the decision of the scientist to remain within the frame of accepted scientific theories. Even so, it is the good scientist who is capable of providing a successful hypothesis. The hypothesis must describe past experiments and predict the outcome of future experiments, and thus it is confirmed.

To ask why we have knowledge and how we ever arrived at building up a system of science is not a question the philosopher can answer. This psychologism is an attitude typical of traditional epistemology. When we pose the problem of knowledge in this manner, we automatically prejudice any possible answer : for we then search for the *genesis* rather than the *analysis* of science, and for a *psychological explanation* instead of a *logical re-construction* of scientific method.

This prejudice is revealed also in the traditional problem of the empirical basis of science. When, like Bertrand Russell, we ask, Granted science is true, how do we know it to be true ?, we are once more in danger of falling victims to the psychologizing attitude of epistemology. For it seems to imply that there is some information about the world which is more basic than any other, or that there are statements enjoying a special status— protocol statements or sense data statements—which are to be preferred for their reliability. Such sentences are supposed to be needed so as to provide a ground for our knowledge ; they are often believed to be absolutely certain, and incorrigible, since they require no inference. For it is argued that unless there are such ultimate statements the whole of science would collapse.

Such an interpretation of the foundation of science however betrays many of the bad features of epistemology. There is the universalist tendency, when we are expected to give a guarantee for the *whole* of science ; but we cannot possibly question *all* the theories of sciences at the same time, for what could we offer as basis for such a colossal doubt? We cannot even put into question a whole theory, in this sense, only some statements of such a theory ; while others must be kept, at least temporarily, to supply the context and the standard of comparison, so that we can carry out a test of the questioned statements.

Nor is it possible to accept the view that there are some sentences *intrinsically* more basic than others. No doubt there are sentences which, *in a given context*, we prefer since we take them to refer directly to experience ; and such sentences are often of the sense data kind. But there is no special virtue in the fact that these sentences are of a certain grammatical form and refer to my own person, to space-time location, and to simple qualities. Such an estimate is conditional upon the peculiar theory of perception inherited from the associative psychology of previous centuries, and there is little reason to-day for accepting it. Basic sentences in this sense are simply sentences which we take as directly expressing experience in a given context. They are not incorrigible, even if we forget the possibility of verbal mistake : we do change them—we do look more than once to read the scale of the measuring instrument, and we correct our previous readings. We may assume that each time the same observation is repeated we obtain a completely new sentence, and that all these sentences are unrelated ; then, I suppose, we can say that each observation sentence is incorrigible. But this merely indicates our decision how to use the word 'incorrigible' in this context. From the logical viewpoint we cannot object to such usage, but psychologically it seems to be a dangerous recommendation. It suggests that a certain kind of sentence represents the rock bottom of experience, a natural basis upon which to build the system of science. Apart from the strange theory of perception this view entails, it is equally mistaken to say that certain sentences are never subject to correction. We may accept some sentences in a given context, but—in another context—these same sentences may be questioned, and they may be shown to involve a long chain of inference.

P

Let us consider a series of observation sentences, say, a sequence of readings of a meter. We find the numbers scattered around a certain mean value. We may of course say that each reading is incorrigible ; but the net result of the whole series is one number—the mean value—which we take to represent the *correct*, that is the *corrected*, observation. We do in fact question the individual observation sentences, on the basis of other statements which are not at the same time being questioned : we accept the theory of errors, the theory of instruments, and a host of other scientific statements. Thus it seems more natural to say that certain sentences are accepted within a given context ; we accept them tentatively but are prepared to change and even to drop them, if need be, at a later stage. To ascribe absolute incorrigibility to them is misleading since it suggests that they are never questioned within any context ; and this is palpably untrue.

Although we must have some sentences to start with, it is not important what kind these sentences are, whether they refer to sense data, or things and events, or whatever else : they do not enjoy a special ontological status. We need neither 'ultimate facts' nor 'a priori principles' as a basis for constructing the system of science. But it is equally impossible to make science without presuppositions. While the aprioristic theory is no longer much in favour to-day, there are still some philosophers who believe that Newton's famous dictum 'hypotheses non fingo' has to be interpreted in their sense. Such an attitude seems to show a profound misunderstanding both of Newton's position and of modern science. It was relativity theory which brought out most clearly that physics pursues the *hypothetical-deductive* method. A statement contrasting this modern attitude with the ideas current in the 19th century was given by Einstein in his Spencer Lecture (1933).

Whenever we wish to ask questions, we must first hazard a guess as to what possible answers we can expect : we cannot formulate a meaningful question unless we know what the question is about, and this entails that we know a possible answer. Indeed, in science as anywhere else it is more difficult to ask the right question than to find an answer to it ; and to formulate the right question presents the main task.

Now, this sounds very paradoxical. What is the use of asking questions if we already know the answer? Of course, we do not know the answer in this sense. We start with a hypothesis which is usually rather general and vague and which is suggested to us by previous experience ; and we test it by performing an experiment. This test, and the confirmation so obtained, is often not very conclusive. So we narrow down the hypothesis until we obtain a satisfactory confirmation, at least for the time being, and sufficient for the purpose we have set ourselves. Moreover, there are many different hypotheses between which we must choose. By this process of trial and error we eliminate the various possible hypotheses until only a few, or perhaps only one, hypothesis remains ; we are guided in this choice by the criterion that any new hypothesis must, in some way or other, fit into the accepted theories of science as we know them. This criterion of *correspondence* often suffices for selecting a successful hypothesis. It is not only psychologically but also logically relevant ; for it shows that science cannot be made without presuppositions, that is, without some previous knowledge. This knowledge is not certain, or absolute, or eternal ; it is merely tentatively assumed, although it is usually highly reliable since we take previous, and well tested, theories in order to construct new ones. But we may find that this previous theory is defective, in some way or other ; then we use our new theory in turn to correct the old theory which, originally, served as starting-point. This *self-correcting* character is most important for the understanding of what we mean by 'scientific method'.

The scientist designs an experiment in order to find the answer to a specific question. He has a hypothesis in mind which he wants to put to the test by experiment ; and if the test is successful, the hypothesis is confirmed. In the practice of inquiry the scientist not only invents hypotheses but must also find the evidence. Starting with a vague hypothesis he 'works out' the data at least a little ; thus the hypothesis becomes clearer, and he 'works over' the data once more, and so on. Hypotheses are not inferred in this way ; but Mill's canons, for example, are procedures of experimentation which may help us to improve them. This psychological process cannot be formalised by rules. The Bacon-Mill school is therefore mistaken in assuming that we somehow read off our hypotheses from the facts. In this manner induction is taken as a procedure of 'generalisation from particulars' or of 'abstraction from facts'. Some sort of logical method is assumed that would lead, by means of inductive inference, from singular existential sentences to the universal hypothesis or law.

But there is no possible demonstrative inference by means of which we could get from 'This is a swan and it is white' and 'This is another swan and it is white', etc. to the universal sentence 'All swans are white'. True it was recognised that this kind of inference is logically invalid ; nevertheless it has been held to be indispensable, and various attempts have been made to justify it.

The difficulty is that if we construe induction as an inference from particular to universal, we seem to require a *principle* of induction which itself cannot have been obtained by experience, that is, by means of an inductive inference. Thus we are told that the 'uniformity', or 'regularity', of nature is the guiding principle, a principle implanted into nature or into our minds by a benevolent agency. How could we otherwise accomplish inductive inference—which, in fact, we seem quite capable of doing— and how else could we justify induction? If we reject this *apriorism*, we seem to be thrown into the sceptic's position of saying that induction is completely irrational, an act of animal faith on the part of human beings, or a habit which even past experience could never provide with a logical guarantee. If 'induction' is so interpreted, surely Hume is right ; and the fact that the sun has risen every morning since time immemorial cannot justify, in any logical sense, our firmly held belief that the sun will rise tomorrow.

The sceptic's reaction to the problem of induction when it is posed in this manner, as a riddle, has contributed however a good deal towards elucidating the situation. For it has shown convincingly that the problem of justifying induction is not a problem at all. If we understand by 'justification' the demand for a logical derivation of the principle of induction (whatever that may be) from some other, higher principle, clearly we are confronted by an infinite regress. Thus, to justify induction can only mean that our theories are successful in describing past experience and in predicting future experience. The great merit of the Humean kind of scepticism is to have emphasized that it is the *criterion of success* by which we judge a scientific theory.

That no specific justification of an inductive principle is needed has become widely accepted, both among philosophers and among scientists. But the sceptical attitude towards induction still carries with it the traditional interpretation of 'induction' as an *inference from some to all*.

On this view inductive reasoning leads from limited evidence to a more comprehensive hypothesis by the rule of induction. The new hypothesis is supposed to be found in this way, and so the rule must have added some knowledge to the evidence. The *predictive power* of the inference lies in the *rule* since it says something about the future course of events, over and above the given evidence. Unfortunately, nature does not always follow our prescriptions, and so it is said that the hypothesis is not certain, only probable. In the empiricist version the rule is expressed by saying that the relative frequency of characteristics observed in the past will persist in the future. This makes the rule itself a sentence arrived at by induction, and so we have an infinite regress and the traditional puzzle. The task of induction is taken as inferring a hypothesis from the evidence, in the sense that the hypothesis is the conclusion. The rule used for this purpose, e.g. Mill's rule of enumeration, supplies the extra information and is expressed in a factual, or synthetic, sentence.

Naturally, if we take induction as a psychological process of discovery and, at the same time, as a logical method of proof, we end up with an insoluble problem. This is exactly the fault of the epistemological theories of induction (including that of empiricism) that try to make psychology do the job of logic. Neither Hume's scepticism nor Mill's belief in the uniformity of nature are solutions of the inductive problem, but rather they are attempts to banish a riddle.

There is, to-day, an ever-increasing number of philosophers as well as of scientists who reject this *inductivism*; and they advise us to drop the term 'induction' altogether when describing scientific method. If I continue to speak of induction, it is for two reasons. The word has such a wide currency, even in every-day life, that it seems strange not to use it. And though 'induction' will be given a completely different sense here, let us not forget that the philosophers who tried to work out a theory of induction had in mind the same purpose as we have to-day even if, as we can see now, they were mistaken. In fact, we learned from their mistakes—without which we would have nothing that could be called 'induction'. Similarly, we continue to use the word 'atom', for instance, though in a sense quite other than what Leukippos and Demokritos understood by it.

In what sense, then, can we speak of 'inductive inference'? We want to confirm a hypothesis on evidence. The hypothesis may be formulated in the sentence 'It will rain soon' and the evidence is 'The sky is overcast'. Is the hypothesis about the future warranted on the present evidence, that is, can we say 'It is probable that it will rain soon'? That this is an instance of inductive inference carried out by everybody every day can hardly be contested.

The task of induction is therefore not to discover a hypothesis but to *judge* it on the evidence. There are no rules for discovering anything ; still less is there a fixed rule (like the traditional rule of induction) to be used on all and every occasion ; though there may be practical procedures for obtaining the experimental evidence. The *predictive power* lies in the hypothesis which is invented by the scientist but is not the conclusion of an inference. What we do infer is whether or not the hypothesis is supported by the evidence, i.e. the sentence 'It is probable that . . .'. We establish the probability of a hypothesis by rules which are formal or tautologous, and do not prescribe the future, that is, the rules of probability calculus. Our expectation of the future or, in general, of an unknown state of affairs, is expressed in the hypothesis, and the rules check it against the evidence. In other words, induction is the same as what, technically, is called 'statistical inference'.

4. *Theories, laws and hypotheses*

The scientist starts with a hypothesis which he wants to put to the test by experiment. But what is a hypothesis? Here the difficulties begin. For the choice of our basic terms, e.g. of *theory*, *law*, and *hypothesis*, will decide what we shall understand by testing, and confirming, a statement.

Naturally, no re-construction of scientific method will be very relevant to physicists unless we follow as closely as possible the actual usage they make of these terms ; moreover, we must consider what other concepts are, in fact, involved when we say that an experiment confirms a hypothesis. The highly idealised conceptions current to-day will certainly distort, if not hopelessly misdirect, all efforts to give an adequate account of theory construction. It is notorious that scientists find very little resemblance between the methodology described in books on the philosophy of science and the methods they believe themselves to follow.

It is of course not necessary to assume that the physicist working in the laboratory or at his writing desk is always right in his criticism. The experimentalist tends to mistake the practical procedures used to obtain results with the theoretical methods designed to explain these results ; and the theoretician is inclined to mistake his formalism for 'a picture of reality'. All the same, it cannot be denied that all present-day methodologies are insufficient, to say the least.

Take, for example, the sentence 'All swans are white' which, so we are told, is a scientific law. Everyone is of course well aware that this so-called law is none too reliable ; but even to-day, in the most advanced treatises on logic and probability, we find this very sentence (and others like it, e.g. 'All ravens are black') being advertised as stating a law, I suppose, of zoology where such simple classifications may be of import. It is not difficult to guess why such a law is chosen as a specimen : first, because it can be made to represent an 'empirical generalisation'; and, second, just because there are known exceptions to the law so that it is natural to call it probable rather than true. But what connexion has this sentence with a law of physics, e.g. Newton's laws of motion? No physicist has ever found exceptions to any law so conveniently placed at his disposal—like black swans— when he wanted to test it.

For example, our understanding of what statistical inference can do is obscured by the empiricist scheme prescribing that all laws are hypotheses, and by the logicist scheme of taking all hypotheses as universal implications, e.g. $(x) (fx \supset gx)$. For laws are not the same as hypotheses : we speak of Snell's law of reflexion, and we would not be understood if we were to speak of Snell's hypothesis. And hypotheses are not always universal sentences holding for an infinite number of instances, for all times, and for all places. Of course, it is often a historical accident whether a scientific sentence is called a principle, a law, or a hypothesis ; but this does not relieve us from the task of finding out the logical distinctions, if any, between them.

Laws, it is true, are very general sentences : they may be represented, logically, as universal implications though this is by no means necessary or always useful. Hypotheses, however, are very specific sentences and, mainly, concerned with the happenings in the laboratory.

While hypotheses may be probable to some degree or other, what can we say about laws ? We must realise that there are different kinds of laws in physics : some which appear to us to be indispensable are often called 'principles', while another kind— variously called 'empirical law' or 'rule'—is regarded as tentative only since it cannot yet be incorporated into any proper theory. Finally, there is often more than one, acceptable, formulation for any law, and so its translation into logical symbolism need not be uniquely determined.

For example, Newton's first law (which is always given in words) finds a 'natural' translation as, e.g. $(x) (Rx \lor Ux \supset \sim Fx)$, if the functors R, U, and F mean 'being at rest', 'being in uniform motion', and 'being acted upon by a force', respectively. But what about Newton's second law which is more usually given in mathematical notation, e.g. $f = m \cdot a$? Although it is possible to torture almost any statement into the logical form of an impli- cation, is it wise to do so here? For the universal implication has become the standard logical form because of the view that laws describe how events hang together, i.e. the antecedent is followed by the consequent as cause is followed by effect, and a law so becomes *eo ipso* predictive. But this string-model of causality, even in the refined version of causal action, is of limited and very doubtful value, as we have seen. The point is, then, that the choice of logical form may bring with it a peculiar interpretation of 'law'.

There are at least two ways in which laws seem to be used within physical theory. We may remember that laws have been found wanting on occasion, e.g. Ohm's law or, even, Newton's second law. What do we do then?

We do keep the law, naturally : it has been too successful in the past to be simply rejected. But it is not quite true to say, as is sometimes suggested, that we stick to our laws, no matter what happens. Ohm's law, for instance, states that for all electric conductors the current flowing through it is proportional to the voltage applied and that the proportionality factor is constant (for a given temperature) ; this factor is characteristic of the given metal and called its 'resistance'. But in certain phenomena, e.g. the conduction of electricity through a gas, in a discharge tube, this is no longer so. Instead of abandoning Ohm's law, we restrict its applicability and invent a new theory describing electric conduction in materials other than simple metals. In this manner we explain the negative characteristic of a carbon arc, by introducing concepts like 'ion', etc. This new theory is, of course, freely invented ; neither deductive nor inductive rules can ever lead to it from the known evidence ; and it is not a deductive system but, rather, pieced together out of various models, loosely joined to one another by all sorts of assumptions. The point here is that law and theory go together ; we save the law, though at the expense of the theory whose domain of application is restricted.

Similarly, Newton's law was modified and classical mechanics restricted in its range of application, when it was found that the mass of a body depends on its speed. Newton's second law in its customary form, e.g. 'force equals mass times acceleration', applies only when the masses concerned are in slow motion. For high velocities, relativity theory applies ; even then we can keep the law, provided we re-write it as 'force equals the time-rate of change of the product of mass times velocity (i.e. the momentum)'. In other words, Newton's mechanics becomes a first approximation to relativity mechanics, as determined by the correspondence principle.

The second way of using laws is to obtain from them, by various means, single existential sentences which may function as hypotheses. Then we can speak of probability, but only of the hypothesis so derived, and not of the law. Laws are, then, part of the logical or, better, semantic skeleton of a theory ; the law and the theory stand and fall together. If the original law, or theory, was reasonably successful, we keep it though, possibly, in a modified form. This is not a question of induction, in the usual sense of this word, or of probability of the law, in any direct way. It is a question of how we construct theories, namely, by following the correspondence principle that governs the succession of theories. But whether or not we are able to devise a new theory and so, indirectly, save the old law is a matter of luck and of the scientist's ingenuity.

This, of course, is too brief a description of how laws function : but it shows that laws are simply accepted or rejected, though a previous acceptance may be qualified later by restricting the range of the theory to which the law belongs. We speak of testing a law ; but we do not say 'this law is probable', and we never assign a definite degree of probability to a law. For laws, being universal in scope, cannot be said to be probable since an infinite number of instances alone would suffice to confirm them ; and any finite number of instances can only result in zero probability (or degree of confirmation) : that is, the concept of probability does not apply to laws. But a universal sentence is equivalent to the negation of an existential sentence, e.g. $(x) (fx \supset gx) = \sim (\exists x) (fx . \sim gx)$. Therefore, a single negative instance decides the rejection of a law. And in the so-called instance confirmation, what we confirm (or obtain the probability of) is the hypothesis derived from the law : we say that, in this way, the law is tested. We may say, of course, 'it is probable that this is a law', or wonder whether we should incorporate permanently a certain statement into a given theory. But this is not the same as to say 'this law is probable'—we use laws differently from hypotheses.

What, then, is a law? The first alternative of adapting it to experimental evidence, i.e. by restriction, suggests that a law is presented as an analytic sentence within a theory. Though, strictly speaking, the meaning of the sentence is changed, this is shown only by placing it within a different context, or a more restricted theory, and not by changing the sentence. The second alternative, i.e. by instantiation, similarly suggests that we use the law as an empty schema : we fill it with a particular set of data—the initial and boundary conditions—and so obtain a specific hypothesis which can be tested by experiment.

Therefore we cannot say that we stick to our laws come what may ; but, equally, we cannot say that they are formulated as factual sentences. This peculiar rôle laws play in science, or at least in physics, has often been noted. Schlick, for instance, spoke of laws as prescriptions ; and nowadays some philosophers say that laws are inference-licences (though it is not quite clear how the licence is, in fact, used). It has also been said that certain laws are disguised definitions, e.g. the conservation laws ; and I have argued previously that these seem to function as semantic rules. But, in all these views, the law is expressed either in a factually empty statement within the theory, or in a statement belonging not to the theory but to the corresponding meta-theory : and this is, in a way, shocking to one's prejudices. Physicists, especially, like to remember that the laws and principles were discovered, originally, in connexion with simple experiments.

However, this does not necessarily fix the logical status (within a theory) of a sentence so discovered. The naive view— which, perhaps, is right for a less developed science like zoology —that we call 'laws' those factual sentences which are most important in a theory does not seem tenable in physics. The factual content of a theory is brought out by the specific hypotheses which can be obtained from the theory.

This leads to another point. We talk of the probability of hypotheses, *not* of theories. A theory is constructed for a definite universe of discourse and re-constructed as a language system, with primitive concepts, rules, etc. A hypothesis is a sentence within such a theory and is more or less probable according to evidence. A theory is *adequate* if it allows testable hypotheses to be formulated which suffice to describe and predict the phenomena. Fresnel's elastic theory of light is not improbable (though abandoned) but inadequate, since it breaks down, e.g. in the treatment of polarisation. To say that a theory is probable is to assume that it is no more than a single sentence ; but a theory is a language system in which a sentence is formulated. When we speak both of Newton's 'law of gravitation' and of his 'theory of gravitation', we must not confuse them though it is true that the inverse-square law is the most important part of gravitational theory ; but neither can be said to be probable. It is impossible to assess the probability of a theory : this can be done for hypotheses alone and, even then, only if they are of suitable form.

The aim of the scientist is, indeed, to be able to say 'It is probable that . . .'. Though ordinary as well as scientific language allows us, only too easily, to formulate sentences of this sort, not all such sentences are proper hypotheses. This is, I think, a most important point : for it shows that the concept of probability is not as widely applicable as we are usually led to believe. Because everything we say in science is put forward tentatively, it is assumed that all scientific sentences are probable only ; but not all sentences occurring in a theory are hypotheses. This attitude of *probabilism* is as unjustifiable as the opposite one, that is, that probability plays no rôle in science and that we can never ascribe a certain probability (or degree of confirmation) to any sentence. Both attitudes arise from the same mistake : it is the over-simplified, and biased, conception of what we take as theories, laws, and hypotheses. It makes, however, good sense to say, in ordinary life, 'It is probable that it will rain to-morrow'; just as it is reasonable to state, in physics, 'The neutrino has probably a negligible mass, no charge, and a spin of $\frac{1}{2}$', i.e. the neutrino hypothesis.

What, then, is a hypothesis? The term seems to be used in at least two different ways, and on different levels of explanation. The neutrino hypothesis, I should think, is one that all physicists would like very much to put to the test by experiment ; unfortunately, at least at present, there is no prospect of doing this. Though indirect evidence, e.g. the β -ray decay, together with the principle of conservation of energy, lends some support to the hypothesis, this does not amount to a proper test ; it merely shows that the hypothesis is compatible with present-day theories and, in fact, useful. The (nearly complete) absence of a theory from which this hypothesis could be derived prevents us from testing it.

But when we speak of the 'hypothesis of central forces' in mechanics, we do not think of subjecting this hypothesis to a test ; rather, we take it as an assumption which helps in formulating testable hypotheses. On this level of explanation, the *general* hypothesis is used to make the theory more definite and so more applicable. From the many kinds of forces that are, theoretically, possible we select one kind, and our theory is accordingly restricted. This kind, e.g. of central force acting along the line connecting two particles (or centres), is in fact very frequent in nature ; and so we are tempted to treat all forces on this model, the more so since their mathematical description is relatively simple.

When discussing scientific method it is necessary, then, to distinguish two tasks. We construct theories ; and we formulate *specific* hypotheses in terms of a theory. We may use a model, or models, to build up both a formalism and an interpretation, that is, a theory. The oscillator model, for instance, is taken as a basis for the classical theory of specific heat, etc. Once the theory is constructed, in some way or other, we can relate it to experiment, by model, and to the lower theory, by approximation, in this instance, to mechanics.

The general relation between theories, by the correspondence principle, is not considered as confirming a theory. Rather, it safeguards both the internal consistency of the whole of physics (taking 'consistency' here in a very loose sense) and the observational basis of the most 'abstract', i.e. advanced, theory. We do not claim that the special theory of relativity is confirmed because it contains ordinary mechanics as an approximation. But we accept relativity theory because, with its help, certain optical experiments can be explained which, before, defied a mutually compatible explanation in terms of the aether, e.g. Bradley's aberration, the Fresnel-Fizeau drag coefficient, the Michelson experiment, etc. And, of course, other explanations as well as new, and unexpected, predictions were supplied, e.g. the mass-energy formula. In other words, very specific hypotheses formulated in terms of relativity concepts are confirmed by experiment.

To make our ideas more precise, let us consider a simple law of classical physics, e.g. of free fall. Surely, we need not put ourselves in Galileo's position and discover the law anew ; we only mean to test it. How do we do this? We have a simple apparatus, like Atwood's machine, a clock, and a set of weights ; we want to determine the distance through which a body falls as a function of the time elapsed. We need to know, then, the position from which the body starts, that is, the initial condition. This is given by any constant values of the space and time coördinates x and t supposed to hold for the beginning of the experiment ; for convenience we choose, e.g. $x = 0$ for $t = 0$. By using bodies of different weight and noting the distance covered in a certain time, we find that the distance is proportional to the square of the time, within a reasonable margin of error. The law may be given, e.g. $x = \frac{1}{2}gt^2$, where g is a constant (indicating the value of the gravitational acceleration). Then we see that the hypothesis holding for a single weight (or for the finite set of weights) is derivable from the law, by instantiation, and is confirmed by each experiment ; and so the law is tested.

According to the way we ask the question, different existential hypotheses can be derived from the law. We may say, for example, that for a given weight the distance of fall is proportional to the square of the time elapsed ; or, that it is so for all the weights used ; or, finally, we can determine a value for g. But whatever we do, the hypothesis is always about a finite set of values ; and the fact that a finite number of instances of the law is confirmed leads us to accept it. Though, psychologically, Galileo may have 'generalised' from existential statements, i.e. his data, to universal law when he discovered it, we test the law, logically, by *instance confirmation*. Galileo's inventiveness is the more to be admired since historians have shown that the primitive apparatus he employed, e.g. an inclined plane, could not possibly have given values anywhere near the ones needed.

This example is often given in accounts of scientific method ; though acceptable, it is too simple an example. Most laws are more complicated, that is, they are expressed, mathematically, by a differential equation of the second order. To solve this sort of equation we have to specify, apart from initial conditions, also boundary conditions.

For instance, we might study the transversal vibrations of a string which are described by the wave equation : $\dfrac{\partial^2 u}{\partial t^2} = c^2 \dfrac{\partial^2 u}{\partial x^2}$ Here u is the displacement, and c the velocity, of the vibrations ; x and t are the space and time coördinates, respectively. We need to know the displacement as well as its time rate of change in order to give a complete description of the motion, and so we must state the initial values of both for every part of the string. That is, for t=o, we prescribe as initial condition for the displacement, e.g. u=f(x), and for the change, e.g. u̇=g(x), where f and g are known functions. The functions are specified only in the interval $o \leq x \leq 1$, if 1 is the length of the string.

We also require boundary conditions which express, for all times to be considered, the limitations of the motion we investigate. Mathematically, or syntactically, these conditions select certain solutions of the equation from the infinite, or at least indefinite, number of solutions that otherwise satisfy the equation. Semantically, the conditions prescribe the allowed range of the phenomena we wish to deal with, that is, they limit the universe of discourse and specify the possible states that may be found in this universe. The modes of vibration of a string, for instance, will differ according to whether one end is tightly clamped, or free to move, etc. A set of boundary conditions is, e.g. for all t, and x=o (one end of the string), u=F(x) and $\dot{u}$=G(x) ; for x=1 (the other end), u=H(x) and $\dot{u}$=K(x), all functions being known for the given values of the argument.

It suffices to say, then, that we have a solution of an equation, that is, a certain function on which we base our prediction. We have the hypothesis that a certain value, or set of values, will be found when a measurement is made under the conditions assumed. Whether and how well the results of the measurement agree with the values predicted, decides the confirmation of the hypothesis.

Usually, we do not take many results though, of course, the more measurements of the same quantity we make, the more firmly do we rely on the value obtained. If we have an extended series of values, we may apply the theory of errors and, in simple cases, we take the average as the correct value. This is not a matter of mere mathematics but involves additional hypotheses concerning the particular experiment. We may assume that the errors are distributed at random ; or, we may neglect observed values which are very much 'out'; and these assumptions are, obviously, not based on mathematical grounds. For we say that something has gone wrong with the apparatus, or that we have made a mistake, or that the set of readings should lie on a smooth curve, and so on. These factors are usually not evaluated numerically but only qualitatively introduced, as part of the evidence.

But even if we have a perfect set of data, we must still make the main decision whether their agreement or disagreement with the predicted values confirms the hypothesis and, possibly, to what degree. Usually, we aim at, and achieve, complete agreement, within a small margin of error : and so we have a practically complete confirmation of the hypothesis. The highly developed techniques of physics allow us, nearly always, to say yes or no to a hypothesis, and we rarely need to find the exact numerical degree of its probability. Together with the highly developed (i.e. mathematized) theories of physics, this might give the impression that the 'inductive' decision was, so to speak, automatic.

This would be an oversimplification, however. The hypothesis and the evidence do not completely agree ; the predicted values and the experimental result are not the same, and it depends on theoretical as well as practical considerations whether or not we take the experiment as supporting the hypothesis. That is, there are rules for deciding the issue, beyond mere agreement or disagreement. The point I want to make here is this : we refer to a singular hypothesis and to a specific experiment as evidence. We do not take the hypothesis to hold for an infinite future ; this is a matter of speculation which is truly metaphysical, that is, outside physics. The (logical and mathematical) concept of infinity is most useful in simplifying our symbolism ; it is not a descriptive, or physical, concept. To regard all hypotheses as universal is part of the unwarranted idealisation to which, traditionally, induction has been subjected.

Thus, the methods of science are in some ways directly opposite to what philosophers have thought fit to prescribe. We do not generalise from singular statements ; rather, we derive a singular statement from a more general, or universal, sentence. It is this hypothetical-deductive method which modern science has developed. It is hypothetical, since we start with a guess, an unconfirmed hypothesis ; and it is deductive, since a scientific theory is regarded as a deductive system and since we test the laws of the theory by deriving from them existential statements which are confirmed by experiment, that is, the evidence. But we do not 'generalise' the evidence in order to *justify* the hypothesis. We *judge* the hypothesis on the basis of evidence.

5. *Induction as statistical influence*

The formula for the free fall, e.g. $x = \frac{1}{2}gt^2$, allows us to predict a specific set of values for the space and time coördinates x and t (suitable units for both being presupposed). Another set of values is obtained in the experiment. If the result agrees with the prediction, within a certain *margin of error*, the particular hypothesis is confirmed and the law tested.

The mathematical language of physics permits us to express both hypothesis and evidence in numerical terms ; and the coördinate language reduces these expressions to a set of values for space and time. We do not have to refer to the falling mass, only to its position at a given time ; these represent the arguments in the mathematical function f(x,t). A possible state of the falling mass, predicted by means of the formula and expressed by a set of values (x,t), is thus compared to an actual state found by experiment.

It is, really, somewhat unfair to take a well tested law and a very simple hypothesis as an example since here we are inclined to reject the evidence rather than the hypothesis. It would be preferable, at least psychologically, to discuss e.g., how we arrive at the probable age of the earth, on geological, astronomical, and other evidence ; or, how we come to say that the μ-meson has a mass of 209 (in units of electron mass) : that is, examples in which we doubt the hypothesis more than the evidence.

However, the methods we apply for making a decision are essentially the same. We must not forget that the numbers we deal with are interpreted ; and the comparison of, or the agreement between, prediction and experimental result depends on their interpretation. We must take into account the theory in terms of which the problem is formulated, the performance of the apparatus, and possibly all sorts of other assumptions regarding the experiment. Our decision will be affected by the number of experiments, their repetition as well as their independence, that is, whether many different types of apparatus were used. For example, to test the free fall formula, we employ not only Atwood's machine but also an inclined plane and, perhaps, we make direct observations by dropping a mass from a great height, etc. In physics, at least, it is very rare that we are satisfied with one experiment only and, even, with one type of experiment.

Scientists know how to judge a formula by the result of an experiment. This technical task is carried out by *statistics*, and there are a great number of such methods. These methods work best if both the hypothesis and the evidence are represented by a large, though finite, set of numbers ; but methods for judging a very small 'sample' have been developed. We must guard here against the misconception, arising from the popular understanding as well as from the mathematical formalism of statistics, that there is an infinite set of numbers involved : in fact, there never is. But the main point is that even for judging the agreement (or disagreement) of two sets of values *we do use rules*. No physicist accepts an experimental result unless its accuracy is given.

We say that the result of an experiment is such and such, with a certain % error, and this is only another way of saying that the result is probable ; therefore, we cannot help acknowledging that the agreement of predicted and experimentally found values is probable only. In practice, the error is extremely small and the probability amounts to near-certainty ; we speak of the probable result rather than of the probable agreement since it is understood that we always aim at agreement ; and the probability arises not from the uncertainty of our prediction but from the difficulty of the experiment. But this must not blind us to the fact that we make use of probability for judging a hypothesis on evidence, even if we take agreement as the standard. The claim sometimes made nowadays that probability plays no rôle in testing and confirming hypotheses is untenable.

The reason why we say that a certain result is probable is, of course, quite different from the reason given by empiricist philosophers. We do not introduce probability because of the philosophic belief that every event in nature is 'contingent' and, therefore, only probable; or, because our human powers of foreseeing the future are fallible, and so our predictions can be merely probable : speculations of this sort are gratuitous. It is conceivable that, if our experimental techniques were perfect, complete agreement could be obtained ; but even the imperfection of our measurements is not decisive, logically, for speaking of probability here. We use statistics as a *technical* method for judging a hypothesis on the *actual* evidence we have been able to obtain.

In the free fall experiment, for example, we obtain a set of numbers. These are the evidence, and we describe them usually in statistical terms by stating the *dispersion* of the results (as given by the standard deviation or other measures). Probability so plays a rôle in selecting the evidence. We want a precision experiment which gives reproducible data of high accuracy. For we reject an experiment as evidence if the results are scattered over too wide a range. This involves a decision which is taken in view of the inductive (statistical) rule we are going to adopt, and so we accept an experiment as reliable only if it produces uniform results. If an experiment is difficult to perform, for instance, we are willing to put up with a larger error than we would otherwise. If the evidence is accepted, however, the error becomes part of it. Over and above this descriptive use of probability we then state the rule for accepting the hypothesis. If we take agreement as our aim we demand that the predicted values must lie within the margin of error of the experimental values. The % error so becomes a numerical measure for the probability of the hypothesis on the evidence, i.e. for the degree of confirmation. If we do not, or for some reason cannot, aim at agreement, we may specify only that the two sets of values lie within a certain interval or show some correlation ; and there are rules by which we then estimate the probability of the hypothesis, e.g. by means of significance tests, etc.

But how can we 'translate' our mathematics into ordinary language, that is, speak about the relation of hypothesis to evidence when these are sentences, and not numbers? Our judgment, and what statistical methods we employ in order to arrive at it, depends of course on what the numbers mean. To say, then, that a scientific theory represents a hypothetical-deductive system does not suffice : we must add that the system consists of a (logical and mathematical) calculus and of an interpretation in terms of experience.

A theory represents a definite universe of discourse and is intended to give an account of a circumscribed realm of phenomena. It thus provides a boundary and delimits the possible states of the world to be considered ; and this limits our predictions. Newtonian mechanics, for example, treats only of such phenomena as can be described in terms of a few concepts, e.g. masspoint, force, etc. The world is taken to be an aggregate of masspoints moving in space and time under the influence of forces ; this model describes our actual experience in so far as it can be 'caught' in mechanical terms. Classical mechanics does not speak of charges or light rays, and so on : this is the task of other theories, i.e. of electricity and of optics.

This might be thought a trivial remark, and in one sense it is ; but there is a point of logic to be made here. A theory, when considered as a semantic system, specifies the individuals and their properties and so prescribes the kind of variables and the propositional functions that are satisfied significantly by the variables. This is not to be regarded as an ontological assumption, i.e. as saying what the world is 'really' like. Rather it represents a choice of a suitable language in terms of which a certain set of events is to be described. It is true that, historically, the advent of Newtonian theory gave rise to the mechanistic interpretation ; but that this is a mistake is already seen from the development of other theories that do not make use of mechanical concepts. The choice of a language need not commit us to any metaphysical asumptions but merely expresses our decision to accept certain concepts as suitable for describing our experiences. If we are successful in this task, all is well ; otherwise we must invent another vocabulary and different rules.

The propositional functions become propositions or statements when the variables 'x,y,z...' are replaced by the constants 'a,b,c...', which may be assumed to refer to physical individuals. In this way, we attribute to them properties and relations and establish the kind of sentences that are to be admitted to the system. A state-description is a sentence which tells us, for every individual and for every property (primitive predicate), whether or not the individual has this property ; and, similarly, for relations. A sentence of this sort, then, describes a possible state of affairs, and so we know what may happen so far as these individuals are concerned. An experiment, of course, is needed to show us which one of the states is actual, under the given conditions. An atomic sentence (in the system) ascribes a property to an individual ; any state-description will either affirm or deny such a sentence ; and the range of the sentence is determined by the number of state-descriptions in which it holds. The sentences therefore possess a definite logical range, and it is by virtue of this range that the sentences are meaningful. For we must know what possible facts would satisfy a (factual) sentence if it is to have meaning.

In mechanics the individuals are masspoints ; and let a few of them be denoted by the letters a,b,c, etc. Their properties are expressed by propositional functions such as the space-time functor ' . . . has position x,y,z, at time t', or by ' . . . has velocity v', or ' . . . is attracted by a force proportional to $1/r^2$ to . . .', where the . . . may be filled in by a,b,c, etc. It makes no sense to introduce different constants denoting other individuals, e.g. α, and to say 'α is attracted . . .', since by definition an α does not significantly satisfy the propositional function in question. Thus we cannot say 'A wave is attracted . . .'. This is simply nonsense since it violates the rules for forming sentences which we have stipulated. The word 'wave' may however occur significantly in another theory, say, in optics, where we would find sentences such as 'The wave has a velocity v at time t'. In other words, another theory makes use of different individuals and usually employs different propositional functions, although similar properties may be described in two theories, e.g. having velocity.

It is this notion of logical range which is of primary import when we wish to construct a theory and when we use the theory for making predictions. For it must be at least logically possible to verify or falsify a sentence occurring in the system, and we can speak of the meaning of a sentence only if we can say what possible states of affairs we would count as verifying the sentence. That is, we must show how, and to what sort of things, we wish to apply our theory, and to what purpose we want to put it, if the theory (or language-system) is to be accepted into science.

Unless the sentence within a theory, and so the theory itself, delimits the universe of discourse, there is no possible way of verifying (or falsifying) a sentence, and there would be no meaning. This is no mystery. As Humpty-Dumpty said, we must *make* our sentences mean what we want them to mean.

After all, ordinary language is normally used for the purpose of making meaningful statements, and scientific language is designed for this end as well. Since ordinary language is often vague and the rules of grammar not sufficiently strict, we try to make them more adequate for scientific use. So we list, for example, all the individuals and their properties and provide a catalogue of admissible sentences. We usually deal with an indefinite number, both of individuals and of properties, and so we may only be able to give rules which apply to classes of them. In this way, we try at least to give exhaustive characterisation of the language system to be employed for a specific purpose.

In science, then, hypotheses are always so constructed that we can establish their range and thus know what can be asserted in the theory. The best hypothesis is the one which is most specific about what can happen ; its logical content is increased while its range is decreased. The narrowest hypothesis is for this reason better testable than any alternative, that is, if only a single state of the physical world would be compatible with it. The Michelson experiment was therefore crucial since of the many aethers only one, the luminiferous aether, had remained ; and, as Einstein said, '. . . immobility (was) the only mechanical property of which it (the aether) has not been deprived by Lorentz'.

How, then, can we explicate 'statistical inference' (or 'induction' if you like) when the hypothesis and the evidence are sentences, and not numbers? Black clouds are a partial condition for rain ; knowledge of temperature, wind speed, etc. is also needed. The weather inference (as it is called nowadays) is carried out within the framework of meteorological theory. The hypothesis of rain includes more possibilities than the evidence of black clouds. The interpretation of 'probability' in terms of logical range is suggested here and usually accepted.

The inference is then determined by a relation between two given sentences, e.g. the hypothesis and the evidence. But does this not make induction the same as deduction? No, for the hypothesis is *not* derived from the evidence. In deduction the logical range of one sentence is wholly contained in that of the other (i.e. one sentence logically implies the other) and the inference is complete or demonstrative. Here the hypothesis is only partially contained in the existential sentence (the evidence), and the 'inductive' or statistical inference is thus incomplete or non-demonstrative. The ranges of the two sentences overlap but do not coincide, nor is one contained in the other; and the amount to which the two ranges overlap can be taken as a measure of the probability of the hypothesis on evidence.

It is clear, then, that our judgment of a hypothesis will depend on the language system or theory, or model, which we have adopted. The sentences, i.e. the hypothesis and the evidence, are synthetic or factual ; and they are so only in relation to the theory in which they occur and to the rules according to which they are used in the theory. It means that if we are not clever enough to invent a suitable theory the power of our statistical methods is severely restricted. Once more we see that the traditional account of induction is highly misleading.

If we want to predict the future we can do so only *within* the framework of a theory. How can we be sure, otherwise, that the hypothesis is about facts? Take as example the cosmological hypothesis of finding the age of the universe on astronomical, and other, evidence available to-day. What do we mean by 'age of the universe', and is this age determinable for the whole universe, like the age of a human being? Even if we take one of the modern, and highly speculative, cosmological theories as context for this hypothesis, it seems impossible—apart from the logical difficulties involved—to decide whether or not the hypothesis is factual.

Again, think of the language which professional statisticians are prone to adopt : they regard everything that happens as the process of drawing black or white balls from a bag. This bag-and-ball model is often very useful ; but sometimes we feel quite irritated when we are told that such and such is *the* solution to a certain problem. For the probabilities so calculated depend on the model chosen, and we sometimes simply cannot accept the model as being suitable for the problem, however correct the mathematics may be.

Our judgment of a hypothesis will depend on the theory to which it belongs. A theory, or model, tells us what possible events may happen ; the future event is unexpected since any one of the many possibilities allowed by the theory may materialise ; but it is not *absolutely* unexpected in the sense that something not foreseen, that is, not describable by the theory may happen. The theory is then not applicable, and we have no basis for a statistical (inductive) inference. In spite of the popular, optimistic, belief probability is not a device for overcoming our ignorance.

The neglect of the limitations which a language system imposes is, I think, responsible for the view that laws are counter-factual conditionals. This depends of course also on the interpretation that laws are universal implications. If the antecedent is not related to the consequent by a logical implication—but by a 'causal', 'nomological', etc. implication as proposed by some writers—this would be another way of avoiding the difficulty.

I do not want to deny that technical problems of logic are raised in this way which merit discussion. Laws, however, when interpreted as universal implications, seem to become *vacuously* true. Newton's first law, for instance, may be formulated as a universal implication, like this. It holds for all bodies that if no forces act on them, then the bodies remain at rest or in uniform motion. And there are always forces since friction can never be wholly eliminated : thus the antecedent is factually false. So this law would be true only because from a false antecedent anything may follow ; it becomes a counter-factual (subjunctive) conditional.

This is surely not what we intend a law to be, and there are good grounds for doubting such an interpretation. Some general remarks about idealisation as a *technical device* may be in place here. Laws are part of a theory ; and a theory describes a certain set of phenomena. The situations described are therefore idealised, since we leave out features which we consider as irrelevant for the purpose of the theory. Whether or not the idealisation is acceptable in a given instance, depends on the success of the theory so obtained. In fact, the Newtonian idea of frictionless motion—contradicting common sense as well as the Aristotelian conception—was immensely fruitful ; without it, inertia and gravitation would be hard to describe. All description makes idealisation inevitable in this, technical, sense ; perhaps, it is better called 'simplification'.

If laws are taken as universal implications, one may argue that it is merely technically impossible to produce the antecedent conditions, not physically or logically impossible. No known physical law, within the theory in question, would contradict the antecedent expression. There are no frictionless motions in nature ; but we can approach this condition to a high degree, in practice; and Newtonian theory is, anyway, not concerned with describing the phenomena of friction.

This is a general requirement for simplification (if we prefer to call it so) to be permissible in science. Frictionless motions and weightless pulleys, etc., represent idealised conditions that we can approximate in an experiment, and they do not violate any law either of logic or of the given theory. For, even that bodies have weight, is not a law of mechanics but simply a fact ; and we may disregard it when we employ a pulley for some purpose and do not study the behaviour of a pulley as it depends on weight.

Thus, laws when regarded as sentences of a semantic system need not be counter-factual conditionals. If we choose the state-descriptions as representing the ideal (possible) conditions, then the antecedent is true (within the theory) and the law becomes a simple, universal implication. The idealised character attaches to the system as a whole ; and the success of the theory shows the idealisation to be acceptable within the demands for detail and precision specified for it.

It seems possible to extend this argument to other kinds of counter-factual conditionals, and even to modalities, i.e. whenever we have to consider possible states of affairs. To construe subjunctive conditionals syntactically appears to be hopelessly wrong ; and many conditionals of this kind cannot possibly be truth-functionals. Such sentences must be analysed in terms of semantics, since their meaning depends upon the specific situation to which they refer. If the laws of physics are supposed to be counter-factual conditionals, clearly syntax alone cannot suffice for their analysis ; but we must consider their extra-linguistic reference and the theory in which they occur.

6. *Probability*

We want to confirm a hypothesis on evidence or say 'It is probable that . . .'. How do we use the word 'probable'?

To show that there are at least two concepts of probability it is perhaps best to begin with an analysis of probability-sentences as used in ordinary discourse. Grammar allows us a wide latitude in the formation of sentences, and so a re-construction in logical terms is required since we wish to state more precisely the rules according to which probability-sentences are formulated and used. This re-construction need not exactly coincide with actual usage but must approach it to a degree sufficient to reveal the differences, if any, between the various uses to which we put the term 'probability'.

Roughly, two kinds of probability-sentences seem to occur in normal usage. First there is the *inductive* sentence which *predicts* future events, e.g. (A) 'It is probable that it will rain to-morrow'. Such sentences may also *retrodict* past events, e.g. (A¹) 'It is probable that Caesar crossed the Rubicon'. Finally, a sentence of this kind may *make a claim* about a present, though unknown, state of affairs, e.g. (A²) 'It is probable that there exists no life on the planet Mars'.

The second form is the *frequency* sentence which *describes* the actual occurrence of a property or event within a (finite or infinite) sequence of events, e.g. (B) 'The probability of obtaining one point with one throw of a single die is $1/6$'. This formulation, however usual, is already somewhat misleading. For the probability is assigned to a specific, given, die by observing a long series of throws. But when we speak of *a* single die and of *obtaining* a certain result we suggest the inductive hypothesis that all single dice will behave so in the future. So (B) must be interpreted with caution if we wish to separate the two kinds of sentences. For this reason a sentence taken from the more technical discourse of statistics furnishes a clearer example, e.g. (B¹) 'The probability of suffering a traffic accident in London last year is so and so'. In this instance we are less tempted to use the sentence inductively. What the chances were of dying in the streets of London last year is no matter of great concern now ; moreover, significant changes have occurred influencing the accident rate, for petrol rationing has been abolished since and so the density of traffic has increased. Although it is possible to take last year's data as the basis for prediction to-day, we should be conscious of the fact that we lack relevant information. In other words, we take last year's statistics as a summary of what has happened, or as a description. This is made more obvious since in the sentence (B¹) we may substitute for 'probability' words such as 'rate', 'incidence', or 'frequency', and these usually refer to actual observation and are construed with the present tense, instead of the past or future.

There is a third form of probability-sentence in which the adverb 'probably' occurs, e.g. (C) 'It will probably rain to-morrow'. This kind of sentence is obviously predictive and so reduces to (A), for the modality shows that the sentence refers not to actual but to possible, i.e. future, events. We need not deny however that on occasion this sort of sentence may also be construed as being of kind (B).

The two kinds of sentences do show significant differences.

(1) Inductive sentences often do not give numerical values. 'It is probable that it will rain soon', we say, and mean that we are willing to accept the hypothesis expressed in the sub-sentence 'It will rain soon'. No number need be combined with the use of 'probable' though some qualifying terms such as 'very' or 'highly' may occur. Frequency sentences nearly always state a numerical degree of probability. For the purpose of induction the unqualified term 'probable' often suffices, and so such sentences are used to express a somewhat weakened assertion, or warranted assertibility (to use Dewey's phrase).

(2) The inductive sentence uses the predicate 'probable' while the frequency sentence employs the noun 'probability'. Frequency sentences are not of much use unless they give a numerical value, and so grammar decrees the use of a noun. It is

more usual to say : The probability is so and so, than to say : It is probable to the degree so and so. Inductive sentences are useful even without such values. This is of course not a strict distinction (although noticeable) since in many instances we demand numerical information even in induction, e.g. in gambling.

(3) The two kinds of sentences often differ in tense. For the inductive sentence—or, rather, the hypothesis contained as sub-sentence in it—is usually about the future or the past. At least, it concerns a state of affairs which is not known *now*, and the sentence as a whole assigns a probability to the hypothesis on the basis of evidence. We must guard here against the traditional view that induction is necessarily tied to statements about the future or the past ; but the time factor comes in, though perhaps not essentially, even when we judge a present, unknown, state of affairs. For (on occasion) we utter a probability-sentence of this kind and merely mean that a certain hypothesis merits support : we hope later to find, or at least improve, the evidence for it. To-day, for lack of conclusive evidence, we can only say 'It is probable that there is no life on Mars'; but one day, sooner or later, we shall be able to go to Mars and find out. In all these 'inductive' examples, however, probability is a concept which applies to sentences and so is a logical, or semantic, property of sentences. The *pure* frequency sentence describes actual events in the timeless present and so states a physical property of events on the basis of comparison with other events.

(4) Finally, the frequency sentence always refers to a large, possibly infinite, number of events, while the inductive sentence may or may not do so. There is no sense in speaking of a frequency unless a large number of events is involved. But we may be interested in predicting, or retrodicting, a single event such as Caesar's crossing of the Rubicon. There is off-hand at least no way of interpreting this single event in terms of a frequency. Certainly, when we speak of the probability of a single event of this kind what we *mean* is not a frequency. Although a frequency interpretation may be constructed, it becomes very far-fetched to invent a series of similar events. We do not believe that Caesar crossed the Rubicon, only because we may know that Hannibal crossed the Alps, Alexander crossed the Indus, etc. This seems to suggest that history repeats itself : a most question-

able assumption which I am sure the advocates of the frequency interpretation would not wish to maintain. And if we try to construct a reference class for the single event by arranging into a series historical records, eye-witness reports, etc., we are not much better off. How do we know that the historian was reliable ; he may have made a mistake about this single event, and all subsequent writers have copied it. Anyway, when we speak of the probability of Caesar's crossing we do not *mean* to refer to the reliability of historic reports but to an actual happening.

These are the main differences which seem to occur among probability-sentences, and so there are two kinds of usage for 'probability'. This gives rise to the two concepts of probability which have been widely discussed in the literature and are now generally accepted. Of course we should not want to deny that the term 'probability', or any of its numerous cognates, is used in conversational language in a great number of ways. In these usages the term mostly refers to states of belief, i.e. it is used within a psychological context. All we wish to claim here is that the two concepts of probability represent the main usage in scientific discourse. In so far as logical meaning is important in conversational language it may be claimed that this scientific use of the concepts also represents their use in everyday life. Of course we must not forget that concepts are not found, or discovered, in nature like crocodiles or black swans. They are not a natural species, but they are words—key-words—used frequently and importantly and for which we can give rules of use, at least to some extent. Often concepts are 'distilled' from conversational usage, i.e. a logical re-construction is given which comes close to this usage ; sometimes they are freely invented. But we must always provide some rules for using them, that is, a certain degree of formalisation is introduced. It is then possible to construct an axiom system for probability and syntactic rules for using the symbols, and this constitutes a formal calculus. The syntactic rules attached to the system are chosen in view of possible semantic interpretation. That is to say, the form of expressions to be admitted to the calculus will depend to some extent on the meaning we wish to attribute to them. This explains why there exist various, slightly differing, axiom systems for probability.

Inductive probability (or degree of confirmation, or logical probability, or probability of hypotheses) is then given a precise explanation, or explication, in terms of the overlapping ranges of two sentences within a semantic language-system. It is a function whose arguments take sentences as values. Frequency prob-ability (either as ratio within a finite class or as limit of a ratio within an infinite sequence) is a function whose variables are classes of physical events. The two functions are of different logical type and so they are entirely different functions. They have a mathematical calculus in common to some extent and are possibly based upon the same set of (uninterpreted) axioms, but they differ in interpretation.

To-day most authors accept this distinction of the two con-cepts of probability, but there are some who believe that all usage of 'probability' may be reduced to one concept. This view, I believe, arises from an understandable desire for simplifi-cation, but partly also from historical reasons, and from grammar. When the Chevalier de Méré asked Pascal for mathematical help in order to improve his gambling, the problem from which probability calculus developed required two answers. First, it was necessary to derive formulae describing the frequency of favourable (relative to unfavourable) cases in various games of chance. Second, on the basis of this statistical evidence successful bets were to be laid, and so formulae for predicting the outcome of such games were wanted. No doubt the main use for the con-cept of probability is for the purpose of prediction. But it is here that the greatest difficulty arises, when the frequency sentence is used as evidence for an inductive hypothesis about the future. The sentence (B) is taken as expressing a bet, e.g. 'The prob-ability is 1/6 that one point *will* be obtained with one throw of a single die'. This sentence combines both predictive and descrip-tive characteristics, and so we might think that these two cannot be separated.

Grammatical usage has contributed to this confusion. When a hypothesis is judged by evidence, we should say : It is probable that the probability of obtaining one point with one throw of a single die is 1/6. The phrase 'it is probable that the probability', and similar iterations, are shunned by grammar and so are con-tracted in speech. This distinction however is vital for a satisfactory analysis of probability-sentences and of induction.

Another difficulty arises from the verbal habit of formulating probability-sentences incompletely so that their usage is elliptical. This has brought about the so-called *absolute* concept of probability, or the concept of *chance* which seems to play a rôle in every-day life. But the analysis of probability-sentences has shown that these are (logically) meaningful only if they make use of a relative concept. Probability is taken, in its logical if not in its psychological meaning, as a relation of comparison. Inductive probability is assigned to a sentence (i.e. the hypothesis) only relative to another sentence (i.e. the evidence). Frequency probability is attributed to a class of events (i.e. as a property) relative to another class of events (i.e. the reference class). To be meaningful a probability-sentence must be complete, and so probability has to be taken as relation of at least two terms. When not explicitly mentioned the second term of the relation is tacitly implied and this makes for ambiguity, for the sentence in question may be completed in at least two different ways.

Both the hypothesis and the evidence are synthetic sentences (in the language-system chosen), for they are used to refer to extra-linguistic facts. The hypothesis contained in the sentence (A) refers to the occurrence of rain and the suppressed evidence is represented by weather observations and similar information. The sentence (A) can be re-constructed as : 'The hypothesis of rain to-morrow is confirmed by meteorological evidence to the degree p'. The inductive sentence is then also concerned with physical events, although indirectly. The frequency sentence speaks about a physical property of a sequence of physical events. The inductive sentence speaks about a hypothesis about physical events and judges this hypothesis on evidence. It is an estimate of the occurence of a property (or event) relative to *known* instances of occurrence, and the estimate is given according to certain rules, i.e. the logical and mathematical rules of estimation. Frequency probability is then a physical property of events, inductive probability is a semantic property of sentences since it depends on the meaning of the sentences involved.

It follows from the definition of 'frequency probability' that a sentence containing this term always refers to a large number of events. The relative frequency of any given property can of course be observed only in a finite segment of a sequence. Bernoulli's theorem shows that, under certain conditions, the value of the frequency will remain within prescribed limits when the sequence is continued indefinitely. It is argued sometimes that this confers a predictive character on a probability-sentence of this kind.

This argument is incorrect. When a mathematical theorem like Bernoulli's is applied, this must involve an additional hypothesis about facts. That any *actual* sequence of events can be so described, or that the mathematical formalism is applicable, is naturally an assumption. When the frequency sentence is taken as holding for the unobserved continuation of the sequence it is no longer purely descriptive. Rather it incorporates the prediction in the form of a hypothesis that the observed frequency will remain stable in the actual, future, sequence. In other words, the concept of frequency probability is not applicable without *presupposing* that of inductive probability. This of course has often been noted.

A so-called inductive conception of relative frequency probability has been formulated by Reichenbach in order to overcome this objection and so to merge the two concepts of probability. But is such a conception permissible? The existence of a limit must then be postulated as the principle of induction, and it becomes a necessary condition for predictability that we can apply inductive method. So we are forced to define what we mean by 'predictable' since it 'will turn out to entail the postulate of the existence of certain series having a limit of the frequency'. This is an ontological assumption, for it is tantamount to prescribing a property nature must possess. It makes no sense to say that only such events are predictable whose sequence has a certain property, for it is just this property (as well as other properties) that we might wish to predict. Prediction is possible, but this is not because nature, or certain event sequences, behave in a prescribed manner. And induction is not a search for suitable causal sequences but a logical method of confirming sentences about them.

The future continuation of an *actual* sequence can never be postulated to be Bernoullian, i.e. to follow a mathematical law, even if the frequency is stable in the observed segment of this sequence. Such behaviour cannot be prescribed, only conjectured. A hypothesis is thus introduced than can and must be tested by observation and confirmed on the evidence so obtained. The concept of frequency probability alone does not suffice to ascribe a predictive character to a probability-sentence, and its inductive conception achieves prediction only at the cost of prescription.

Of course this Bernoullian argument falls in with the prejudice of traditional epistemology according to which inductive inference leads from limited evidence to a more comprehensive hypothesis by the principle of induction. Bernoulli's theorem, when used as such a principle, is a synthetic sentence, since it then says something about future events. It means that induction becomes an illegitimate deductive inference disguised as a mathematical theorem. If 'probability' is defined in terms of relative frequency in the long run, or as a limit, or in any way as referring to an as yet unknown future, it must introduce a hypothesis about this future whenever it is applied to actual instances. When used only within a mathematical calculus the limit is merely a mathematical expression formed according to certain rules. A limit is then no more than a convenient notation, and there are no objections to its use. On the contrary, the invention of the infinitesimal calculus has been the main support of modern science. But it is a matter of interpretation when the calculus is applied. Bernoulli's theorem, since it speaks about the continuation of a sequence according to a rule (otherwise there would be no limit) is interpreted to hold for the future of actual sequences. But a deductive relation can never be predictive. If the frequency concept is used for prediction, it requires an extra hypothesis in order to guarantee the stability of the frequency, and this changes the character of the probability-sequence. A *pure* frequency sentence is only descriptive.

Of course, we are rarely interested in purely descriptive probability-sentences in scientific practice. When we gather statistical material we mean to use it for prediction. However, weather records or mortality statistics for a given year say nothing about what is going to happen the following year, unless a suitable hypothesis is introduced. And this hypothesis need not express the stability of observed frequency if the mortality tables concern a year in which a serious epidemic occurred. Statistics by themselves are merely a convenient manner of presenting data. 'One can prove anything with statistics', i.e. as with all mathematics it depends on our interpretation whether or not we use it correctly.

That most probability-sentences of the frequency kind are

also used for prediction and so contain another concept of probability seems to be one reason for well-known difficulties in defining 'probability' as 'relative frequency in the long run', that is, in terms of a limit. The sequence described in terms of this probability must satisfy two contradictory conditions : it must possess a limit, i.e. there must be a rule of formation for the members of the sequence ; and it must be random, i.e. there must be a general independence between the members. The limit character obviously belongs to a *mathematical* sequence, and so is part of the symbolism used. Randomness is a characteristic that belongs to a *physical* sequence of events : such a sequence may be regarded as statistical, that is, its members possess a certain physical, though collective, property designated by 'frequency probability'. For in certain causal sequences every member of the sequence possesses the same characteristics, and this is described by a law of the deterministic type. Other causal sequences are such that only a certain number of its members possess a given characteristic, and this is described by a statistical law. When we find that a causal sequence is random in the sense that only some of its members have the property prescribed, we reject a deterministic law for its description but choose the probability law. The failure to separate the two concepts of probability confuses the rule of formation of an expression with the condition of its applicability ; and this engenders the contradiction.

7. *Confirmation*

There is general agreement in saying that induction consists in applying probability to sentences, but disagreement how this is to be done. This dispute concerns mainly the logical analysis of inductive sentences, not the mathematics. In every textbook on Probability we find the same solutions for typical inductive problems. The examples are usually taken from gambling, i.e. concern the outcome of statistical problems. To discuss the difficulties arising from applying the concept of probability would make necessary a presentation of the mathematical theory. But there are some points of logic which can be discussed without recourse to detailed mathematics.

We want to find out, for instance, to what extent a present, or known, state of affairs allows us to predict a future state, for induction consists in confirming one sentence (the hypothesis) with respect to another (the evidence). This means, of course, that we introduce a model of the world, in the sense that we must say what possible states or events may occur, so that we can judge how much, if at all, our present knowledge warrants a prediction of the future. Induction cannot provide *absolute* predictions, that is, judge a hypothesis about the future regardless of what may happen. We need a universe of discourse, or we must construct (at least in outline) a theory describing the possible states of the world which may, in our view, arise.

In practice, say when solving problems of dicing, the context is obvious and so need not be explicitly mentioned. This often holds in every-day problems. We know the relevant factors to be considered and need not take into account possibilities that are, in this context, irrelevant. When we throw dice we know that nothing matters save that the dice are thrown in a haphazard manner. Rather, we assume it. For it is conceivable that a skilled gambler may roll the dice in such a manner that he can influence the outcome of the throw ; or the surface on which the dice are thrown may not be smooth ; or the beaker (if one is used) may be so constructed that it favours one result rather than another. All these assumptions, just as our knowledge that, in a given case, the dice are not loaded, are founded on previous experience which we use to visualize the possible happenings. So we come to the conclusion that the various outcomes of a throw are all equally probable, and this assumption of equiprobability if often made, though sometimes unjustifiably. It all depends whether or not such a model of the possible states of the world (i.e. possible outcomes of a throw) fits the actual occasion.

The mistaken assumption of equally probable events is a typical example of the difficulty confronting us when we wish to apply probability. For it was assumed that there exists a universal principle of *insufficient reason* that allows us in all cases to evaluate the possible states and assign equal probability to them. Ignorance, in the sense of no reason to the contrary being known, was taken as basis for constructing a model world, or universe of discourse. The classic example is Laplace's rule of succession derived on this assumption. It states that the probability of an event is given by the formula $(m+1)/(n+2)$ if after n trials the event has occurred m times. If m and n are sufficiently large we may approximate the formula by the expression m/n. Laplace therefore concluded in answer, I suppose, to Hume's problem, that the odds are 1,826,214 to 1 in favour of the sun's rising to-morrow, since he assumed that the sun had risen for at least 5000 years, or 1,826,213 days.

This answer is rejected by common sense, and modern writers on probability have strongly condemned Laplace's argument. We cannot say that it is equally probable whether the sun does or does not rise, nor is the probability of successive occurrences constant : the laws of planetary motion, and the laws of physics in general, bring overwhelming evidence in favour of its occurrence, etc. The point I want to make is merely this. It seems at first odd to say that we must specify the universe of discourse before we can make an induction. But there is no other way. Whenever we apply mathematical theory we must interpret it. A model world is assumed, or a language system, which describes the possible states of the world so that we can assign probabilities to them. Whether the model fits and whether the initial probability assigned to each state of the world is correct can only be judged by experience. That in practice we often need not mention the model is simply because the context of many problems is familiar ; but it remains as a *logical* requirement for applying the concept of probability to hypotheses. The sentences admitted to the language system describe the possible states of this model world, i.e. are state-descriptions. A hypothesis is made about the unknown past, present, or future : it is, then, a sentence concerning possible states, it has a certain logical range and so has the evidence which is concerned with actual states of the world. Modern statisticians describe this by saying that probability theory can be applied meaningfully only if we agree on what we wish to take as possible results of an experiment or observation. Each such outcome is represented as a *sample point* in a *sample space*, and this allows us to make use of measure theory and other mathematical tools for setting up a calculus of probability.

The hypothesis is confirmed if its range overlaps with that of the evidence, that is, by the degree of confirmation as we call probability when applied to hypotheses. Can a calculus be set up for the degree of confirmation so that we can have a logic of induction ? Yes, to deny this is too radical though it is obviously not an easy task. But we have a mathematical-statistical calculus already ; and hypotheses and evidence are usually formulated in ordinary language so that it must be possible, in principle, to re-construct a set of rules for the use of probability-sentences. Statisticians do apply probability to sentences all the time, though they 'translate' them as quickly as possible into mathematical language, by means of various and often very limited models, e.g. the bag-and-ball model.

There may also be many possible systems of inductive logic, and our demands must not be unreasonable. Are the odds in favour of a certain horse simply determined by the frequency with which it has won previously, or must we not consider also the skill of the jockey, the state of the track, etc.? Many factors that we know must influence the probability are difficult to describe in practice, to say nothing of evaluating them numerically. The best we may be able to do at the moment is, perhaps, not very impressive, that is, construct a system of rules which applies only to logically very simple sentences ; and so we must be content, in present practice, with a description by model when applying probability to logically more complex sentences. But this is no reason for denying that a better system may not be constructed in the future.

Both the hypothesis and the existential sentence confirming it belong to a theory or language system, and confirmation is relative to the evidence which *can* be expressed in the system. If numerical values are assigned as a measure (for the overlapping ranges), they will depend on the rules of range adopted for the system. This is of course always so : we cannot give, say, the length of something in centimetres unless a standard length is previously defined in terms of centimetres. So we cannot derive values of probability except from other probabilities previously specified, e.g. the initial probabilities. What number is correlated with the width of the ranges of the two sentences is arbitrary but need not be subjective ; just as any scale is arbitrary but can be used to determine an objective measure, relative to the scale chosen. There may be various scales depending upon extra-linguistic considerations—that is, on scientific practice. We do not derive or prove the hypothesis but judge its probability (on evidence) ; and judging is always relative to a given standard. Only actual science can provide a standard for accepting a hypothesis.

How are we then to assign numerical values to the probability of a hypothesis? Again, I do not wish to give a mathematical theory but only to bring out a point of logic. If the hypothesis is statistical, i.e. concerns a frequency, this is often fairly simple, and the textbooks on Statistics give many methods for evaluating the probability of hypotheses of this type. It is general practice to take as the estimate of a relative frequency (i.e. as the probability of the hypothesis) a number close to, or the same as, the expected value of the observed frequency. In recent writings on the theory of confirmation this usage has been re-constructed as the *best estimate*, and so its scale, or metric, is given by a definition. To return to the example : the estimated value of the probability that we will obtain one point with one throw of a single die is made to approach the value of the actual frequency of this occurrence in the long run. For we know of course that, with a true die and under normal conditions, the relative frequency is stable so that by continuing the series of throws we increase the evidence favourable to the hypothesis. This is the reason why the scale of the estimate is chosen according to the convention given.

The scale, or metric, is always a matter of definition, and so there is no question of an a priori judgment being tacitly introduced here, as has sometimes been alleged. Nor can the objection be upheld that a principle of uniformity is thereby smuggled into the theory of confirmation and of induction. To specify a metric is a mathematical (i.e. formal) method. And the assumption of uniformity, or stability, of a frequency—either suggested by evidence or arbitrarily made—is justified only by practice.

This is illustrated by the well known statistical method of maximum likelihood. The method requires three different kinds of information : the statistical evidence, a mathematical law of distribution, and a hypothetical population of which the evidence is a sample. The problem normally consists in finding that hypothetical population for which the known evidence is the most likely sample.

This method is purely mathematical, and is a typical instance of statistical, inductive, inference. The hypothetical (or original) population is not derived from the sample but constructed by means of a distribution function assumed to hold for it. Moreover, the sample is not only obtained by a random process (otherwise it would not be unbiased) but also has been selected from the hypothetical population by a specific law or rule. For instance, if the distribution of the original population and the probability of sampling follow the Gaussian law, then the sample also follows the same law, and so on.

Suppose a small sample is found to possess a certain property with the relative frequency r. Can we predict that among the N members of a very large population this property will occur and what will then be the value of its frequency? Assume this value to be p, for the moment : we want to find out whether the values r and p are the same or not. We make a hypothesis or choose a distribution law for the population ; the mathematical function representing the distribution contains at least one free parameter ; and we adjust this parameter so that the sample, for the given law of selection, has the greatest probability of occurring. In other words, we constructed or invented a hypothesis and make it fit the sample by adjusting the scale. If we fail, then we may have to find either new evidence or invent a new hypothesis or choose a different law of sampling, or any two of these items, or possibly all three of them.

For example, a penny is tossed 100 times and found to give 50 heads, i.e. r equals ½. We estimate its 'true' value for a large number of tosses by choosing the hypothetical probability p to have the same, or nearly the same, value as r. This value makes the observed sample the most likely one for the hypothetical population assumed, and any other value would make the sample less likely to occur. Usually, if we find that for a given hypothesis (distribution law) the probability of the sample is very small, we reject the hypothesis since we accept both the sample (the evidence) and the rule of sampling.

Incidentally, this description of the maximum likelihood method is found in every textbook on Statistics. And yet, in some of them, the author also describes induction as a method of *deriving* a hypothesis from the data : how can one call inventing a hypothesis, adjusting its parameter, and choosing a law of selection a 'logical derivation'? The empiricist prejudice which tempts people to say this is, indeed, very strong, but it is obviously not true that we simply read off our hypotheses from data.

The best estimate as mentioned before then appears as an instance of the application of this method (though, of course, there are other methods as well for this purpose). The relative frequency in the long run is the most likely value, or best estimate, if the distribution law according to which the hypothetical population is given is simply a *constant*. We make many trials, say consisting of 100 tosses with a coin, and in each series so obtained the frequency of heads is practically $\frac{1}{2}$. In other words, the constant frequency of an event sequence—the datum—is the most likely sample of a population of frequencies that all have the same value. This choice of the best estimate cannot be said to bring a principle of uniformity surrepetitiously into the metric of inductive logic. It is merely a mathematical definition specifying a rule which is suitable to the problem in hand.

Estimation is a branch of the mathematical theory of probability, and many methods have been developed for this purpose. The estimated value of any variable is given by a formula, and so is obtained by formal means. Since it is the task of inductive logic to state rules for estimating, i.e. for finding the probability of a hypothesis on evidence, we see that, at least for certain instances, it is possible to give rules and to determine numerical values.

If the hypothesis refers to a single event no such method is readily available. We must try to construct a language-system so that we can ascertain the ranges of the two sentences involved, i.e. describe the class of facts which would make each sentence true. What scale is to be applied to the ranges is however, as before, a matter of convenience and convention. The practical difficulties, at least at the present time, are overwhelming since descriptive semantics has not been sufficiently developed to allow the formulation of sentences (for the hypothesis and the evidence) of the logical complexity needed in application. The language-systems so far exemplified do not suffice in logical richness, but the simple systems which have been worked out illustrate that it is in principle possible to define a metric for them. The choice will obviously be guided by the decision to make the probability of a hypothesis (or degree of confirmation) approach our judgments in practice, and the choice of the metric as well as of the language-system as a whole can only be justified by success. What is important for the understanding of induction is, however, to see that it is a *logical* method.

To illustrate that induction in every-day life is no different from what it is in science, let me tell a true story. While riding on a bus in the beginning of August I saw a friend standing in front of Selfridge's with a large, paper covered, box in his hand ; the box seemed to be very light and to be held by some sort of handle. I inferred (a) that the box was a newly bought suitcase and (b) that my friend was going on his holiday soon. These two hypotheses were confirmed when I jumped off the bus and asked him. That is, in ordinary contexts it is very easy to invent suitable hypotheses and to evaluate them, since the possible facts which make them true are quickly visualised.

That it is in practice often difficult to specify a suitable metric for inductive sentences is, I suppose, one reason why inductive logic, or at least the numerical evaluation of inductive probability, has often been rejected. But it is not a good argument against this thesis that an explicit and complete formulation of such systems has not yet been achieved. Actual science is not completely formalised but we can make it work all the same ; just as we can use language without being able to state precise grammatical rules. It is an odd view that denies the use of semantics on this ground : like the inverse view that took deductive logic to be a finished system and so retarded its development for two thousand years. Since a sufficiently rich descriptive semantic system cannot be constructed as yet, we must use simpler models, approximations, and so are often forced to fall back on some sort of psychological intuition for judging hypotheses. This is shown by the trivial example about the suitcase. A better logical re-construction of inductive method may be hoped for with the development of descriptive semantics. The main point I want to make is this. Induction is a logical and mathematical (statistical) method and so a calculus and rules can, at least in principle, be developed.

If the probability-sentence is of the inductive kind, what is then the correct analysis? The sentence (A) 'It is probable that it will rain to-morrow' expresses the probability of a future event, or it assigns a probability to a hypothesis. A prediction is made in the clause 'It will rain to-morrow', and its probability is judged on evidence, but neither the degree of probability nor the evidence are explicitly mentioned. This is a standard form of an inductive sentence, and such sentences always refer to some unknown state of affairs.

This probability-sentence must then be regarded as the *con-*

clusion of an inductive inference which is not explicitly made. The suppression of the evidence, i.e. in this instance the weather records and similar knowledge, tends to obscure the logical character of the sentence. According to the modern conception, induction is a non-demonstrative inference relating two sentences The rules are given by the calculus of probability suitably interpreted so that it applies to the semantic language-system in which the sentences are formulated. The conclusion of this inference is thus a sentence stating the degree of probability assigned to the hypothesis on evidence and so is derived by inductive logic. It follows that the inductive probability-sentence must be *analytic*. The sentence is analytic with respect to the language-system in which it is used since the probability relation between the two sentences is determined by the rules of a calculus. We need not even know whether the hypothesis and the evidence are *actually* true or false. If we know their meaning (i.e. their *possible* truth), and so their logical ranges, the degree to which these overlap can be computed.

When we predict an event with a certain degree of confirmation and the event fails to occur, what do we say? The empirical character of the hypothesis and of the evidence seems to confer some sort of factual import on the inductive sentence. But this failure may embark us on two different courses of action. We may abandon the hypothesis if the evidence is considered reliable, or we may search for more evidence. The low degree of confirmation does not tell us what to do : a good hypothesis may fail for lack of evidence ; and a poor hypothesis may obtain more support than it merits for the evidence may turn out later to be incomplete or biased, *vide* the case of the Piltdown man. In other words, the actual truth of the hypothesis and of the evidence does not affect the probability which evaluates the relation between them, and so the inductive sentence can only be analytic (in the language system used). Only success in practice can justify a given inductive method.

The analytic character of certain probability-sentences (here called 'inductive') has often been noted. Such a view does not create difficulties, but rather rescues us from the traditional puzzle. If inductive sentences were empirical, they would themselves have to be subject to inductive inquiry, and there would be an infinite regress (which is acknowledged in the frequency interpretation). This is serious enough in itself. But the empirical character of such sentences also entails that the rules of inductive inference are used as synthetic sentences, and this is impossible. For it implies *a priori* assumptions about the world, and so induction would achieve prediction only at the cost of prescription. Unless the sentences of the form 'It is probable that . . .' stating the conclusion of an inductive inference are analytic (for a given language system) no logical re-construction of inductive method seems possible.

If the probability-sentence is purely *descriptive*, i.e. states an observed frequency, then it is of course an empirical sentence, and so it is verifiable. The given series of die throws has a certain, rather *elusive since collective*, physical property. This property does not belong to the single die alone nor to the single throw, but to the whole sequence of throws with a particular die. This is a description of fact and cannot be construed as prediction. For a loaded die the various results of a throw do not occur with the same frequency and this is easily decided by appeal to experience: it may of course require a large number of observations. It is in this way that it differs from other factual sentences, for which a single observation suffices to test the presence or absence of a given property.

A probability-sentence of the pure frequency kind is descriptive, and completely verifiable by experience, in the same sense in which any factual sentence is verifiable. If finite sequences are used, the frequency of any property occurring can, in principle, be found by counting. If finite, mathematical, sequences are used, the limit of the relative frequency represents merely a convenient notation and has by itself no predictive import. It must be read as the value of the frequency within a certain interval, for the finite number of observations that can be made, and so it is again completely verifiable if the interval is included. This is exactly the same situation as when we take acceleration as the limit of the time rate of change of velocity : the use of differential calculus does not make acceleration, or any other physical property so described, an unobservable quantity. Only if the limit of the frequency is taken to refer to an *infinite but actual* sequence, then it is not verifiable ; but in this instance it includes an inductive hypothesis, and this changes the character of the probability-sentence.

A probability-sentence of the inductive kind, i.e. a sentence judging a hypothesis on given evidence, is analytic, and so no verification by experience is required or indeed possible. The inductive sentence, in its full formulation, contains two sub-sentences (the hypothesis and the evidence) both of which are used as synthetic sentences. But this does not entail that the probability-sentence as a whole must therefore be synthetic (factual) : it is simply not used for saying something about the world. This task is already performed by the hypothesis and also by the evidence—one sentence saying something new about the world and the other saying what is known. And the inductive sentence is used to judge whether this new knowledge is war-ranted by the known data. Such a judgment says nothing new about the world but is the result of (actual as well as hypothetical) knowledge in which it is already implicit, and inductive rules make it explicit.

We say, for example, 'It is probably raining now', and then we open the window to see whether it does or doesn't. This appears to make the probability-sentence factual, but only because it is incompletely formulated. For by uttering the sentence I state not only the hypothesis 'It is raining now' but also give my judgment, on the basis of whatever evidence I have at the moment of speak-ing. When I open the window I obtain new evidence which will change my judgment ; and if I actually see the rain, there is no longer any reason for making a hypothesis (or for judging it), and I simply assert that it rains.

A probability-sentence of this kind is the conclusion of an inductive inference, and it is agreed that this conclusion cannot be proved factually true, nor even probable. There are no mysterious epistemological reasons for this as is sometimes argued and no ontological assumptions are involved, but merely logical reasons. For the hypothesis is an invention of the scientist suggested by experience, and statistical (inductive) rules check it against the evidence. So the conclusion of an inductive inference is not the hypothesis but the sentence judging it on the evidence, i.e. the inductive probability-sentence ; and both the hypothesis and the evidence are factual sentences available before the judg-ment can be made at all. If the hypothesis is confirmed on the evidence, then it does represent new knowledge, and this con-firmation is expressed by an analytic probability-sentence. Only in this indirect sense can induction be said to provide knowledge. For we gain knowledge by learning ; and we learn by experience, at least sometimes. Though we use induction to establish new knowledge, that is, a new hypothesis, we do not obtain it in this way. To believe that we learn by induction is part of the inductivist myth which identifies a psychological process with a logical method : this is a rationalisation—that is, the human mind is taken as functioning in a simpler and more orderly way than it really is. Thus the inductive probability-sentence states a logical relation between two sentences, or a semantic relation, since the meaning of the two sentences is involved. Inductive method applies probability calculus to sentences according to rules, and the corresponding probability-sentence is analytic.

Consequently, it cannot be maintained that probability-sentences are factual but incapable of factual verification : some of them are analytic (i.e. the inductive kind) and others are synthetic (i.e. the frequency kind). The confusion of the two concepts of probability has given rise to the view that all probability-sentences are peculiar in the sense that they are not verifiable, since the rules according to which one sort is used are taken to apply to the other. Indeed, on this basis, an argument is brought forth not only denying the classification of (declarative) sentences into synthetic and analytic, but even rejecting the criterion of verifiability.

No one would deny that, in ordinary discourse and sometimes perhaps in science, probability-sentences are used in an ambiguous manner. We do not quite know what we want to say and so we do not use our sentences clearly and correctly. This does not mean that we can never use language properly, or that we cannot attempt to make our linguistic usage clear by giving a logical re-construction and by providing rules. Moreover, any re-construction here intended is of the informative use of language, and the non-informative use (emotional, etc.) is disregarded, though this may on occasion occur even in science (e.g. persuasion by authority).

It has been argued previously that the distinction of analytic and synthetic applies only to declarative sentences. This is merely a classification convenient to show that such sentences are used in two different ways. And that factual sentences must, in principle, be capable of factual verification is no more than a definition of the term 'factual' ('empirical', 'synthetic') in its normal usage.

To say, therefore, that probability-sentences are factual but incapable of verification is to ascribe meaning to them while refusing to give a rule for their usage. But how then can they be used? If our sentences are to be meaningful, we must say what we want them to mean. To refuse to give rules of usage is to abandon the informative use of language, although a persuasive or, in general, an emotional use may still be possible. (When we say that science rejects metaphysics, all we mean is that such sentences do not provide any information though it is claimed that they do, since we are told no rules of use can be given for them.) According to our analysis, however, we can give rules of usage for probability-sentences, at least within the context of science.

8. *Corrigibility and scientific method*

The epistemological view of a unique, synthetic, *rule of induction* suggests that there is a universal mechanism, either imposed upon nature by the human mind or inherent in natural processes. But rules are not facts which may be found by observation or by self-observation. Rules apply to language—they are made so that they approximate as closely as possible to an actual or a new, proposed, usage of our sentences. Nor must it be believed that we must use rules in the sense that we cannot help it whenever we speak or write. In ordinary conversation we need not make use of grammar in the sense of consciously following the accepted rules ; to speak correctly or grammatically merely means that our sentences, when analysed, are found to follow a certain pattern ; and it is only when we are in doubt that we check our usage against the rules. If we want to ensure that we make sense, then we specify explicitly the rules, and these may be either well known, like grammar, or the less familiar but more exacting rules of logic. But to apply logic (or mathematics) to our expressions does not mean introducing factual knowledge ; it is making this knowledge more explicit. To improve the formalisation of our language, or to give rules, is to say more clearly what we mean.

The rules of induction, or of statistical inference, are given by the calculus of probability applied to the two sentences (the hypothesis and the evidence), and so they are *tautological*. Like all rules, they belong not to the language we speak but to the meta-language, or terminology, which we use for speaking about our expressions. They do not introduce new knowledge ; for tautologies are compatible with all possible states of affairs. If the rules were not of this kind, they would say something about the world (unless they were contradictions), and this would limit their applicability. We use tautologies in order to make clear what we are saying about the world ; but what we say need not therefore be a tautology.

There are *many* kinds of statistical (inductive) inference. There is no one principle of induction, but various rules are used by scientists for confirming their hypotheses. Such rules will depend on the form of the sentences involved and on the situation to which they apply. There is no reason to assume that every sort of hypothesis is judged by all sorts of evidence in exactly the same way. And new inductive methods may be invented with the progress of science, e.g. Fisher's method of maximum likelihood was developed in relatively recent years.

To discuss in detail the different rules of inference it would be necessary to describe how to construct a formal calculus of confirmation, and this in turn involves logical and mathematical formulae. The probability of a hypothesis on evidence must depend on the logical form of the two sentences, since this affects their logical range and so the degree to which they overlap ; and so on. It must suffice here to point out what is of general interest.

In statistical theory, for example, we sometimes wish to predict the characteristics of a sample selected from a population. We may have reasons for assuming, e.g. that in a very large number of nails produced by a machine every twenty-third is defective. We buy a small packet of nails, and assuming the nails well mixed before packing, we want to know how many of the nails we bought are unusable. This has been called the direct inference. But we may have only a sample at our disposal and make the inference from one sample to another, in a predictive inference. Or we infer by analogy, a form of inference that, in spite of certain difficulties, is often used in science with good success. The evidence says that some individuals have a certain property, and a few among them are found to possess still another property ; the hypothesis to be judged is whether the remaining individuals also possess the second property. Then, there is the inverse inference from sample to population, etc.

Finally, there is the universal inference ; but it is not as universal as is generally supposed. Traditional theory is concerned with this one kind of inference only, according to which a universal sentence is confirmed by limited evidence. This arises from the traditional view that all laws are hypotheses and that all hypotheses are universal, i.e. apply to an infinite number of instances. If laws are construed as being unrestrictedly universal in scope, that is, as holding for all, actual and possible, events so that the law can never fail, then the sentences expressing them are analytic (within the theory). This has been pointed out before. We can use the law for a genuine prediction only when we obtain from it a singular, existential, hypothesis by instantiation, that is, by making use of the initial and boundary conditions which may hold for a specific instance. This is the so-called instance confirmation which allows us to find out whether the *next* instance of an event has, or has not, the properties predicted by the hypothesis. And we need no more than this. For we do not wish to find out whether *all* future instances have the property the law ascribes to them when taken as a hypothesis, or predict for all eternity. Such a demand is outside science ; and it arises from the epistemological myth that events happen according to the iron rule of law. But it is not a factual question to ask for an infinite number of confirming instances : infinity is a concept that has logical, but not physical, meaning. So universal sentences of this kind can only be analytic. It also shows that probability-sentences containing a prediction cannot be interpreted in terms of relative frequency. Frequency probability, by definition, cannot say anything about the next occurrence of an event, or about a single instance.

The rules of statistical (inductive) inference must not only take account of the logical form of the sentences but also of the situation in which the inference is applied. This is shown by the so-called variety of instances. A single (positive or negative) instance will often count more than a great number of similar instances in the confirmation of a hypothesis. This depends on many factors. In certain applications, the distribution of instances is of import, so that those that are better distributed (say, with smaller variance) will strongly affect the degree of confirmation. It also depends on the logical *strength* of the property, i.e. the range of significance of a composite property. The fewer individuals there are that can satisfy significantly the corresponding propositional function, the narrower is its range ; but the more important it will be if such an individual is found. If a property is described in the language system chosen as conjunction of many simple properties, then the longer the conjunction, the stronger the composite property.

This strength of a property is not easy and, in practice, nearly impossible to determine. For example, if we say 'It is probable that it will rain in an hour', then we have to evaluate the various pieces of evidence available now, e.g. black clouds, the wind velocity, the humidity of the air, a recent fall in barometric pressure, and so on. Are all these indications of equal strength in supporting the hypothesis, and if only some of them are found and others are absent, how do we proceed then? Clearly, this depends on the theory we have telling us how rain comes about ; and a theory which is sufficiently detailed so as to bring in all these factors is not easy to construct.

The confirmation of hypotheses in actual science is very complicated and involves many steps. Not only the hypothesis but also the evidence may be sentences of great logical complexity. When we confirm a hypothesis we use not only our data as evidence but other laws as well. This *concatenation* is so strong that, at least within the framework of a well established theory, a decision whether to accept or to reject a hypothesis can be obtained by very few experiments. The point I want to make is only this. There are many rules of inductive, statistical, inference, and not only one ; and these rules are tautologies.

Both in science and in every-day life, we often do induction implicitly rather than by an explicit inference, and so we tend to forget that there are rules and what character they possess. But deduction is also done intuitively, so to speak, and we do not always state an explicit syllogism. This I suppose is the reason why logic was once regarded as the art of thinking ; and it is one reason why, even to-day, some people want to take induction as a special power of reasoning of which human minds are capable. We guess and anticipate and we want to be certain of the future : so we take psychological credibility for logical confirmation.

Nature, or the human mind, is expected to supply not only a clear-cut hypothesis but even an exact value of its probability, for we want the *best* of all possible hypotheses. But this is, once more, the pseudo-problem of justifying induction. We demand too much and we are not omniscient : we can never have a catalogue of *all* hypotheses that can be formulated about a particular problem. Nor can we ever have *all* the evidence that can or will be found in the future ; and our results are not unique in this sense. It is not true that only one theory, or hypothesis, is accepted and a solution to every problem found, ultimately : the history of science does not bear this out. This belief in the omnipotence of science is, in fact, making a mockery of science : for this *scientism* represents the same, superstitious, attitude which, in previous times, ascribed such power to a supernatural agency.

The attitude underlying science is quite different. It is shown by the *corrigibility* which is indeed the most important feature of science. It is this which distinguishes scientific thinking from all other forms of thought : religion, and philosophy also, have only too often claimed infallibility. But to reject such claims does not mean that the scientist must be a sceptic. A scientific theory is never ultimate, as J. J. Thomson once remarked, and its object is physical rather than metaphysical. 'From the point of view of the physicist, a theory . . . is a policy rather than a creed'.

For we learn by experimenting, by trial and error, and not by induction. Learning is a psychological process, and the ability to learn is a measure of intelligence of which, alas, we sometimes need more than we have. Induction is a logical and mathematical (statistical) method. It does not describe how we obtain knowledge ; nor does it prescribe what we must do in order to acquire knowledge. The method merely re-constructs in logical terms the rules we actually use for judging a hypothesis on evidence. To have learned from experience is then to construct new theories and hypotheses and to show that this knowledge is better confirmed than what was previously known.

Thus we are enabled to correct past mistakes. Scientific method is self-correcting, for it allows us not only to check our theories against experiment but also to change, and even to abandon, them if the evidence so requires. How is this done? The mathematical method of successive approximations is the usual illustration of inductive corrigibility. An equation is assumed to possess a solution that is not directly obtainable and so is represented by a trial solution, say, by a power series. When the coefficients of successive powers in the variable are determined, the solution gradually improves, provided the series satisfies certain general conditions of convergence.

This property belongs to a mathematical method, but not to nature—it is not as if nature possessed ultimate characteristics which we slowly but surely discover. Nor does there exist a final world-formula, as yet undiscovered, which is gradually approached by science. Ideas of this sort are a refinement on the principle of uniformity and an illegitimate answer to the epistemological question : What is the Nature of nature? Self-correction cannot be conceived as a mechanism, like the governor on a steam-engine ; and although difficult to analyse it cannot be so automatic. (This seems to suggest the idea of mind as a concealed mechanism, with cog-wheels whirring and levers clicking, and we don't even have to push a button.) What it expresses, after all, is the simple fact that we do learn from experience, at least sometimes. We use the trial and error method ; but the new trial is not a logical outcome of previous error. Whether or not we are inspired by failure to invent a new, and better, hypothesis is a matter of psychology. But we can judge whether we have learned from experience by applying inductive (statistical) rules to the new hypothesis and establishing its confirmation.

We cannot learn from experience, however, unless our theories are so built that we can apply the trial and error method to them. Corrigibility then means that certain logical requirements must be met when theories are constructed. A new theory (i.e. language system, or universe of discourse, or model world) is to be constructed so that it contains the previous theory as a lower approximation, e.g. quantum mechanics contains Newtonian mechanics as prescribed by the correspondence principle. And the higher theory must allow us to formulate new hypotheses and so provide new possibilities for testing. We build up a scientific theory so that it is *open* to experiment.

This manner of theory construction has nothing to do with probability (as the empiricists would have us believe). The corrigibility of scientific method does not consist in constructing probabilities of probabilities of probabilities, ad inf., as the frequency theory of induction suggests, but in making successive estimates of the same (or a different) hypothesis on the basis of different (or the same) evidence. But it is up to us to invent a new hypothesis and to search for new evidence.

The willingness to expose our theories to the test, to change and, even, to abandon them is what most characterizes the scientific attitude ; and it finds its expression in the way in which we construct theories. We reject as unscientific any theory which is *closed* to experiment. Such a theory, e.g. astrology, might well describe experience in some manner as indeed its adherents claim that it does; but we cannot accept this as a test. 'Experience' is a word that has come to mean almost anything. It is the experiment which, alone, can be accepted as a test ; and an experiment is deliberately performed in accordance with a hypothesis which has been derived from a theory. Science as we know it to-day began only when the experimental method was discovered. In this way hypothesis and experiment are united, and we can test our theories significantly and show their success or failure. It is for this reason that we may say that scientific method is the best means for making our knowledge secure.

I have attempted to give a semantic analysis of the main concepts of physics and of scientific method. Since science makes use of formalism, this non-technical account is necessarily inadequate. There are no doubt many sins of omission and of commission, and so I may have sometimes given the wrong impression. But I want to make clear that nothing I have said, or tried to say, implies that I have a doctrine to spread, or a new *-ism* to found. Our knowledge is contained in the theories, laws, and hypotheses of science and these are expressed in statements and formulae the task is to give their meaning. To apply logic and semantics (like applying mathematics) to problems of knowledge, or to make clearer the meaning of our sentences, is not a matter of dogma. Science does not claim infallibility, nor does it provide ready-made solutions for all and every problem. The scientific attitude is to solve problems, and if unsuccessful, to start anew, always guided by a hypothesis and corrected by experiment.

INDEX

GEORGE ALLEN & UNWIN LTD
London: 40 Museum Street, W.C.1

Auckland: 24 Wyndham Street
Sydney, N.S.W.: Bradbury House, 55 York Street
Cape Town: 58–60 Long Street
Bombay: 15 Graham Road, Ballard Estate, Bombay 1
Calcutta: 17 Chittaranjan Avenue, Calcutta 13
New Delhi: 13–14 Ajmere Gate Extension, New Delhi 1
Karachi: Haroon Chambers, South Napier Road, Karachi 2
Toronto: 91 Wellington Street West
São Paulo: Avenida 9 de Julho 1138–Ap. 51

The Laws of Nature

R. E. PEIERLS *Demy 8vo 21s. net*

How big is an atom and why does it not collapse ? How do we know that neutrons spin ? The development of Physics, from Newton's laws to relativity and quantum theory, the structure of atoms and nuclei and the recent discoveries of new particles are explained without technical jargon and without mathematics. This is the contemporary physicist's world expounded in lucid English. It is a book which can be read by an engineer, by a general practitioner, by a philosopher or by a sixth former with an enquiring mind.

Popular books in this field are not uncommon, but this is a "popularization" by one of the most senior of the British team which worked on the atomic project in the U.S.A. during the war. Professor Peierls was amongst the first scientists in England to see the possibilities of atomic energy and he worked on this undertaking from 1940 until the end of the war, after 1943 in the United States. He is a Vice-President and past President of the Atomic Scientists Association, which he helped to found. He also has experience of lecturing to audiences ranging from mathematics professors to housewives, an experience which has stood him in good stead in writing this book.

Introduction to Nuclear Engineering

RAYMOND L. MURRAY *Demy 8vo 30s. net*

This book on the techniques and methods of nuclear engineering is for the person with a background understanding of the fundamentals of conventional engineering who wants a working knowledge of nuclear physics and atomic energy in their relation to practical problems.

Dr. Murray first defines what he means by nuclear engineering and describes its broad scope. Not only is the term applied to the nuclear reactor—its design, construction, testing and operation—but also to such related activities as : the accumulation of nuclear fuel and other materials with unusual properties ; the handling of radioactive chemicals ; the design of instruments for experimental particle detection ; establishment of standards and practices in radiation protection ; and the use of isotopes for industrial and biological purposes. The technology and problems of the use of atomic energy in all its phases is discussed in detail. Some of the highlights are : an overall view, presented clearly and compactly, allowing you to see each problem in relation to the whole field ; four separate chapters devoted to the problems in the auxiliary field of development and research—radiation hazards, radioactive waste disposal, shielding and reactor control instruments ; description of benefits of nuclear engineering to scientific research, medicine, engineering and agriculture ; presentation of prospects for the use of nuclear energy in the production of electrical power and propulsion together with the types of calculations performed by workers in the field.

GEORGE ALLEN & UNWIN LTD